Celebrating the
Cherry

Growing around the world

By Gib Hancock

*"We respond to cherry orchards with a delight
that a cabbage patch or even an elegant
vegetable garden cannot provoke"*

Jane Grigson

Contents

Foreword

Growing and supplying fresh cherries is one of the most time-consuming, or rather all consuming, jobs you can have in the world. It is also a passionate and risky business where the stakes are high and Mother Nature can, at times, be very cruel.

Growers must fight hard for the perfect large, juicy fruit they are striving for. They have been known to spend entire nights in their orchards, protecting their trees from the harsh frosts that can destroy a crop literally overnight. Cherry farming is not just a job, it is a complete way of life.

In addition, the climate needed to grow perfect cherries means they are found in some of the most beautiful parts of the world. Orchards are often set alongside gleaming glaciers, plunging valleys, or dramatic mountain ranges. Set the fruit aside and the scenery is one of the greatest joys of cherry farming.

It's no accident that all over the world, the people you meet in the cherry business do what they do with such passion. From the small family farmers in Spain's Jerte Valley to the large producing companies of the United States, everybody loves their job.

Above all, everyone is extremely proud of the business they are in.

My father once said to me on my return from a "Cherry" trip; "Why don't you write a book about all these wonderful places and fantastic people". After much deliberation I came round to the idea and so I set about convincing him to write it!

This book aims to provide an insight into some of the main countries involved in supplying good quality fresh cherries, the growers, and, naturally, the fruit itself. The wine industry has boomed as shoppers have come to understand more about different varieties of grape, and developed a hunger for understanding the hard work that goes into producing the perfect bottle.

We would like to see the same thing happen for cherries.

I would like to thank all the breeders, growers, exporters, importers, freight companies, marketing organisations and countless others who have helped to put this book together. Special thanks go to my father, Gib Hancock, for coming up with the idea for the book, researching and writing it, and for taking such an interest in what we do.

Matthew Hancock, Norton Folgate

Introduction

Cherries are a part of folklore all over the world. In Japan, the Sakura, or ornamental cherry tree, has for centuries symbolised the fleeting nature of life. The short life of the cherry is compared to the samurai warrior, who was expected at any time to sacrifice his life for his master. The saying goes: "the cherry is among flowers as the samurai is among men".

There are over 400 varieties of ornamental cherry grown in Japan, derived from a number of separate species, such as prunus contradinae, prunus incisa, prunus serrulata and prunus sargentii. These are grown for their dazzling springtime blossoms. For a few weeks every year, the trees sprinkle the streets of towns and gardens with white or pink confetti, as the breeze lifts the delicate petals off the trees.

The Japanese hold parties and picnics in their parks and open spaces at cherry blossom time. Many people dress in traditional costumes to celebrate the beauty of the trees. These "hanami" or "flower viewings" take place throughout the country, beginning in the south where the early blossoms appear, and gradually moving north.

In China, meanwhile, the ample blossom of a cherry tree represents femininity, female beauty and sexuality.

But ornamental trees produce inedible fruit rather than the juicy delicious cherries celebrated throughout this book.

There are two broad categories of cherries for eating. The sweet cherry, and the bitter-tasting tart cherry used for cooking and distilling into alcoholic liquor.

The Roman general Lucullus found edible cherries when he arrived with troops in the town of Giresun, on the Black Sea coast of Turkey. When he returned to Rome in 74 BC, he brought back Italy's first trees, where they were planted and eventually grown in suitable locations throughout the Roman Empire and beyond. It is still unclear whether these first trees produced tart or sweet fruit; however, their Turkish origins remain today: it is from the Turkish word 'Kiraz' that we get the English word 'Cherry'.

Left: Japan's oldest known cherry tree
Right: Ornamental cherry blossoms in Japan

The original wild cherries were called mazzards. They were grown in China over 3000 years ago and also possibly in Britain in the Stone Age. The Roman historian, Pliny, provided the first record of cherries in Britain, noting that Rome sent trees to the country in the first century AD.

Within 100 years, the cherry was well established across western Europe and by the 15th century had become a widely grown and well loved fruit in the region. Records from the Middle Ages show some 15 varieties being grown here and, when European colonists began to push back the frontier of the United States in the 17th century, they were delighted to find cherries growing in abundance.

Today, although there are hundreds of cherry varieties growing around the world, only a handful of these are produced commercially. Amongst the more common modern varieties of the sweet cherry are Bing, Ziraat, Sweetheart and Lapins. Bing is grown all over the world for its large, sweet and well-flavoured fruit. There are specialized varieties, too, such as the stalkless Picota cherry, which is found principally in Spain's Jerte Valley.

When it comes to tart cherries, the Morello dominates. It has been grown for many centuries and has a myriad of uses in cooking, making jams, and of course as the basis for an excellent cherry brandy.

Cherries are now grown in many parts of the world, but as cherry growers will tell you, there is no one perfect place. Everywhere you find a cherry orchard, you also find an ongoing battle between the farmer and the elements. When the farmer wins and the needs of the cherries are met, the harvest can be a rich one. When the elements win, an entire crop can be destroyed overnight.

Cherry trees are notoriously fussy. They need rain and warmth, but not too much of either, and then only at the right time. These basic climatic conditions play a huge role part in producing good fruit.

If it rains while cherries are ripening, they will start to take in water, which will cause them to crack. No one wants a cracked cherry. So, over the years, farmers have learned to cover their trees when there is a threat of rain. Protecting their fruit in this way adds cost, but the cost of not doing it would be far higher. One farmer in Argentina has developed a noisy sonic device that causes explosions in the atmosphere designed to break up rain-forming clouds – a resourceful approach, which works.

Cherry farmers must do everything possible to minimise the risks involved. Growing tender, tasty, luscious, cherries requires lots of tender, loving, care.

Cherries also demand that the temperature is absolutely right at each phase of the growing cycle. In the dormant phase after cherries have been harvested, a cherry tree typically needs 700 to 800 hours of "chilling time" - when the temperature is between freezing and seven degrees centigrade. If the tree doesn't get this, it will become stressed and will refuse to produce fruit later. So there are many parts of the world where it is impossible to grow cherries successfully.

Cherry production regions:
northern and southern hemisphere

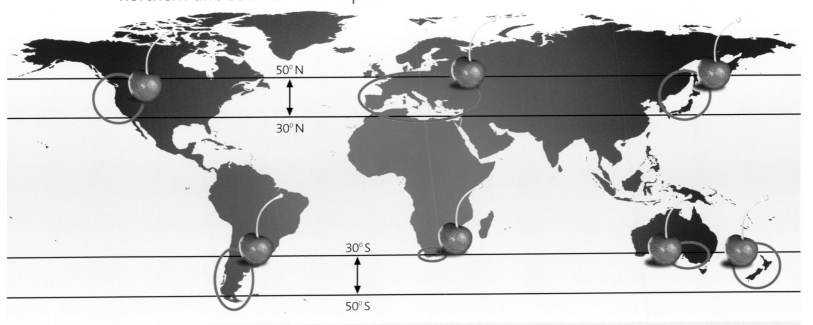

Later in the year, when the trees are in bloom, they decide they can no longer tolerate the cold. A late frost can destroy the embryonic fruits as they form at the centre of the blossom and has caused many a crop failure, and heartbreak for the grower. The risk is greatest where the cherry orchards are situated on flat land or in the bottom of valleys, where the cold air will fall to the valley floor.

Growers have fought back by installing large blowers that keep the air moving through their orchards and discourage frosts from forming. The blowers come on automatically when the temperature falls to a preset level. Growers have also developed heating systems at the base of the trees, small stoves or simple burners.

The latter have to be lit by hand when frost threatens. On some farms the heaters and the blowers work together to protect the tender blossom.

The temperature must be right as the fruit matures and ripens. Cherries need warmth to produce and ripen. If they don't, the sugars will not develop and the fruit will be sour and insipid tasting. Daytime temperatures should ideally fall between 26 and 32 degrees centigrade, while the nights should be cool and crisp. Again, rain on ripening fruit can spell disaster.

The two narrow bands on the map show the areas where climate fulfils the requirements for successful cherry growing.

This is a graphic explanation of why we have gaps in availability between our hemispheres. If production could be shifted north or south in either hemisphere it would provide fruit to fill these gaps. However, although growers are working to producer earlier and later varieties of cherry that have extended their seasons by a few days, to date nobody has found a location that will promise cherries throughout the year.

Successful cherry farming is not just about overcoming the problems of nature. It demands a commitment and a skill that only a dedicated farmer can provide. The farmer has to understand his orchard, and have the answers to many questions: What makes my trees flourish? What care and attention is needed to produce the best possible crop? Am I planting this variety in the most suitable location?

The most successful of growers have a deep-seated passion for what they do. They walk through their orchards daily; they observe and understand what is happening to the trees, and what condition they are in. They understand the differences between one variety and another, and between one part of their farm and another. They can predict and react to problems even before they develop, and they are continuously learning new ways of solving them. They acquire a feel for their orchards.

Growing is perhaps nearer to an art form than to a science. The local knowledge needed cannot be learned from a book, and is usually passed one from one generation to the next.

Farmers don't simply grow their fruit, they nurture it. Successful cherry growing is a way of life.

Cherry smoothie

Spain

"During harvest, work starts each day before first light, and goes on late into the evening"

Aragon

Madrid ■

Valencia

Extremadura

Bottom left: The renowned Picota cherry
Bottom right: Deserted street, Extremadura

From Huesca in the north to Seville in the south, cherries are grown throughout the Spanish mainland and even as far south as the Canary Islands.

Aragon

The region around Aragon is Spain's largest producer of the fruit, accounting for around a third of the county's cherries. Extending south from the foothills of the Pyrenees, it's an area rich in history, as well as being the birthplace of Catherine of Aragon, the first wife of Henry VIII.

This region, along with Navarra and Lerida in the Ebro valley, was only a marginal cherry producer until the late 1950s. From then Aragon began a huge expansion until it became a major force in Spain.

The country's oldest cherry orchards can be found in the Calatayud region of Aragon – where cherries are the main livelihood for a large number of farmers. In the beginning, most cherries were grown for industrial processing as there was a well-developed infrastructure of small jam processing plants in this area and a strong tradition of preserving various fruits in sugar or syrup.

So until the 1980s, most of the cherries grown in the area were bi-coloured or pink and very sweet – perfect for preserving. At the end of the 1980s, some 70% of the 13,000 tonnes of cherries produced in Aragon were processed for many important export markets, France in particular.

However, in the last 20 years we have seen a huge transformation and renovation of old orchards being modernised with large, good eating and firm varieties. During this time we have also seen a huge growth in the planted acreage of cherry trees and with this growth farmers have moved beyond the traditional boundaries in Calatayud towards Cape-Mequinenza and the Fraga area.

These two regions, still within the Ebro valley, both offer much earlier cropping of the orchards with their distinctive microclimate. Land in these areas is now hard to find and is worth a premium with its good access to water. There has also been a move northwards towards Lerida and the Catalan borders.

In these new areas the focus of production is the early market. Since Spain's production window comes after the six-week break between Southern Hemisphere and Northern Hemisphere seasons, there is an annual frenzy to have the first fruit to market and the ensuing premium that the market will offer growers who can produce good quality fresh cherries at the end of April and early May.

Inevitably, the growers in this region have planted varieties that will also mature in the mid- and late-season through June and mid-July respectively. By the middle of July temperatures start creeping into the low to mid 40s and the delicate cherry can no longer withstand the heat. While the fruit still looks great on the tree, the heat stresses the cherry, and it will no longer withstand the 2- to 3-day trip to European markets without softening and going mouldy. This is the time that retailers and marketers switch countries and start buying their cherries from Turkey and Washington State.

Valencia Province

This is the third largest cherry growing area in Spain after Extremadura and Aragon. The region of Castellon is the most important with towns like Segorbe, Viver, Bajo Maestrazgo being important and two main nucleus towns of San Mateo and Salsdella. Not far from this area you move into the region of Alicante and the Valle de la Gallinera and into the hills known as the Montana de Alicante. These areas have seen a similar change and modernisation of the sector from traditional cherry varieties to the modern imported varieties from the US and France in particular.

This region is very similar to Extremadura in terms of the large numbers of small-scale farmers growing in mountainous terrain. There has also been extensive conversion from olive and almond production into cherries.

left: Picota cherries are one of the most eagerly anticipated fruits on the international market
Centre: The Jerte Valley   Right: The gate to Caceres, Extremadura

Harvesting the Picota cherry

Extremadura

The striking region of Extremadura in the west of Spain also has a host of historical stories, and is home to another hub of Spanish cherry growing, the Jerte Valley (Valle del Jerte), located 200 kilometres west of Madrid at the northern end of the Caceres province.

Savvy visitors coming from Madrid shun the dual carriageway that runs to the south of the valley and instead take the old National 110 Via Avila. In spring, this historic road is populated by hundreds of nesting storks, which build precarious homes at the top of pylons that line the route.

The route may be slightly longer, but as it passes up into the Credos Mountains at over 1,200 metres it offers up an astonishingly rewarding panorama.

The River Jerte is a shining ribbon, which winds its way over 70 kilometres through a narrow valley with peaks rising sharply on either side. From the hillsides, streams come cascading down into the main river. Fast and often frightening waterfalls roar past on their way to the valley floor. Higher up, where there are fewer trees, cattle graze in the meadows, and the view becomes even more spectacular. It is a staggeringly beautiful place.

The valley is covered in cherry trees: there are more than two million of them, forming the foundation of the Jerte economy. The Jerte climate is near perfect for cherry farming. During cold winters it is frosty enough to stimulate new growth, after which there is abundant rainfall while the fruit is developing. Crucially, springtime in the valley is usually free from frost as the delicate blossom is forming. While the cherries are ripening, the summers stay dry.

The Cherrypickers

In mid-August 1811, during the Peninsular War between the French Napoleonic Empire and the alliance of Spain, Portugal and Britain, a patrol of ten soldiers from the British 11th Hussars regiment were sent by Wellington to the Extremadura region in the west of Spain on a reconnaissance mission. Looking for something good to eat, they stopped in St Martin de Trebeja, just south of the Jerte Valley, dismounted from their horses and helped themselves to handfuls of deliciously ripe cherries that hung from the trees surrounding the village. Their commander failed to see an approaching detachment of French cavalry, and he and his men were captured.

The men of the regiment – now part of The Royal Hussars – are still referred to as the Cherrypickers.

Subtle variations in climate arise from differences in altitude and the position of orchards on the northern or southern side of the valley. This, in turn, gives Jerte the longest harvesting season of any area in the world. Farmers maximise their natural advantage with an array of cherry varieties, including so-called early and late cultivars, and well-loved favourites, such as the renowned Picota.

The stalkless Picota is without question the most famous cherry in the valley. Unique to the Jerte region, the Picota ripens slowly – taking twice as long as some varieties. This long development creates a characteristic deep colour and intense flavour. It also means a protective skin forms between the fruit and the stalk connecting it to the tree. When the pickers arrive to harvest the ripe cherry, the fruit comes away easily and undamaged, leaving its stalk behind.

The Picota cherry season runs for less than six weeks between mid-June and July. This short run and the Picota's clear difference from other cherries make it one of the region's most eagerly anticipated exports.

The valley supports more than, 5,000 farms, almost all of which are run by families, and average just six acres each. This production culture is rare in the modern fruit business. The farmers produce olives and chestnuts, along with a few other fruits, but this treasured cherry remains the focus and livelihood of the vast majority of growers.

The workers on the Jerte Valley's farms are typically family members who plant, prune, pick and prepare the fruit for sale. You can often find three generations of a single family engaged in the diverse tasks involved in preparing for the year's harvest.

Individual farms would not survive without the cooperatives. These organisations, such as Agrupacion del Valle del Jerte, which accounts for around 70 per cent of cherry production in the valley, collect the cherries and market them throughout the world on behalf of the growers. Cooperatives such as these provide a vital link between the old, traditional and otherwise fragmented way of producing fruit on small family units and the demands of the sophisticated world markets they supply.

Opposite and above:
The Picota cherry is grown
by around 5,000 family-run
farms

Main picture: Cherries
growing in the Jerte Valley
Right: Nesting storks,
Extremadura

Cherry farming dominates the Jerte Valley region throughout the year. As the harvest finishes around mid-August, and the trees begin to shed their leaves, preparations begin for the year to come. The farmers turn and fertilise the ground, prune the trees and plant new ones. Harvest time aside, this is the busiest period of the year.

Come winter and the hills surrounding the valley are often covered in snow, which can sometimes reach the trees. It is a time of rain, storms and strong winds. According to local folklore, it is during this bad weather that the cherries are 'conceived'.

Sure enough, after a couple of months the earliest buds begin to show – the first signs of the crop to come. As spring arrives, the first blossom appears, almost overnight, and towards the end of March, the valley is transformed as white blossoms appear on the thousands of trees scattered over the hillsides.

If the trees escape the spring frost, their flowers are replaced by developing fruit as the weather gets warmer. As the cherries grow and ripen, the branches of the trees begin to sag under the weight. The colours on the trees vary from the deepest red to tones of yellow, depending on the variety of the cherry.

The Jerte summer is all about cherries. The families in the valley have worked throughout the year to produce the best possible fruit. Now is the time to earn their reward. The harvest determines how the family will live for the next 12 months.

It is a time of feverish activity. Work starts each day before first light, and goes on late into the evening. All cherries are harvested by hand. Pickers spend their days up metal ladders, filling baskets and taking care not to mix varieties, sometimes tying branches back to make the job an easier one. Many trees will be visited three times before all their fruit has been collected.

When the baskets are full they are sorted into sizes and packed – the larger the fruit the greater the price – before the cooperative ships the fruit across the world.

The harvest finishes, and the autumn arrives. The cycle of cherry production in the Jerte Valley begins once again, and continues, as it has done for hundreds of years.

Opposite:
Top left: Harvest time
in Jerte
Bottom left: Quality
control for Picota cherries

Major cherry varieties

The following are some of the most important commercial cherry varieties.

Early varieties

Brooks

An early ripening cherry, the Brooks is large, firm and juicy, and has a rich sweet flavour.

Sequoia

An up-and-coming cherry related to the Brooks, Bing and Tulare varieties, the Sequoia is a trademarked variety developed in California. This cherry – actually a series of three similar cultivars: Glen Red, Glen Rock and Glenoia – is deep red, large and has good sugar levels.

Mid-season

Bing

Known as the 'King of cherries', the Bing cherry is typically very large, high quality, sweet and filled with lots of juice. The fruit is very dark red, almost black, when completely ripe. This is one of the most popular cherries for production and export around the world.

Ziraat (Napoleon)

This is a bright red to mahogany-coloured variety, which originates in Turkey and can produce cherries that are almost 3cm across. It has a long shelf life, travels well and is available from the end of May/early June until early August. This variety is also known as Napoleon.

Late

Sweetheart

When grown correctly the vivid red Sweetheart cherry is excellent quality and remains firm to bite into after it has been harvested. This is a vigorous variety, and trees need pruning to stop them from producing large quantities of small fruit.

Staccato

Staccato is similar to Sweetheart but ripens later, allowing growers to extend their season with later fruit. It is firm with good flavour.

United States

"US cherry farmers grow big, luscious fruit, and they harvest big volumes"

Washington

Oregon

Michigan

California

Washington DC

The Columbia River Valley

Growers in the United States do cherries in a big way. They grow big, luscious fruit, harvest big volumes; and, in a good year, the business is big. Bumper harvests from all sources mean the country's combined production of sweet and tart varieties can reach 300,000 tonnes.

About a third of the US's big, bold cherries are tart and two-thirds are sweet. The former are concentrated in the Midwest state of Michigan, the latter in the Pacific coast states of California, Oregon and Washington.

Colonisation of the cherry

Early European settlers introduced tart cherries to North America in the 17th century. They were followed by French colonists from Normandy who brought with them cherry stones, which they planted along the shores of the Saint Lawrence River and by the Great Lakes. Many of these Gallic settlers also planted cherry trees in their gardens as they set up home in new cities, such as Detroit and Vincennes.

It wasn't until 1852, however, that the foundations of modern production were laid by Peter Dougherty, a Presbyterian missionary living in northern Michigan. Dougherty planted cherry trees on Old Mission Peninsula, which is near Traverse City.

Neighbouring farmers and the local indigenous people were amazed when they saw Dougherty's trees flourishing. They followed his lead as they began to realise the area surrounding the lake was ideal for cherry growing, as proximity to the lake tempered the winter winds and cooled the high temperatures in summer.

Tart cherry farming went commercial in 1893, on Ridgewood Farm, close to the site of Dougherty's original holding. The venture was successful, and more people established farms. By the early 1900s, the tart cherry had become big business for the area, with large orchards around Traverse City and along the shores of Lake Michigan. The first cherry processing plants were built here early in the 19th century.

The Montmorency cherry has been the most important in the area since these first orchards. The fruit is grown for processing, canning, freezing, drying or juicing, and finds its way into a range of foods, from pie fillings, jams, jellies, cheesecake and drinks. Michigan also grows sweet cherries, but mainly for the Maraschino market.

Traverse City remains the centre of cherry activity in Michigan and is known in the US as the Cherry Capital of the World. The city has hosted the National Cherry Festival at harvest time in July, since 1924.

Top left: Cherry trees getting winter chill time
Top right: Cherry blossom against clear spring skies
Bottom left: An orchard at ripening time
Bottom right: Empty road with trees in blossom

The Cherry Festival is no country fair (visit www.cherryfestival.org for an idea of the sheer scale of this event). It attracts visitors from around the world who come to take part in the festivities and catch a glimpse of the crowning of the year's Cherry Queen.

After a record crop the previous year, 2002 was calamitous owing to heavy frosts in the spring, which destroyed the new buds as they formed. The situation improved in 2003, but growers are still recovering from the financial impact – estimated to be in the region of $20 million – of the crop failure.

The consequences are far reaching and underline the fact that cherry farming is not for short-term gain. Growers – in Michigan as in the rest of the world – know this is a long-term business. Cherry farming can be challenging, as well as rewarding.

Top left: Central Park with cherry blossoms
Top right: Washington Monument (Washington DC) and cherry blossom

Kaley Schroeder,
the National Cherry Festival's
Cherry Queen for 2006/2007

Top left: Quaker on an Oregon street

Top right: Blossom-lined street, Oregon

Bottom right: Portland, Oregon

Bottom left: One of the US's large and juicy cherries

The cherry goes west

A Quaker from Iowa, Henderson Lewelling, introduced sweet cherries to the American Northwest. In 1847, he travelled west on the Oregon Trail by ox-drawn wagon. Along with his wife and eight children, he brought with him around 700 one-year-old tiny grafted apple, pear, peach and cherry trees packed into earth-filled boxes.

Among the cherry trees packed into the wagon was the Napoleon Bigarreau, which Lewelling called the Royal Ann. The variety is still grown in the Northwest region today.

The family settled near Milwaukee in the Willamette Valley just south of Portland, where Henderson's brothers John and Seth and his son-in-law William Meek joined them. Together they established an orchard and opened the first fruit tree nursery in the Northwest.

By 1851 they had produced more than 18,000 fruit trees for sale, which grew to more than 100,000 trees over two years. The family sold their trees to professional growers and to other nurseries for between $1 and $1.50 a tree.

Before the Lewelling nursery, fruit growers in the valley relied on growing their trees from seed. It was an unreliable method that often resulted in small trees which were prone to disease, and produced low yields of flavourless fruit.

The Lewelling family moved fruit growing in the area forward by a giant step. In doing so, they laid the foundations for fruit growing to become a major industry in the Northwest states of the US.

Seth Lewelling, in particular, is remembered for breeding promising new types of cherries by careful cross-pollination. Seth developed the Black Republican cherry in 1860; from this, he derived the new seedling that was to become his greatest achievement, the Bing. He named the new cherry after the head of his Chinese work crew: Mr Bing. The dark, sweet and juicy Bing is now the most celebrated cherry in the Northwest – and is one of the most popular amongst growers and shoppers around the world.

California

Cherries thrive in California's sunny days and cool nights. Frost is rare at those times that are critical for cherries. The region has fertile soils, providing a great growing environment for the fruit.

Large cherry farms and their orchards spread out over around 22,000 acres of California and are still expanding. The oldest farms in the area can be found in the San Joaquin and coastal valley regions of Hollister and Gilroy in the north of the state. New orchards have been planted further south in the regions around Bakersfield and Arvin recently, as growers work to make fruit available earlier in the year.

Bing and Lambert have long been northern California's most popular varieties. Lambert ranges in colour from deep pink to red and has deep red juice; it ripens earlier than Bing and is slightly smaller. Bing produces large dark red cherries with a great sweet flavour. Bing keeps for longer and travels better than Lambert.

Growers have developed new varieties especially for planting in southern California, so they can bring the beginning of their season forward with an earlier harvest. These varieties include Brooks, Tulare, Chelan, Tieton, and Seqouia, which produce fruit to harvest from the beginning of May until early June, when first the northern fruit is ripe. In the north, Lambert cherries are picked first, followed shortly after by Bing.

The California season lasts for eight weeks. Every tree has been harvested by the end of June. As the season draws to a close, fruit begins to arrive from Oregon, California's neighbour state to the north.

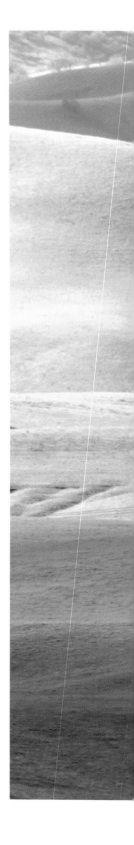

California's coastal range as
seen from the central valley

The impressive Mount Hood,
with orchards in foreground

Oregon

Oregon's farmers grow some tart cherries, but are best known for their sweet varieties.

The cherries are grown in the Hood River and Wasco County area in the north and central part of the state, as well as the smaller area around the Willamette Valley south of Portland, where Henderson Lewelling settled.

Wasco County is an hour's drive from Portland. The road follows the vast Columbia River - the second largest river in the US – as it runs through some of the most breathtaking scenery in the Northwest. Pine-covered hills rise steeply up from the river, and the views across the valley to Washington reveal spectacularly large and open countryside.

The sweet cherry farms are situated above the Columbia River in the area surrounding the riverside town of The Dalles. The fruit is grown in neat orchards on the beautiful undulating hills at the foot of the Cascade Mountains. Something close to three quarters of a million cherry trees cover this truly breathtaking landscape.

This remarkable countryside is dominated by views of Mount Hood, the dormant volcano that is Oregon's highest (3,439 metres) and best-known landmark. Mount Hood appears to preside over the entire area and provides a dramatic backdrop to the cherry orchards throughout the year. The snow-capped peaks of Mount Adams and Mount St Helens can also been seen in Washington state, some 40 miles away.

Almost all of Oregon's fresh cherries are grown in Wasco County, as the weather is more reliably dry and quality is more consistently good. Over half of Oregon's sweet cherry crop is brined for Maraschino production; 15 per cent is canned, frozen or made into drinks.

Over in the Willamette Valley, the weather has proved to be less stable, and severe frosts during blossoming and untimely rain at the June and July ripening stage have damaged the crop several times in the last 15 years. This unpredictability means farmers here are more likely to sell their fruit for processing, rather than into the fresh fruit sector.

SUPER SWEET
RAINIER
CHERRIES
$5.99
A POUND

Top left: Mount Rainier
Bottom left: Rainier cherries on sale in a US market
Right: Rainier cherries on the tree

Washington

Cherries and apples are Washington's flagship agricultural product. Cherries alone have an annual value of in excess of $200 million for an average crop of 200,000 tonnes.

The state is the largest producer of sweet cherries in the US by far, the Bing being the most prolific variety. The bi-coloured Rainier has increased in attraction as growers have planted this variety specifically for foodie customers who understand the attraction of this unusual cherry.

Fans of the Rainier appreciate the contrast of creamy yellow flesh, which gives the blush of the skin a sunny undertone, and the exquisite sweetness of this sublime fruit.

Washington's growers farm around 25,000 acres of sweet cherries, almost all of it on the foothills of the Cascade Range. The southern part of the range stretches south into neighbouring Oregon.

The root of the matter

Like most highly developed and sophisticated things that grow, the cherry is the product of two parents. The parents of the modern cherry are a root stock, a carefully selected "tree stump" with an established rootsystem, and a scion, a bud of the variety that has been selected. The two are grafted together to provide the qualities required in the new tree.

Making the right choice of rootstock is an essential first step for cherry growers, as this forms the direct nourishing link from soil to tree as it matures. Growers look for the rootstock best suited to the local conditions, From the mineral content and ph level of the soil, to the availability of water.

The rootstock can have a direct influence on the character of a cherry tree as it develops after the graft. It can determine how fast, how big and what shape the grafted tree grows, and the size and quality of the fruit it produces. This, in turn, affects how much maintenance and pruning growers have to carry out throughout the year.

The bud from the variety of cherry tree required is grafted onto a healthy rootstock. Once planted the two separate parts will gradually fuse together.

Matching rootstock to the graft is a delicate process. Create a tree that is too vigorous and it may become extremely leafy, producing a surfeit of small, lower quality fruit. Not vigorous enough and you can face low yields and an uneconomical orchard.

Traditionally, most cherry producers grew cherries on tall trees of up to seven metres. New varieties of so-called dwarfing rootstocks, which produce smaller 'Spanish bush' style trees, however, are the choice of commercial growers today. Not only are shorter trees more accessible for maintenance and harvest, they also allow growers to plant more of them, increasing the productivity of an orchard.

The rootstock is so vital to the production of lots of large, juicy cherries that many growers have opened nurseries to produce their own. Research into improving existing rootstocks – and developing new ones – continues around the world.

Turkey

"Turkey is the cradle
of civilisation and
the motherland
of the cherry"

Bursa
Izmir
Afyon
Isparta
Ankara
Giresun

Turkish sunset

The world's first ever towns developed in the region we now known as Turkey, starting in Mesopotamia along the fertile plains of the Tigris and Euphrates rivers, and spreading north and west into Asia Minor and Anatolia. One of the world's first of these, called Catal Huyuk, was founded in Turkey in approximately 7500 BC, around 4,000 years before Stonehenge.

Turkey is also renowned as the birthplace of the cherry. According to the Roman historian Pliny the Elder, the Roman general Lucius Licinius Lucullus took cherry trees back to Rome from the Turkish city of Cerasus/Cerasion – translated as the 'City of the Cherry' – around the year 70 BC. The general had defeated Mithridates VI, king of Pontus, in the city, which was known for its abundance of cherry trees as well as its annual cherry festival.

The city was rechristened as the Turkish province of Giresun long ago, but the old name lives on as the origin of the English word 'cherry'. The celebrated cherry orchards remain in the region, although today farmers in the area grow a wide variety of fruits. Turkey has become one of the world's largest producers of fruit.

About half the population of Turkey works in agriculture or fishing. The main products include cotton, tobacco, cereals, sugar beet, nuts and fruit. The total value of the country's agricultural exports is close to £1.5 billion.

The country produces in excess of 11 million tonnes of fruit, including grapes, peaches, apricots, plums, citrus, apples and pears. Cherries are one of the country's best-loved products, and, of all its agricultural crops, one of those that bring the best rewards for growers.

Large areas of Turkey, with its 5,000 miles of coastline, have benefited from a boom in tourist interest in recent years as holidaymakers eager for sun and an exotic location have come in increasing number.

The same climate of warm summers and mild winters that captures the imagination of travellers, has also formed the background to the burgeoning cherry industry. Cherries have brought prosperity to an increasing number of regions, notably around Bursa, Izmir, Isparta and Afyon.

From 1965 to 1985, Turkish cherry growers planted significant quantities of new trees, and production began to rise. This process is still continuing, albeit at a slightly slower pace, with output of varieties such as Bing, Bigarreau, Lambert and Napoleon on the rise.

The motherland of the cherry is sending more of its fruit to destinations such as the UK, Germany and Italy than ever before, as its growers have improved the volume, variety and, above all, the eating quality of their cherries.

Top left: Turkish tourist
destination
Top right: One of Turkey's
famous cherry festivals
Bottom left: Harvesting
cherries in Turkey
Bottom right: Mosque
with cherry blossom

Opposite page: Turkish delight
Top left: A Turkish family
at harvest time
Top right: Turkey boasts the
first recorded cherries in Europe
Bottom: Turkish valley
and orchards

Growing up together

The tall trees in a traditional cherry orchard often stood eight metres or more apart. Trees would be left to grow naturally with little or no pruning.

As growers have learned more about their orchards, they have become more concerned with the development of each tree. The most popular type of tree today is small – referred to as a 'Spanish bush' – and can be spaced as little as three metres apart, or even less. This allows for more trees per hectare. It also means that the grower must spend more time in the orchard.

This, combined with better understanding of suitable management practices, means good growers are constantly maintaining their trees both in and out of the growing season.

Even family growers in locations such as the Jerte Valley – where trees may be sparsely distributed throughout orchards growing many varieties of fruit – the farmers pay particularly close attention to their delicate cherry crops.

Demand for bigger fresh cherries has increased, and growers now regularly cut back branches on their trees to create the conditions needed for the cherries to grow to a consistently large size.

In a single season it is possible to produce yields of up to 40 tonnes of cherries from a single hectare of orchard. However, higher yields will result in smaller fruit. Controlling the yield to 15 to 20 tonnes is one of the secrets to producing regular crops of the large fruit everyone wants.

Growers' responsibilities to their cherries also includes making sure they get enough rain when they first start to grow, but are protected from direct contact with rain while ripening. Water is easily absorbed at this stage and can split the fruit. Growers around the world have developed a number of solutions to cover their crops from harvest rains.

Cherry trees need temperatures between 0°C and 7°C in the dormant phase of the growing cycle, but early frosts at the blossom stage can decimate a crop. Growers and their families have been known to spend all night protecting the blossoming crops from the threat of frost with fans and heaters to warm the air in the orchard.

UK

"English growers are taking up the challenge to revive cherries as a national crop"

Herefordshire

London

Kent

Bottom left: Harvesting tall cherry trees is a time-consuming task
Right: Kent is home of the English cherry

Kent has been the British home of cherries for hundreds of years, thanks to Henry VIII. The king's fruiterer, Richard Harris, brought the first trees to Teynham in the Garden of England in 1533. Production flourished, and by the 20th century over 20,000 acres of cherry trees had been planted across the region.

Every spring they produced huge drifts of pink and white blossoms, which brought out the very best of the lush Kentish countryside. Cherry growers enjoyed a dominant supply position in cherries and in a wide range of other fruits for more than 400 years.

In the 1950s, however, the amount of fruit grown in Kent began to fall dramatically. More than a third of the area's fruit orchards have been grubbed (removed) and converted to cereal farming.

Cherries suffered more than most fruit. Although a limited number of new cherry orchards have been planted in the Malvern Hills in Herefordshire, in Kent the 18,000 acres that existed in 1950 had dwindled to just 2,000 by 1990. By 2005 this had fallen to less than 1,000 acres, and yearly production of around 20,000 tonnes of fruit dwindled to less than 1,000 tonnes.

The decline was brought about by a combination of factors, but the starting point can probably be found in the trees the original English farmers decided to grow. For centuries growers nurtured huge, tall trees, of up to 40ft high, with branches that spread out almost the same distance wide.

These relative giants were extremely expensive to manage and tricky to harvest. Tall trees took up to 12 years to produce a decent crop of cherries, with perhaps another ten years before the farmers saw a return on the cost of planting the tree and growing the fruit.

Critically, it also took far more time and needed more pickers to harvest the larger trees, compared to the small bushy trees grown by the modern farmer. The number of people who were prepared to undertake the lengthy harvest fell. Fruit began to be left on trees and was wasted.

High rainfall in the run-up to the harvest didn't help the industry either. If cherries come into contact with water as they are ripening, they absorb it and the fruit cracks, making it unsuitable for sale. During the 1980s, there was enough rainfall in the month of July to cause significant cracking in five out of the ten years. In these years, growers lost around half of the cherries they expected to harvest. In three of these five years, they lost up to four fifths of their crop.

Cherry farmers stopped investing in their businesses - they quite simply couldn't afford to. Little was done to research the new varieties or new rootstocks that might have helped the introduction of more profitable smaller trees. Growers fell further and further behind the game.

One of England's remaining
large trees in blossom

Declining and rising

The British industry was being eroded at a time when demand for cherries was increasing around the world. From 1990 to 2000, UK consumers alone increased their intake of fresh cherries from around 8,000 tonnes to over 23,000 tonnes. In the UK, retailers had to go elsewhere during the traditional British season to meet the rising demand for fresh cherries. They began to import from countries such as Turkey, Spain and France. These countries have proved they can supply good quality fruit at fully competitive prices and in quantities that will satisfy market demand.

Today, people in the UK spend around £60 million on cherries in shops. Domestic suppliers have fallen from total dominance of the market to being a niche player, and now have less than a five per cent share of their home market.

Opposite: A modern cherry
orchard during the autumn

Main picture: A cherry tree
in full autumnal colours
Top right: Oast houses, Kent
Bottom right: Canterbury
Cathedral

The future for the home-grown cherry

But all is not lost for the British cherry.

Domestic farmers know they do not have the competitive strength to win back lost market share from the lower cost suppliers who now dominate. However domination is no longer on their minds. Since the 1990s, farmers have been grafting cherry varieties onto dwarfing rootstock to produce shorter trees of no more than two metres in height. Harvesting these trees presents fewer problems, and good fruit is no longer left on the branches to rot. The new trees start producing fruit within five years of planting, which makes investment much more attractive.

These more adventurous growers have recognised the potential to stop the decline in domestic cherry farming. Shoppers like to buy home-grown fruit. If English growers can produce reliable harvests and top quality cherries, there is the potential to build a much stronger niche.

Growers are also looking at opportunities to extend their traditional harvesting season. English cherries are available from the beginning of July until the middle of August, coinciding with fruit from Spain, Italy, Turkey and the west coast of the US – sources with good quality fruit, which is under less threat of rain damage.

New varieties being developed in Kent should extend the English picking season into September, when none of the major growing countries have cherries available. This will enable the English growers to ask a higher price for their fruit and help justify their investment.

To command a premium price, however, the fruit will also have to reach the market in optimum condition. This can only be achieved if the cherries are cooled as soon as they are picked (see technical section, page 54) to preserve the quality. This is standard procedure in other parts of the world, but it hasn't been adopted widely in the UK. Investment is needed.

Protective tunnels may also help. By covering these new shorter trees with tunnels, growers can safeguard against problems caused by the English weather. Tunnels help extend the harvest period and enable growers to produce fruit from new plantings more quickly.

Trees are planted in the open, and after two or three years, before they start fruiting, they are covered in specially developed polythene tunnels. The tunnels are designed to let air circulate freely and allow machines to work between rows. They give control back to the grower, who is no longer at the mercy of the elements.

Although tunnels add cost, the fruit is home-grown, which is a great advantage to the grower, and, if the cherries are protected from the vagaries of the English weather, they can be harvested when large volumes of imported fruit are not available.

All these factors will encourage the UK growers to believe that they can sell their cherries at the premium price they will need to cover their additional costs.

However, English growers perhaps have one further battle to win. While more shoppers than ever might prefer to choose fruit grown in the UK, the environmental issues surrounding increased acreage of polytunnels are still being debated.

A revival in the UK cherry business is nevertheless underway, and growers have planted 300 acres of new varieties during the last few years. They are taking up the challenge and fighting to restore a position for themselves in their home market.

Modern English cherry production tunnels before and after covering

The cherry harvest

As they mature, most cherry varieties change colour from green to yellow to red and finally darken to a rich dark red when they are ready to be picked and eaten.

After years in the orchards, good growers know instinctively when the short window opens for the perfect cherry harvest, a harvest which yields large juicy fruit.

Pick the fruit too early and the cherries can be small, pale and tasteless. Harvest too late and you may be left with soft, watery fruit susceptible to damage and decay.

Some growers believe the trick is to pick your cherries the day before the birds start eating them.

Tart cherries are usually harvested using large mechanical arms that shake the fruit from the tree. The fruit is collected on sheets spread over the ground before being chilled in tanks of water at 9°C.

They are then taken as quickly as possible to nearby processing facilities, where they are pitted or stoned before canning or freezing.

Sweet cherries are harvested by hand to protect the delicate fruit. Pickers know that sweet cherries bruise incredibly easily at the harvest stage, so they lift clusters of the fruit gently from the spur that connects them to the tree and collect them in baskets. They transfer the cherries to large bins, which are kept in the shade until full. They are then covered in wet canvas and driven to the packhouse as soon as possible.

Canada

"Canada is at its most spectacular in the spring when the cherry trees are in full bloom"

British Colombia

Ottawa

Canadian golf course decorated with cherry trees

The Okanagan Valley in south central British Columbia is the stunning setting for Canada's cherry orchards. Approximately 155 miles in length, the valley presents a spectacularly diverse and beautiful landscape, boasting mountains, highlands and parks, as well as ski slopes and golf courses.

This glorious region stretches from Osoyoos on the US border in the south to Vernon in the north. It is home to almost half of all the fruit grown in Canada and cherries are one of the area's biggest success stories.

The valley is at its most spectacular in the spring when the cherry and other fruit trees are in full bloom. Cherries are one of the region's earliest crops, harvesting from July through to August. Peaches are ready between July and September, apricots from mid-July to mid-September and pears throughout August and September. Apples and grapes are ready to pick from September to mid-October.

Their unique position in the world market means Canadian cherry farmers enjoy relatively high prices for their fruit. Demand for fresh cherries in the UK, Europe and Asia grows strongly throughout the summer, and shoppers get used to their favourite fruit being around – and will pay a premium if they must.

Naturally, if you expect premium prices, your fruit had better be of the best possible quality and the Canadian cherry definitely makes the grade. Large, dark, sweet fruit has become the hallmark of the Canadian season. The country's cherries are definitely a five-star product.

The 7,000 tonnes of cherries produced in the Okanagan account for the vast majority of those grown in Canada. They are the last cherries available from the northern hemisphere, following on from the harvests from Oregon and Washington.

Once Canadian fruit finishes in August, there is a gap during which no cherries are available commercially in the world until the South American crop is harvested in October. It's more than the true cherry devotee can cope with.

Growers are supported by one of the top horticultural research establishments in the world. The Pacific Agri-Food Research Centre in Summerland provides the research infrastructure to keep Okanagan's farmers at the forefront of growing technology.

Traditional varieties such as Bing are still widely grown, however, newer varieties such as Lapins, Sweetheart and Staccato, which are also grown extensively in the US, have replaced many of the older trees.

Working with the institute, growers are continuously developing further improvements to their cherries. Varieties so new they have not yet been named, such as C2101 and CP1904, are creating widespread interest. These promise to help growers deliver even better quality fruit for their customers, and to extend the Canadian production season with a cherry that ripens later.

The Okanagan Valley of British Columbia is not only a beautiful place – it produces the most beautiful cherries.

Left: Canadian cherry
orchards
Top right: Canada produces
some of the world's best
cherries
Bottom right: Blossom in
the city

Hydrocooling and packing

From the heat of the orchards, harvested cherries are delivered into the cool of the packhouse. The fruit undergoes an inspection to check it is the right quality to be packed and its temperature is lowered in large hydrocooling units. These use chilled water to take the temperature of the cherries down to between 6°C and 4°C, either by showering or by completely immersing them in water.

The cherries then pass along a moving production line developed to keep the fruit cool to sort it and pack it for dispatch as carefully as possible. The risk of damaging the fruit is always highest at this stage. Water plays a constant part of the process, both to keep the temperature of the cherries low and to protect them.

First, a two-stage elimination is carried out by hand to remove excess leaves and other materials from the fruit, as well as any damaged cherries.

It's a labour-intensive process but one that no machine can match. In a typical packing line, the cherries are then carried up large escalators and spread out onto a sizing conveyor. This grades the cherries using wet rollers of different sizes before dropping them into moving flumes of water. These flumes carry the cherries to be packed into bags, punnets or cartons, according to specific size and other demands of customers. Once the cherries have been packed, they are grouped onto pallets and placed in refrigerated storage until they are ready to be loaded onto lorries for dispatch.

Argentina

"In this vast country there are only a few areas well suited to cherry growing"

Mendoza
Buenos Aires
Neuquen
Trelew
Los Antiguos

Bottom left: Argentina produces cherries from a variety of climates
Right: Fresh fruit and vegetables are a way of life in Argentina

Argentina forms the eastern half of South America's long, tapering tail. It is the seventh largest country in the world and the second largest in South America, after Brazil. It is roughly one third of the size of the United States, covering an area of some 2.8 million square kilometres. It is over twice the combined size France and Germany put together.

Unlike its neighbour Chile, which is long and thin, Argentina is long and wide. It has a huge diversity of geographical areas: from wetlands and mountains to open plains and glacial regions. There are several climates, from subtropical in the north, hot and humid in the centre, mild in the north of Patagonia and glacial in the south.

Although the country is vast, there are only a few areas that have proved themselves well suited to cherry growing.

One of these areas is the region around Mendoza, which is traditional home of Argentinean cherry growing. It is here that the foothills of the Andes take over from the Pampas region, and fruit farming takes the place of cereals. Argentina's first cherry farmers set up their businesses here, against a backdrop of vast snowcapped mountains.

Cherries are harvested in December through to January – beautiful fruit grown in a startlingly beautiful place.

Argentinean lake, with
mountains and cherry
trees in winter

Patagonia is one of the most
remote and beautiful parts
of Argentina

Opposite:
Top left: Cherry orchards
with mountains behind
Top right: The colourful
district of La Boca,
Buenos Aires

More recently, farmers have found success in new growing regions surrounding the Rio Negro, Trelew and Los Antiguos regions further south and into the Patagonian region of the country. The move south has occurred as pioneering growers have sought to extend their season later into January and beyond to give Argentina a longer harvest – and a stronger position on the world market.

One of the biggest challenges facing the cherry business in this part of the world is sheer distance from the orchard to the market. From Los Antiguos, in Patagonia to Buenos Aires there are over 1,200 miles of dirt and rudimentary tarmac roads. This is the beginning of a 30- to 45-day journey for fresh cherries on their journey to Europe, the US or Asia.

The fact that we can even contemplate these journeys with such an extremely perishable cargo is a testament to the growers around the world who have the courage and skill in the face of what to most us would seem utter folly. It is possible only because they have developed suitable varieties of fruit, suitable processes for handling and suitable systems for packaging them.

As we have seen elsewhere in the world, cherry farming in Argentina is very much a family business. The biggest growers have seen their business develop and grow over several generations. Some are totally integrated, with their own packing facilities and their own marketing operations. Others rely on the cooperatives to collect their fruit and get it to the markets of the world.

Transport

Whether cherries are sent by air, sea or road, the aim is to deliver them to the shopper in excellent condition.

Most cherries travel from source to destination over land in refrigerated trucks – from Turkey to the UK market, for example. Sea and air transport are used when moving the fruit long distances between continents, with sea the preferred option.

Cherries are able to last the long trip over water thanks to technology pioneered in the US and developed commercially by the Chilean industry in the last decade. During the Chilean season approximately 90 per cent of the cherries now travel by sea. A ship can carry huge volumes of fruit, making it the most favourable option in economic and environmental terms.

The main factor affecting the life of fruit is respiration rate – the faster the rate, the faster the decay. To reduce this process to a minimum, the fruit is sealed inside a breathable bag and 50-60 per cent of the atmosphere is removed from around the fruit. The balance of natural carbon dioxide and nitrogen is altered, and the temperature in the hold of the boat is maintained at a constant 0°C throughout the journey.

Air freight is usually used to get fruit to market when volumes are low and demand is high at the beginning of a season. In the first weeks, growers send shipments of both airfreight and sea freight, the former being sold until the latter arrives. It's 21 days door-to-door across the sea from Chile to the UK, for example, or 40-45 days from Europe to Asia. This compares with 24-36 hours by air.

When it does have to travel by air, the fruit is booked and presented to a freight forwarder, who repacks pallets of fruit into containers that fit in the hold of the plane. Like a marathon runner, the container is covered with a reflective aluminium blanket, which will help keep the fruit cool. This is a key factor in preserving the quality of cherries.

Chile

"Chile provides a variety of climates for growing, and cherries are among the country's best fruits"

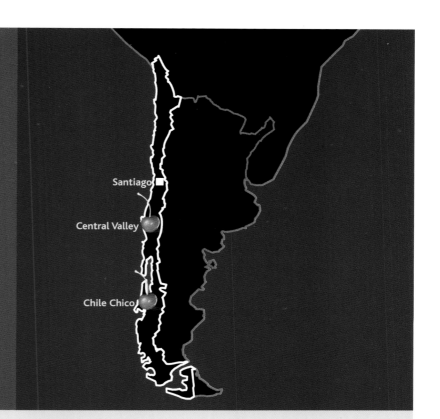

Santiago

Central Valley

Chile Chico

Agricultural land in the south of Chile

Chile is a long thin country that stretches across 38 degrees of latitude. It is over 4,300 kilometres from the top to the bottom and has an average width from east to west of only 180 kilometres.

Its unique shape provides an enormous variety in both climate and vegetation. In the north is the most arid region in the world, the Atacama Desert. Further south, modest rainfall encourages the desert to provide a breathtaking range of colours as plants burst from the soil.

Cherry central

Moving south from here along the Pan-American Highway, you arrive at Chile's agricultural heartland, the Central Valley. Life in Chile's Central Valley is good. The standard of living is high, and there are plentiful opportunities for young people. For those who like to ski in the morning and be on the beach in the afternoon, this is the place to be.

The valley is around 700 kilometres long and is enclosed by the coastal mountain range to the west and by the Andes to the east. It is dominated by impressive Mount Aconcagua, which, at 6,959 metres is the world's largest mountain outside of the Himalayas range. The capital, Santiago, is situated at the northern end of the valley.

This region alone produces more deciduous tree fruit than any other country in South America. Fresh fruit is Chile's third most important sector, consisting of 7,800 growers. Their orchards, groves and vineyards cover a wide variety of fresh produce.

Farmland in Chilean Patagonia, near Torres del Paine

Top left: The Chilean fruit industry has been one of the world's fastest growing

Bottom left: Blossoming branch in Chile

Right: Harvesting cherries in Chilean orchard

Chile Osorno Volcano,
Patagonia

The farmers working in the valley grow a wide range of produce, including grapes for the country's increasingly important wine industry. Fresh fruit growers farm approximately 215,000 hectares, producing more than 75 different types of fruit. These are directly exported to more than 70 countries worldwide.

Exports of cherries, as with so many of Chile's fresh fruits, increased rapidly during the 1990s, and they continue to grow.

The country's cherry industry is based in Curico, 200 kilometres south of the capital, and provides what some consider to be the best cherries in the world. The most important among them are the Bing, Lapin, and Van varieties. Production of Rainier cherries is increasing as their popularity increases.

Chile grows more than 75 different fruits commercially

Moving further south, the agricultural landscape gradually changes from rolling meadows into a world of unspoiled jungle, high mountains, active volcanoes, fast- flowing rivers and numerous mountain lakes. It is a spectacular part of the world, offering a wide range of outdoor sporting activities. Large areas have been made into national parks.

South of Puerto Montt the Andes fall into the sea and create an archipelago of thousands of islands that stretch down to Cape Horn. The islands, hundreds of which are uninhabited, are covered with thick forests and snow covered mountains. Again many of the mountains are active volcanoes.

To the east of this are the plains of Patagonia. Here, near the southern town of Chile Chico, cherry growers from the Central Valley have arrived to develop new orchards to extend their cropping season.

Developing farms in this remote Patagonian area is one of the biggest challenges the cherry industry faces – in the world, let alone Chile. Everything from generators and fridges to equipment for packing and sorting the fruit must be transported over harsh terrain to this isolated and sometimes inhospitable region.

Nevertheless, growers have risen to the challenge, and this development is also turning out to be one of the industry's biggest success stories. The later Chilean (and Argentinean) fruit from the depths of Patagonia, is already appearing on the market.

Chile Chico: The perfect microclimate

The microclimate created around General Carrera lake (the Chilean name for what the Argentineans call Buenos Aires lake) makes cherry growing particularly viable.

As humid cold air from the Pacific Ocean moves east, it hits the Chilean ice fields and gets chilled further before rising up over the Andes mountains. Here, it forms dark clouds that drop large quantities of rain and snow onto the lake's western coast.

As the air moves further east, it hits dry, energetic fronts on the other side of the lake formed from the Patagonian planes in Argentina. The result are ideal microclimatic conditions for cherry growing in the Chile Chico and Los Antiguos regions: good chilling hours for the fruit during winter and a relatively stable climate thanks to the presence of this huge lake (the third largest in South America).

The plantable surface area is restricted in this climatically hostile region. As the mountains surrounding the area fall into the lake there is a narrow plane formed on the south side where the river flows in to the lake. This narrow river plane is sheltered from most of the Patagonian elements and is home to this very resourceful and entrepreneurial group of cherry growers.

Despite the natural protection offered by the microclimate, growers in this area still need to build huge wind breaks to ensure that their orchards are suitably protected from the strong winds. As you drive through the area visitors find the unmistakable rows of poplars towering above the orchards forming rows, criss-crossing the area, guarding next season's most valuable crop. These are some of the latest cherries to ripen in the Southern Hemisphere.

Aerial view of General Carrera/Buenos Aires lake and Chile Chico region

Chile has a diverse
range of climates
and landscapes

Retailing

The retailer is the end of a long road for the cherry. After a year of nurturing, protecting and cosseting, it is in the retailers that the cherry meets its ultimate destiny: the shopper, the person who, with three or four delicious, juicy bites, will destroy what it has taken a year of loving care to produce.

Shoppers love cherries – and they are eating more and more of them. The larger, the juicier, the sweeter they are, the more they love them.

Most retailers now sell fresh produce, particularly fresh fruit, in premium, standard and economy packs. Premium packs of cherries contain the largest, most succulent fruit, which can reach 3cm in diameter. The Bing cherry is a favourite in the premium range and is much sought by the connoisseur.

Aptly know as the Queen of Cherries, the beautiful white and red Rainier variety is a popular premium fruit. Rainier is also another large sized cherry with a delicious taste. It has a very striking appearance that immediately catches the eye of the shopper. It is growing in popularity as buyers realise that cherries don't always have to be deep red in colour to have an unforgettable taste.

Standard packs of cherries also contain well-sized fruit, with a diameter up to 2.5 cm. At the beginning and end of the season, when supplies are limited, these are sold in smaller punnets. They are offered in large packs of between 500g and a kilo.

Retailers used to sell loose cherries straight from the carton. However, too many hands dipping into a box of delicate fresh cherries caused a great deal of damage and large quantities of fruit had to be destroyed. As a result, pre-packed fruit has become the norm.

Although cherries are still perceived to be a bit of an indulgence, as larger quantities are being made available from around the world, more shoppers are buying them, and more of them. The cherry fan club is growing rapidly and while cherries remain a luxury item, they have developed a more universal appeal.

This is encouraged as the retailers play their role giving shoppers choices, good value through special offers and promotions. All this stimulates growth in demand and underlines the important part that the retailers have to play in the story of the cherry. It's not just about what happens in far off places on the other side of the world, it also has to happen at the local store around the corner.

Australia & New Zealand

"Two of the world's most beautiful countries, producing the world's most beautiful fruit"

New South Wales

Canberra

Victoria

Tasmania

Wellington

Cromwell

Two of Australia and New Zealand's agricultural exports

Australia and New Zealand, two of the world's most beautiful countries, have become a very popular destination for tourists from all over the world.

Situated more than 10,000 miles away, it is perhaps understandable why up to now they haven't become major suppliers of cherries to the European market. But increasing demand for excellent quality fruit around the world, improvements in shipping, and expanding horticulture mean both of these countries will become bigger players during the next decade.

Australia

Australia is already beginning to realise its potential as a major international source of fresh fruit and vegetables.

Fruit growing is the fastest-growing part of agriculture in the country, with apples, citrus, blueberries and exotic fruits among those products showing promise.

Cherries are also very much on the up. In the 128 years since the first commercial cherry orchard was planted at Young in New South Wales in 1878, growers have developed cherry farms in five of Australia's seven states. In a good year, the country can produce a total of as much as 9,000 tonnes of cherries. Every year, additional acreage is being planted with varieties that will extend the Australian cherry season.

They have planted new orchards in areas such as Tasmania; Orange, New South Wales and northern Victoria, and we can expect production to increase further in the near future.

New areas are being cultivated which will also help to extend the season. For example in Hillston, New South Wales, new trees will yield good volumes of cherries from mid-October into early November.

In addition, plantings in the cooler climates found at higher altitudes of up to 1,000 metres, mean farms in parts of Victoria and New South Wales will soon be harvesting cherries much later than before.

Varieties such as Staccato grow well at higher altitudes, so growers are planting in these locations with the aim of extending their season as far as early March.

Growers in Tasmania are also looking at expanding their season with later maturing varieties for export around the world. New South Wales has remained at the heart of the Australian cherry business and still produces over half of the country's cherries. Australia's total crop, in a good year, has been as high as 9,000 tonnes.

Cherry production has also developed at Orange, New South Wales. Victoria produces about 30 per cent of the country's total, particularly in Wandin, Wangaratta and the Goulburn Valley. Southern Australia produces around 15 per cent of the national crop, almost entirely in the Adelaide Hills, east of the state capital.

Riverside view, Australia

Tasmania, Western Australia and Queensland together make up less than five per cent of the total production.

Australia's cherry crop may be small compared to the major supplying countries of Turkey and the US, but it is still worth more than A$50 million to the country's farmers. For this reason a great deal of work is being done to improve the quality of the fruit, to make farming methods more efficient and to lengthen the season by developing cherries that can be harvested both earlier and later.

Farmers are also reducing the number of varieties they grow. They are optimising production with the varieties that are best suited to the location of the orchards and that will extend the harvesting season.

The Australian government is supporting growers as they experiment with new rootstocks and with packaging systems that will help them ship cherries to more distant export markets, such as Europe. Experiments are being carried out, growing cherries under covers and higher densities of tree planting. Tasmania alone plans to increase cherry production from 500 tonnes to 5,000 tonnes within the next ten years.

The industry is buzzing with activity, and the renowned Australian energy and enthusiasm is being directed to expanding its cherry farming activities.

The Australians are gaining success in a growing number of fresh products, and they are an odds-on bet to become a force to be reckoned with in world cherries.

New Zealand

New Zealand's south island is hobbit country, providing an otherworldly backdrop for much of The Lord of the Rings film trilogy. The regions of Malborough and Cromwell are also epicentres of the country's cherry industry, as is Queenstown, which is also the world heart of extreme sports such as heli-skiing or bungee jumping.

Cherries from New Zealand are available from Christmas through to early February, which makes the country a natural successor to Australia during the year.

Growers in the country used to supply large volumes of cherries to Australia's eastern states, but have recently started exporting cherries to markets such as Taiwan, the UK and Europe.

Above: Hobbit home, South Island
Top right: Cherry exports are increasing
Main picture: New Zealand's lush landscape
Bottom right: Protecting the orchards (Australia)

The beautiful bi-coloured
Rainier cherry

Other cherry producing countries

"In June, the whole of Europe is alive with the cherry harvest"

Top right: Blossom-strewn path, eastern Europe
Bottom left: Budding cherry tree
Bottom right: Lonely cherry tree, Germany

In June, the whole of Europe is alive with the cherry harvest. France, Italy, Switzerland and Germany are among the most prolific sources. Many countries, Germany in particular, focus on the production of tart rather than sweet cherries, and therefore haven't developed into regular suppliers of fresh cherries.

Eastern Europe

As state-owned businesses in Europe's eastern and central regions have declined, it has paved the way for entrepreneurial cherry growers in a number of European countries to provide cherries, including Bulgaria, Hungry and the former Yugoslavian countries.

Growers in these places harvest their cherries during June and July.

Until recently, farmers in these countries lacked the infrastructure and technology that would allow them to compete on the international stage. But growers are starting to find the means to invest in systems and are bringing a more commercial approach to their business. In time, these growers may be able to compliment the supplies of other countries during the summer period.

Norway

Norwegian growers based around Telemark have been successful carving out a niche as producers of cherries that ripen toward the end of the European season. As in Patagonia, farmers in Norway have had to meet the challenges presented to them by the harsh local climate. The result is large and excellent quality cherries, which arrive on the market around late July to early August – and fetch premium prices.

A cherry tree overlooks a Scandinavian panorama

Main picture: Cherry farm,
Provence, France
Right: European fruit

Top left: Cherry packer, Italy
Top right: Harvest, Eastern Europe
Bottom left: Cherry trees, Germany
Bottom right: Cherry market, Italy

South Africa

The historical growing area for cherries in South Africa is the Western Cape. However, recently a new generation of farms has grown up around Ficksburg and Bethlehem, near Lesotho. Cherries are harvested here from October to December.

Growers celebrate their harvest every year with an annual cherry festival held in Ficksburg. However, heavy rain in recent years has severely damaged their crop and left them with little to celebrate, and the focus of modern developments has returned to the Western Cape.

South Africa has a good climate for cherry growing, but historically, those areas most suited to production have concentrated on the development of apples and pears rather than cherries. Similar to the story in the cherry orchards of England, the country's production has also focused on labour-intensive tall trees, not suited to the demands of a competitive market.

However, with oversupply making the world apple and pear business less attractive, some growers are looking into more niche crops, and cherries have become a more popular alternative. Some South Africans have started developing modern production systems and may be able to carve themselves a strong position on the world market, supplying cherries during late October and early November, when fruit is in short supply worldwide.

Surveying the landscape,
South Africa

Producer study:
The Carleti family

"Where you find cherry growing, you find families like the Carletis"

Top right: Members of the pioneering Carleti family
Bottom left: The old-style grading lines at Carleti's facility
Bottom right: Argentinean cherries

Where you find cherry growing, you will also often find families, families who have been closely involved with cherry farming for several generations. Take the Carleti family in Argentina.

Carleti is a big name in Argentinean cherries. Italian-born Don Vicente and his wife Albina Zingarette settled in Maipu, just south of Mendoza, in the 1920s, and worked for the British-owned railway company.

Don Vicente made friends with an Englishman who had acquired some land in Tupungato, a beautiful area 50 kilometres south of Mendoza near the foothills of the Andes. He wanted to develop a fruit farm and persuaded Don Vicente and his wife to join him.

The three moved south in 1930 and planted an apple orchard. Once this was established they decided to trial cherries, with the aim of diversifying the business. The plants were brought in by train and were protected in thick mud to prevent damage and keep the roots moist. These were the first cherry trees to be grown in this region of Argentina.

The trial was very successful and after a few years quantities of high quality fruit were available for market. The family modified a packhouse originally designed for apples, where the fruit was packed. It was then sent to the markets of Buenos Aires by train.

During this period of development and gaining experience, Vicente became passionate about growing cherries. "The heart of a Carleti is cherry shaped," he would tell his sons Aldo, Italo and Hector.

Ruano, an important company supplying apples from the town of Tunuyan, south of Tupungato, had decided to expand into cherry farming. The company approached Vicente for his expertise in cherries; he joined them, and once again the family moved south.

Vicente and his sons worked for Ruano for several years and helped the company establish its successful cherry business. Then, in 1955, they were able to buy some land of their own: a 12-hectare plot on the outskirts of Tunuyan. Three years of hard work later they harvested their first cherries, and the "Carleti" brand was born.

At the end of the 1950s, there was none of the sophisticated equipment of the modern packhouse. Getting cherries to market involved picking, sorting and packing the fruit in the same day, and all by hand. At the end of each day the fruit was taken 100 kilometres to refrigerated storage in Mendoza to be cooled before shipment by rail or road to Buenos Aires.

The Carletis in the 1980s. Left to right: Standing: Ricardo, Alberto, Fredy. Sitting: Italo, Aldo, Vicente, Hector

Preserving cherries

Bottling cherries is a fairly simple process. Once the cherries are harvested, their stems are removed and the fruit is put into glass containers in a light syrup. The containers are sealed and sterilised, meaning the fruit retains its flavour and has a long shelf life.

Top left: Cherry liquor
Top right: Bright red Argentinean cherries
Bottom: Patagonia, a new frontier for Argentinean growers

The fruit was packed like chocolates – individually in wooden boxes – and protected by decorated tissue paper. Customers loved the fruit and its attractive packaging, and demand grew fast.

To keep pace, the Carletis began buying cherries from other growers. They also built a small packhouse with its own refrigerated storage facility to help get their succulent fruit to the market in top condition.

Many of the cherries grown in the area at the time were not suitable for eating as fresh fruit. They had to be processed and sold for industrial uses, such as juicing or canning. New suppliers had fruit suitable for both sectors of the market; they insisted that the Carletis had to buy both.

Don Vicente was faced with a choice: to limit his business solely to the fruit his family could produce or to expand into the market for processed cherries – an unknown area. In true pioneering spirit, the family chose the latter.

They began by using an outside contractor to process cherries for them, but eventually invested in their own facilities. As Italians they were familiar with how to preserve fruit by bottling it, and bottled cherries were the first processed product the Carletis made.

The family also began to produce Maraschino cherries, another traditional product, which originated in the Swiss and Italian Alps, initially made with – and named after – Maraska cherries found wild in the mountains.

The process involved marinating the wild cherries in alcohol. Not only did the fruit have a distinctive taste, but there was also a large demand for the flavorsome liquor produced.

The wild cherries gradually disappeared and producers had to develop recipes to reproduce both the fruit and the liquor based on cultivated fruit instead. The result was the Maraschino cherry and cherry liquor that we know today. Every producer has his own recipe and naturally believes, with a passion, that his Maraschinos are the best.

Customers loved the old-style presentation of fresh cherries

Opposite:
1980s packing line, Argentina

The Maraschino production process was originally manual. The fruit was placed into wooden barrels with sulphur brine to preserve the fruit and make it easier to remove stems, and to separate the stones from the flesh. Once the stems and stones had been removed the cherries were washed to remove all traces of the brine. They were then put into earthenware vessels, each containing about ten kilos of fruit, and a low concentrate sugar syrup was added, which would slowly absorb the flavour from the cherries.

Once the first syrup was absorbed, a second syrup was added, this time with a higher sugar content. The process was repeated with syrups of increasing sugar content, until the sugar level in the fruit reached a high 55 degrees brix (brix is a standard measurement of sugar levels in the trade). This part of the process took about 25 to 30 days.

Finally, the fruit was put into a syrup containing a combination of essences that simulated the flavours of the traditional Maraska. These were the secret ingredients known only to a few.

Today, much of the production has been fully mechanised and the long process of increasing the sugar content is carried out under controlled vacuum conditions. The process that used to take up to 30 days can now be completed in seven days without any reduction in the quality of the distinctive flavour of the Maraschino product.

While the family's processing concern flourished, its fresh fruit business also continued to thrive. More orchards were planted, and heavy investment was made in refrigerated storage and packing equipment. The main crop for the Carletis – as for other Argentinean growers – is now the Bing cherry, which is harvested from the end of October until the end of December.

The fruit is picked by hand in the early morning and taken to the packhouse. The Carletis inspect it for quality, before sizing the fruit and packing it into boxes as specified by their customers. The packed fruit is stored in refrigerated rooms at just above freezing, until they are dispatched. The aim is to deliver the fruit to the retailers in a 'just harvested' condition

Argentina exports around one third of its cherries, with a large proportion going to the UK. As the country's cherry season is over in two months, the processing facilities of companies such as the Carletis' must be flexible, and able to handle other fruits such as peaches, nectarines and plums at other times of the year.

Cherries, whether from the Carleti orchards or brought in from outside, remain the bulk of the family's growing company. The family has also expanded, and Don Vicente's grandsons, Ricardo, Fredy, Alberto and Eduardo, are now in the business. The Carletis represent a success story of one family who saw an opportunity, took the risks and worked hard to realise their dream.

Left: Chilean cherries
Right: The Andes, Chilean side

Cherries in the future

"We will soon have even more to celebrate about this incredible fruit"

Above: Spain's stalkless
Picota cherries
Bottom left: Modern
technology and cherry trees
Bottom right: Solitary
cherry tree

Over the last 20 years, cherries have become a truly international crop and present an exciting and challenging prospect for growers around the world. The market is there for them; consumers are buying and want to buy more. But they are discerning customers who will insist on good quality at affordable prices.

During the next 10 years, we can expect to see further progress from the growers in two main areas: the availability of cherries around the year, and the size of the fruit we eat.

You can find cherries on shelves for most of the year already, but there are two notable periods during which the world market grows quiet: mid-September to late October and mid-March to late April.

Filling these gaps is one of the great challenges towards which growers in existing sources such as Spain or Chile are working towards. In addition, new sources such as Morocco or Mexico have realized that there might be opportunities worth exploring.

Moves into new geographical areas and the development of new varieties are helping growers bring earlier cherries to market; advances in technology are helping to deliver them in even better condition.

Meanwhile, the trend towards larger, more succulent cherries will continue, as breeders around the world seek out varieties that will yield tasty, large, deep red fruit. Sales of the bicoloured Rainier variety should also increase as consumers learn about and understand the real quality of this fruit.

Behind the scenes, cherry growers will take their own strides forward. Optical grading machines that measure every single cherry are already being used for fruit such as apples, pears, peaches and nectarines. This technology can select and sort according to size, colour and defects. It will soon be able to do the same for cherries – the growers will be able to grade their fruit even more accurately.

Orchards will become larger and more efficient as demand for cherries grows around the world.

However, it is labour above all else that will determine the future of each country's fresh cherry industry. It is the existence of good quality labour that has allowed profitable businesses to flourish. Cherries remain a premium fruit that shoppers are generally willing to pay more for. It is important for the sector that the drive and passion that has seen a small sector flourish into a large success story, continues. For the industry to command the premium it needs it will require continuous product innovation to ensure that their product exceeds consumer expectations.

The outlook for the industry, for the next 10 years is good. If growers have found returns diminishing on other fruits, cherries have provided a good, albeit slightly unpredictable, living for farmers around the world. Production of this fruit has increased drastically during the last two decades and this is set to go on in the years ahead. As the progress continues, both growers and shoppers will find plenty more to celebrate about the cherry in the years to come.

Credits and contacts

Norton Folgate would like to thank the following people and companies with their help in putting together this book:

Argentina
The Carleti family

Australia
Cherry Growers of Australia
Horticulture Australia
Australian Horticultural Exporters Association
Cherryhill Orchards

Canada
Canadian High Commission, London
Profresh Marketing

Chile
ASOEX, Chilean Exporters Association

New Zealand
Summerfruit NZ

Spain
Foods from Spain, Spanish Embassy, Economic and Commercial Office Val de Jerte
Agrupacion de Cooperativas, Sat Riocinca

Turkey
Turkish Trade Office, Turkish Embassy, London
Export Promotion Centre of Turkey
Baris Deniz A S

The US
Cherry Marketing Institute
Northwest Cherries
Orchard View Farms

The UK
Angus Davison

Also:
Eurofruit magazine
Fresh Produce Journal
Mhairi Smeeton, Norton Folgate

Additional research and writing by Dominic Weaver, Red Communications.
Design and layout by Geoff Hobbs, Red Communications.

Published by
RED Communications Ltd
3-4 Free Church Passage
St Ives
Cambridgeshire
PE27 5AY

ISBN: 978-0-9555424-0-4

For further information, please go to:
www.nortonfolgate.com

WOODWORK HANDBOOK

WOODWORKER'S HANDBOOK

Consultant Editor: Peter Metcalfe

SELECT
EDITIONS

A QUANTUM BOOK

Paperback edition published by
Selectabook Ltd.
Selectabook Distribution Centre,
Folly Road,
Roundway,
Devizes
Wiltshire SN10 2HR

Copyright © MCMLXXXIV
Marshall Editions Ltd

This edition printed 2004

ISBN 1-86160-971-X
QUMWH22

This book is produced by
Quantum Publishing Ltd.
6 Blundell Street
London N7 9BH

Printed in Singapore
by Star Standard Industries (Pte) Ltd

Contents

Introduction

It is no accident that the inspiration for this book came from the East End of London, since the area is one of the world's leading centres for furniture making and craftsmanship in wood, very probably because the supply of raw materials was made easy by the nearby docks and canals. Founded at the turn of the century, the London College of Furniture served the training needs of an active, growing community of woodwork workshops, providing a pool of experience and resources, as well as an atmosphere in which fine workmanship flourished.

All along it has been vital for the College to keep abreast of new technology, new materials, and craft and design influences from all over the world. Its success is reflected in the additional status it received when it was incorporated into the Guildhall University in 1990. This book, written by experts in woodworking, provides the opportunity to gain an appreciation of the qualities of fine work as understood by master craftsmen – but only learned by actually doing. Above all, it will help you to attain the level of skill that brings the extraordinary satisfaction and pleasure of a job well done.

Timber in its natural form, the living tree, is stuff of great promise. Transforming it into useful or beautiful objects satisfies several human needs, of which creativity and the love of using tools are only the most obvious. A construction idea, conceived, planned, implemented and completed, right from tree to the last drop of polish or lacquer, provides pleasure and contentment of the lasting kind.

But the promise of wood, like any other, is not necessarily easy to fulfil. Just bringing timber to a workable condition is a lengthy process, strewn with pitfalls. Felling, for a start, is potentially hazardous to life and property. Moreover, large numbers of trees, especially in residential areas, are unserviceable in terms of yielding wood because they contain wire, nails, staples, even rails. A tree or trees offered freely should be approached with caution: discover the reason for the offer before accepting it. Often enough, even the best-managed forestry tree yields a surprisingly small amount of top-quality timber because leaning trunks and branches contain weak, irregular-grained growth.

Assuming a tree has been safely felled, the next stage, conversion into pieces or boards, can begin. At this stage, the natural defects of timber start showing up, as indeed do those of the sawyer. It is all too easy for the unpractised to ruin timber by incorrect cutting and drying.

After waiting months, or in the case of some hardwoods, years for drying to complete, the moment comes at last to select the timber for the project in hand. Wood has a complex structure, and only if its characteristics are understood will there be that synthesis of material and design that characterizes true craftsmanship.

Trees may be a renewable resource, but no longer is the supply inexhaustable. Converting trees to timber is at best a wasteful process—witness the price of wood from a timber yard. The promise of trees is one that should not be denied to future generations. So before embarking on the undoubtedly worthwhile course of putting axe to tree, think about the difficulties ahead; and consider whether it might not be more responsible to recycle 'the old beam in the yard' or to use manufactured board instead.

THE RAW MATERIAL

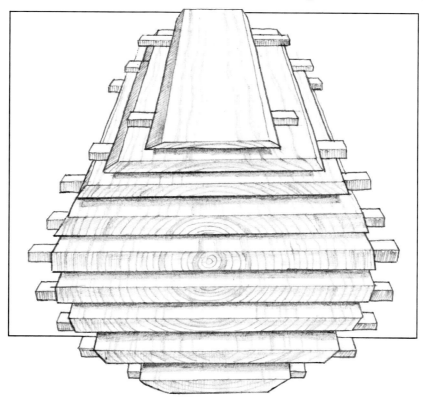

Felling

As a rule, timber merchants stock a comparatively limited number of commercial wood species, cut to standard sizes. Every so often, a woodworking project requires or deserves something extra, and this is when felling a tree, hand-picked for the job, begins to make sense. The process of extracting suitable wood from a living tree is not to be taken lightly, but the effort is undoubtedly worthwhile: the results, if successful, give enormous satisfaction.

Just selecting the tree may be fraught with problems. Examine trees in residential areas, on roadsides or in hedgerows with particular care. The lowest 6 feet (2 metres) or so often contain fence wire, nails, staples or other foreign matter—extremely dangerous when sawing. Avoid trees which are leaning: they are likely to contain irregular growths of 'reaction wood', as indeed do all branches.

If strength is essential for the wood, choose a trunk that is knot-free. Knots are the bases of branches embedded within the trunk as it increases in diameter during growth; knot-free timber, therefore, comes from trunk sections without any branches.

Another factor contributing to strength is straightness of grain. Avoid trunks with spiral grain: it is usually possible to spot them from cracks in the bark that spiral clockwise or anticlockwise.

If a novice at felling, do not start on a large tree, rather leave it to the professional. Choose one of modest size, and if it stands on someone else's land, obtain permission to fell. Even if the selected tree is on your own property, check before felling that it is not subject to a conservation order. Finally, remember that felling usually means removing the whole tree, not just the desired parts.

Before putting saw to tree, study it to decide the best line of fall. Most trees lean slightly in one direction, so try to drop the tree as close as possible to its natural line of fall. If this is not possible, control the fall with rope, wedges and, if necessary, a winch. Never attempt to fell a tree in wind. Check that nothing will obstruct the fall.

If you are felling a tree in dense woodland, where the earth can be wet and soft, it may bring down another tree with it, so ensure that no one remains closer than three times the tree's height when you drop it.

For actual felling, there is a choice of axe, hand-powered saw or chain saw. The last is easiest and fastest, and, with a mill attachment, it allows conversion of the logs at home.

A safety helmet is the most essential item of protective clothing when using a chain saw. Falling branches, even whole trees, are a real menace. Chain saws are not only extremely dangerous but very noisy. Ear defenders prevent both damage to the ears and lapses of concentration.

Heavy-duty gloves protect the hands from cuts, abrasions and splinters and aid handling of timber.

A guard helps prevent accidental contact of the hands with the saw blade.

Safety goggles should not be underestimated, since chain sawing throws up dangerous splinters and dust. Ensure the lenses are shatter-proof, with side shields.

Heavy-duty boots, well-fitting and with steel toe caps, are the soundest way of protecting the feet and ankles. Tuck the laces and your trouser legs inside, to stop them getting caught in the chain. Boot soles should give a firm grip on wet ground.

1 Always start a chain saw with the engine resting on firm ground, right foot through the handle to steady it. Hold the front grip with the left hand and pull the starter cord with the right. Other precautions: clear undergrowth or other obstructions from the area in which the tree will fall; remove any branches which are below head height.

2 It is essential to cut a wedge facing the exact direction of the required fall line. (Try to choose a fall line natural to the lean of the tree.) The wedge's top cut should be at 45°, the bottom horizontal. A wedge's depth should be a quarter of the trunk's thickness to be effective.

3 The final cut should begin 1–2 in/2.5–5 cm above the level of the wedge's bottom cut. Cut toward the wedge, maintaining a hinge of remaining wood that has even thickness along the line of the cut. As soon as the trunk starts to move, withdraw the saw, stop the engine and stand back and to one side to avoid kick-back.

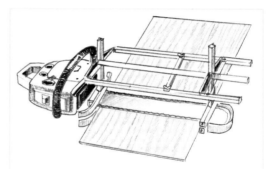

A chain saw mill enables the woodworker to make lumber to his own specifications, rather than limiting himself to the standard sizes available from timber merchants. Once a tree has been felled, topped, bucked (the branches removed) and cut to lengths, logs above 6 in/15 cm in diameter must be converted for seasoning. A mill takes much of the hard work out of this primary conversion; it clamps directly to the chain saw bar without modification.

Ripping chains are necessary to cut logs into smaller sizes. Standard chains are designed to cut across the grain; ripping saws cut more quickly along the grain.

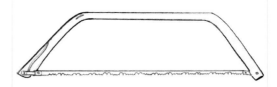

Swede saws (also called bow-saws or buck-saws) are extremely useful for bucking logs. They are easily handled by one man, though two pairs of hands speed the work. Efficient cutting requires a well-tensioned blade with sharp teeth. Today most Swede saws have impulse-hardened teeth, with blue tips, which hold their edge longer than those on regular blades. But they have to be thrown away when they become blunt, for they are too hard to sharpen.

Converting logs

The first stage of a log's transformation into workable timber is known as primary conversion. On large logs, this initial opening-up is performed by the saw mill's large band-saws, which can efficiently slice unmanageable logs into easily handled planks or boards.

Primary conversion has another important benefit: cut planks of timber dry, or season, much faster than whole logs and with a minimum of distortion. However, logs less than 6 in/15 cm in diameter can be satisfactorily dried in the round. Drying larger logs without first converting them is extremely wasteful: as the log dries, it shrinks, and this can cause severe checking, or splitting, along the radius.

The different methods of converting logs yield timber suitable for different uses. Before buying timber for a project, decide what properties and appearance are required.

There are two principal methods of conversion: through-and-through, also known as flat or plain sawing, and quarter sawing. Through-and-through sawing simply means cutting the log in slices along its whole length. Very little waste is produced, and it is the cheapest method of conversion. If the boards cut from a log in this way are kept together, in the order in which they were sliced, they can easily be matched. The figure (pattern) on the faces of such boards is usually a series of loops or arches, properly called cathedral figure.

Quarter-sawn wood is generally more expensive than wood that is sawn through-and-through because much more waste is produced. Logs are first cut into quarters, then the quarters are converted in varying ways. The great advantage of quarter-sawn wood is that it dries to a much more stable condition than plain-sawn wood and so is more suitable for structural work. The difference in shrinkage or swelling can be as much as 50 per cent.

Prominent growth rings show up as alternate light and dark stripes along the grain in quarter-sawn wood. Prominent rays show as ornate silvery or dark flecks; and in timber that has interlocked (double spiral) grain, quarter-sawing produces alternate light and dark bands, which seem to change places with each other as the light changes.

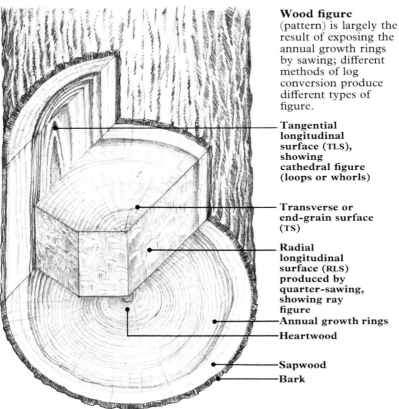

Wood figure
(pattern) is largely the result of exposing the annual growth rings by sawing; different methods of log conversion produce different types of figure.

Tangential longitudinal surface (TLS), showing cathedral figure (loops or whorls)

Transverse or end-grain surface (TS)

Radial longitudinal surface (RLS) produced by quarter-sawing, showing ray figure

Annual growth rings

Heartwood

Sapwood

Bark

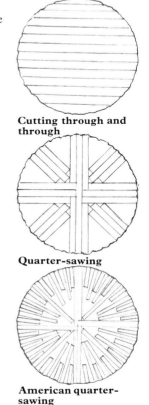

Cutting through and through

Quarter-sawing

American quarter-sawing

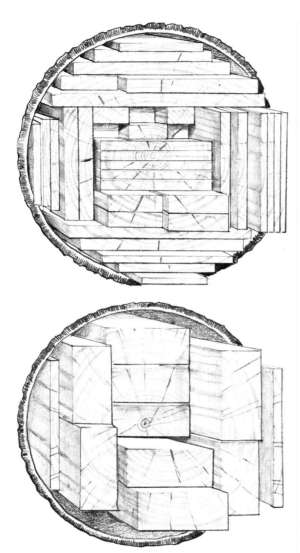

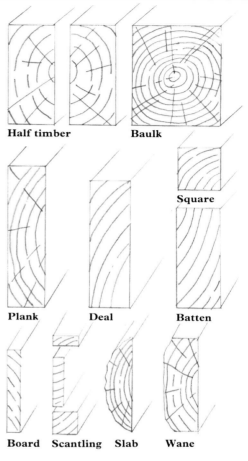

Half timber **Baulk**

Square

Plank **Deal** **Batten**

Board **Scantling** **Slab** **Wane**

Timber terms

The timber trade has precise descriptions for all the different types of timber produced by varying methods of log conversion. **Baulk** is a log squared for further conversion; size 4 × 4 in/100 mm square or larger. **Half timber** is baulk cut in half lengthwise. A softwood **plank** is a length of square-sawn timber with sawn, not planed, surfaces; 2–4 in/50–100 mm thick, 11 in/ 275 mm or more wide. **Deal**, not to be confused with plank, is 2–4 in thick, less than 11 in wide. A **square** is a length with equal width and thickness, 1 × 1 in/ 25 × 25 mm to 5 × 5 in/125 × 125 mm. **Battens** are 2–4 in thick and 5–8 in/200 mm wide. **Board** may have sawn or plain surfaces; less than 2 in thick and 4 in wide. **Scantling** is 2–4 in thick, 2–5 in wide. **Slab** is the slice removed in conversion to a baulk. **Wane** is a converted length, including part of the outer edge or bark. **P2S** means planed on two or both sides. **PAR** means planed all round. **Nominal size** means sawn dimension before planing.

Large-diameter logs can be converted to give the greatest variation in timber sizes. The upper log was converted to yield numerous boards and planks, but it could also have produced a smaller number of larger pieces as shown immediately above. It takes a skilled, experienced sawyer to choose the conversion method that will produce the most valuable timber. A major consideration is the log's knot content: knotty wood is too weak for load-bearing in constructional work. Timber from unmanaged woodland tends to be knotty because the lower branches die due to shading by the upper. If not removed, their bases are engulfed as the trunk grows outward, leaving dead knots in the outer parts of the log.

Buying wood

Woodworkers who cannot fell and convert their own timber usually buy from a timber merchant. His wood comes converted to standard sizes, usually measured in metre lengths and in millimetre widths and thicknesses. Softwoods are sold in standard lengths from 6 ft/1.8 m to 23½ ft/7.2 m with 12 in/300 mm increments. Hardwood is available in lengths from 6 ft/1.8 m with increments of 4 in/100 mm; maximum lengths vary with species.

Timber may be bought either sawn or planed. Sawn timber is rough; planed timber is smooth enough for final finishing at home. Planing reduces the dimensions of a piece by about ⅛ in/3 mm.

Splits at the ends of a timber length are common. When buying for a large job allow 5 to 10 per cent waste.

Due to the inherent variability of wood, timber is graded to give an indication of its appearance or strength. Softwoods and hardwoods are graded in different ways and the rules governing the grading systems vary internationally. Basically, however, grading is in terms of the number of defects. The higher the grade, the fewer and less significant the defects. The most common defects are knots, but there are many others such as sloping grain and splitting.

After grading, the timber is labelled with the shipper's mark, usually applied by stencil; boards, however, carry a gummed label on the face.

The top grades of timber are used for high-class joinery, while the lowest end up, typically, as packing cases. If in doubt about the grade needed, ask a timber merchant.

Softwood is graded in two ways, according to appearance or to strength. The latter method is known as stress grading and is done either visually or by a machine. The British defects system recognizes five grades: I clear, I, II, III and IV. Visual stress grading recognizes two grades: SS (special structural) and GS (general structural). The machine-stress grades, MSS and MGS, correspond to the visual ones.

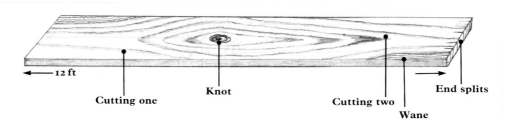

Cutting one Knot Cutting two End splits Wane 12 ft

How hardwood is graded
Hardwoods are graded visually—each individual piece is inspected. Two systems are used: the defects system, similar to that used for softwood, or the more usual cutting system. To become an efficient grader, capable of gauging a board in 15 seconds or so, takes years of experience. Inexperienced graders may have to refer to written specifications.

Grading by the cutting system is achieved, 1, by selecting the poorest face and, 2, measuring the board, length in feet, width in inches, eg 12 ft × 6 in. 3, The grader visualizes on the surface a number of clear, or defect-free, rectangles known as cuttings. 4 He measures each cutting, length in feet, width in inches, and from this calculates the number of cutting units: a 5 × 4 cutting contains 20 units; a 6 × 5 cutting contains 30 units. 5, He calculates the maximum number of cutting units in the board if it were perfect. 6, He consults the grading specifications and allocates a grade. In the USA, for example, these lay down the percentage area of the board that must be in clear cuttings. First grade, for instance, requires 11/12 of the board to be clear in one cutting; second grade is 10/12 clear in one cutting. The next grade down, known as No 1 common, gives 8/12 clear in a maximum of two cuttings.

This board contains a total of 50 cutting units in two cuttings. It does not, therefore, fit into the top US hardwood grade, which requires 11/12 of the units to be clear in one cutting, ie 66 clear units. Second grade requires 10/12 in one cutting, ie 60 units. However, No 1 common requires 48 in a maximum of two cuttings—so the board is No 1 common. In this and lesser grades, the poorest face is the basis for calculation.

Sawn Softwood timber sizes available.

The measurements are metric, in accord with British Standard 4471, 1978.

Thickness (mm)	Width (mm)								
	75	100	125	150	175	200	225	250	300
16	★	★	★	★					
19	★	★	★	★					
22	★	★	★	★					
25	★	★	★	★	★		★	★	★
32	★	★	★	★	★	★	★	★	★
38	★	★	★	★	★	★	★		
44	★	★	★	★	★	★	★	★	★
50	★	★	★	★	★	★	★	★	★
63		★	★	★	★	★	★		
75		★	★	★	★	★	★	★	★
100		★		★		★		★	★
150				★		★			★
200						★			
250								★	
300									★

Sawn hardwood timber sizes available. The measurements are metric, in accord with British Standard 4471, 1971.

Thickness: 19, 25, 32, 38, 50, 63, 75, 100, 125 mm and thicker, rising by 25 mm stages—largest dimensions normally for construction purposes only.

Width: normally 150 mm and wider in increments of 10 mm. Strips and narrows available from 50 mm in 10 mm increments.

Length: normally from 1,800 mm and longer, in increments of 100 mm. Shorts, often available, 1,700 in decrements of 100 mm.

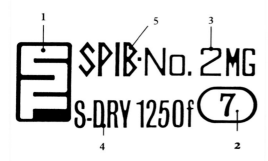

Shipping marks

1, is the shipper's own emblem. **2**, is the mill number. **3**, refers to the grade, here No 2 MG. **4**, specifies the moisture condition: S-dry means ship dry, ie not above 25 per cent moisture content. **5**, is the association whose grading rules have been applied to this particular consignment of timber. There is a large variety of shipping marks, of which these are typical examples.

Timber trade abbreviations

(As defined by British Standard 565, in 1972)

a.d.	Air-dried
C. & S.	Common and selects—combined grade of two lower grades of hardwood.
Com.	Common
d.b.b.	Deals, battens, boards (various timber shapes)
F.A.S.	First and seconds—a combined grade of the two upper grades of hardwood.
f.s.p.	Fibre saturation point.
hdwd.	Hardwood.
h.g.	Home-grown
k.d.	Kiln-dried
lin.ft	Linear foot
m.c.	moisture content
P1E	Planed one edge
P2E	Planed two edges
P1S	Planed one side
P2S	Planed two sides
P1S1E	Planed one side, one edge
P2S1E	Planed two sides, one edge
P1S2E	Planed one side, two edges
P4S	Planed four sides
S/E	Square-edged
sftwd.	Softwood
std.	Standard (165 cu ft or 4.67 cu m)
t. & g.	Tongued and grooved

Shrinkage in wood

A living tree contains a great deal of water, and so does a felled one. The sapwood, which conducts water from roots to leaves, holds most of this water and, on felling, the timber is termed green wood. The amount of water present in wood is expressed by the percent moisture content (%MC) and is the ratio of the weight of water in the wood to the weight of the wood when dry. The MC of green wood is often more than 100 per cent.

When wood has dried to 28–30 %MC, it starts to shrink appreciably. This point, where shrinkage begins, is known as the fibre saturation point (fsp).

Green wood placed in, say, a workshop, will dry until it reaches a stable weight. The moisture in the wood is then in equilibrium with the moisture in the surrounding air: the wood has reached its equilibrium moisture content (EMC). In air with 100 per cent relative humidity (RH), the EMC will be about 28 per cent. At 60 RH, the EMC is about 12 per cent. As the RH changes constantly with the weather, wood is continually absorbing and losing moisture and is thus always subject to swelling and shrinking, or movement. To control movement, wood should be dried to an EMC suitable for the atmosphere in which it will serve.

Wood does not shrink uniformly. Along the grain it contracts by only 0.1 per cent between fsp and 1 % MC. Across the grain, some timbers can shrink 14 per cent.

The most accurate method of measuring moisture content is the oven-dry method. A piece of wet wood is weighed, then dried to a constant weight in a drying oven. The %MC then equals the wet weight, less the dry weight, divided by the oven-dry weight, times 100.

The simpler but less accurate method is to use an electrical moisture meter. Two needle electrodes are inserted into the wood and a current passed between them. This current is directly related to the MC so that %MC can be read directly off the meter's dial. Several readings have, of course, to be taken and averaged because moisture varies in different parts of the wood. The main pitfall of the moisture meter is, however, impossible to avoid. In thicker pieces of wood, the electrodes cannot penetrate to the centre, which is the wettest area during drying. Such readings are thus bound to be inaccurate.

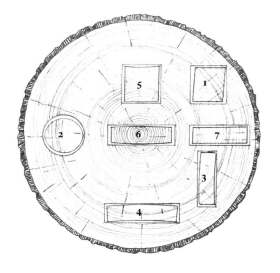

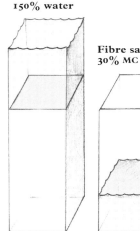

**Green wood
150% water**

**Fibre saturation
30% MC**

**Wood in use
usually $12\frac{1}{2}$% MC**

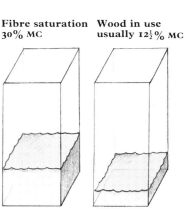

Timber warps during drying if it is cut from wood with a moisture content above 30 per cent. A square section cut as, **1**, will 'diamond'. A dowl or round section, **2**, becomes oval. Pieces cut as **3**, **4** and **5** will 'cup' away from the heart. **6**, shrinks more across its width than its thickness; **7**, becomes wedge-shaped.

Green wood holds considerable amounts of water. If it is compressed, the water can be squeezed out of it: its cells are hollow, and the free water inside them evaporates first in drying. The cell walls contain bound water; as this dries, the wood shrinks.

The chart shows suitable wood moisture content (MC) for specific uses. Too high an MC, and the wood dries and shrinks. Too low an MC, and the wood will absorb moisture, swelling in the process. Such movement makes joints open up. Trying to restrict movement by nailing, screwing or gluing only leads to splitting.

Moisture Content of Timber   %

	%	
Appreciable shrinkage commences at about this point	30	Air drying sufficient to achieve these levels
Suitable MC for pressure treatment, creosoting, fire-resisting solutions	23	
Decay safety line (dry and wet rot can start if MC is higher)	20	
Exterior joinery	18	
Garden furniture	15	
Aircraft, motor vehicles, decking, woodware	15	Artificial heat needed to achieve these levels
Timber for use in places only occasionally heated	13	
Timber to be used in buildings with regular intermittent heating, ie, flooring, furniture, musical instruments	12	
Timber to serve in continuously heated buildings	11	
Woodwork to be used in exceptionally well-heated buildings, eg, hospitals, department stores	10	
Timber to serve close to source of heat, eg, radiator shelves, mantelpieces, flooring to lie above under-floor heating elements	9	

PEG
With special treatment, the problem of timber movement can be overcome. One such treatment is impregnation with PEG—polyethylene glycol 1000. The molecules of PEG replace the molecules of bound water in the cell walls of wood; once there, it cannot be extracted, so shrinkage is effectively ruled out. PEG is most effective on green wood; in fact, it has no effect at all on dry wood. A 30–50 per cent solution of PEG in water is made up, and the wet wood completely immersed in it. The length of soaking required varies according to the size of the piece of timber being treated, but usually at least one week is necessary for the PEG to diffuse into the wood.

Seasoning

Newly felled timber contains a high percentage of water, which must be dried out before the wood can be brought into service. Dry wood is stronger than wet wood and takes finishes better. It is lighter, gives stronger joints when glued, is easier to machine, and, if the moisture content (MC) is below 20 per cent, is less vulnerable to certain types of insect attack; it is also protected from fungal infection and less likely to move—to expand or contract—when in use. Most, if not all, shrinkage occurs during drying, so the strength of a piece of woodwork containing more than one component will be considerably enhanced if all the components have been dried to the same moisture content; they will all move at the same rate when in use. Dry wood can also be more efficiently treated with preservatives and fire retardants

There are several different methods of drying wood, and all require care because, if the process goes too quickly, irreparable damage results. Logs more than 6 in/15 cm in diameter must be converted (sawn into boards or pieces) before drying; those less than 6 in/15 cm in diameter may be dried before converting.

The cheapest method of drying, requiring no specialist apparatus, is natural, or air, drying: the wind and the sun do the work. The timber must be stacked so that air can flow between the layers. Round logs or square-sectioned pieces are stacked on each other, thinner boards are usually 'box-piled', separated by timber 'stickers'. These are $1 \times 1\frac{1}{2}$ in/2.5×4 cm lengths, preferably of the same species as that being dried. Stickers of a different species may cause stick stain, which penetrates deep into the board and cannot be planed off; this is particularly awkward if the timber is pale. The stain is caused by a chemical reaction between the different timbers; some timber yards use plastic stickers to eliminate it. Wooden stickers must, in addition, be free from decay, stain or insect damage which might infect the drying wood.

However converted boards are stacked, the stickers must be placed at regular intervals to prevent the boards sagging. The ends of the boards must always be supported, and the

 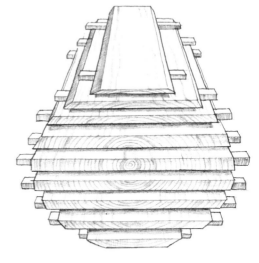

Situate a timber pile where the air circulates freely. Brick or concrete foundations will support the pile well clear of the ground, a source of fungal and insect infection.

To prevent timber warping, arrange the stickers separating the boards so that they transmit weight directly to the foundations. A cover prevents alternate wetting and drying, another cause of warping. Some wood may still warp; weighting the pile may help to prevent this happening.

Before seasoning, peel the bark from the log. It is a waterproof layer that restricts drying and can also harbour fungal spores or insect eggs or larvae, which can later harm the wood.

Boards produced by sawing a log through and through are usually stacked together (boule piling) so that they can easily be matched for figure and colour. To ensure that boards are not separated, the saw cuts may stop just short of one end, leaving all attached.

stickers arranged in vertical columns so that weight is transmitted directly to the pile foundations and not via the boards, causing them to bend. The stack should be raised about 18 in/45 cm from the ground to allow air to circulate underneath, and it should be protected from rising damp. To allow the entire stack to dry at an even rate, the width of the stack should not exceed 6 ft/1.8 m. Length may be determined by the length of the timber, and height by safety and convenience. Lastly, the pile must be protected from alternate wetting and drying by rain and sun, otherwise surface checking (splitting) results. The ideal solution is to stack timber in a Dutch barn or open-sided shed, but a tarpaulin, supported above the stack so as not to interfere with the air flow, can be satisfactory. The ends of timber tend to dry fastest and are prone to split; painting the end grain reduces this tendency.

In temperate climates, such as that of the United Kingdom, softwoods can be air-dried in three months to one year, hardwoods in about one year for every inch of thickness.

The final moisture content to which wood can be air-dried is beyond human control. In a British winter, for example, a minimum of 22–23 per cent can be reached; in a British summer, a minimum of 16–17 per cent. Some tree species contain less sap during the winter months, so timber felled then dries quicker.

Timber surfaces left damp (above 20–25 per cent MC) for several days are liable to become mouldy. Although mould does not damage wood, it does produce coloured spores that must be brushed off affected surfaces. Potentially more serious, damp wood may suffer from sapstain, a fungal infection producing a dark blue-black stain in the sapwood. It cannot be removed, and it devalues the timber; to prevent it, spray the wet surfaces with a suitable fungicide.

Air-dried timber does not have a low enough MC for use indoors and requires further drying. For the woodworker, probably the simplest solution is to purchase a dehumidifier. Placed in a small, enclosed space with the timber, this can dry wood to about 10 per cent MC in a matter of weeks.

A wood-drying kiln is expensive, but it can bring green wood down to 10 per cent MC in days. Proper management of a kiln requires skill. Only one species of timber should be dried at a time, and a recommended drying schedule followed, with appropriate modifications. If two species must be dried together, follow the schedule for the one that needs gentlest drying. Stack timber in a kiln in the same way as for air-drying.

Kiln schedules

Twelve kiln schedules (A to K) have been devised to give the fastest and safest drying times for commercial timbers. Below are two examples. Schedule A is for timbers which must not darken during drying and which are likely to warp but not to check; Schedule G is for those that dry slowly but are not prone to warping.

%MC of wettest timber on air-inlet side	Dry bulb temp.	Wet bulb temp.	Relative humidity

Kiln Schedule A

	°F/C	°F/C	
Green	95/35	87/30.5	70
60	95/35	83/28.5	60
40	100/38	84/29	50
30	110/43.5	88/31.5	40
20	120/48.5	92/34	35
15	140/60	105/40.5	30

Kiln Schedule G

Green	120/48.5	115/46	85
60	120/48.5	113/45	80
40	130/54.5	123/50.5	80
30	140/60	131/55	75
25	160/71	146/63.5	70
20	170/76.5	147/64	55
15	180/82	144/62.5	40

Drying defects

Many timber defects are caused by incorrect drying and as such are quite easily spotted. As might be expected, they differ widely in severity and, if slight, can be ignored.

Commonest of the drying defects is splitting, or checking, which usually occurs along the grain at right angles to the annual growth rings (ie, radially). The most likely location for splits is the ends of boards; take careful stock of how long the splits are, for this determines the amount of timber that will have to be discarded as waste.

Internal splitting, by contrast, cannot be positively identified until wood is cut. It is, however, often associated with a fault known as collapse, caused, like internal splitting, by drying wood too fast; though collapse is distinguished by the timber having been unusually wet at the start of drying. The outward signs of collapse are depressions in the timber's surface that often give it a corrugated appearance, known as washboarding. Such timber should be suspected of both collapse and internal splitting and so should be approached with extreme caution. The splitting (also known as honeycombing) makes it unsuitable for load-bearing, and collapsed areas of timber, being denser than normal wood, present dangers to the operator when machining.

Warping, another common defect, is likely to have been caused by cutting timber to size before it finished drying. It usually occurs across the grain (shrinkage is greater across the grain than along it) and gives rise to a range of different effects, going by names such as diamonding, cupping, bow, spring and twist. To detect warping, position your eye at one end of a board and peer along it.

Casehardening, when the wood's outer surface is compressed and the core under tension, can be detected only by a prong test (*described opposite*). Like splitting and collapse, it is caused by drying wood too quickly and presents dangers when sawing.

Discoloration, most often caused by the stickers placed between drying boards, can penetrate to considerable depths, and it is unwise to assume that it will be simple to remove the discoloration by planing.

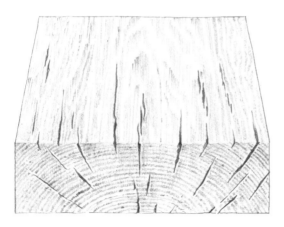

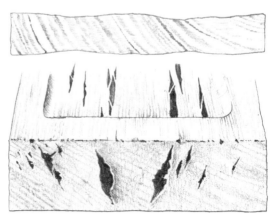

Surface checking, or splitting, is usually a minor fault; if the splits do not penetrate far, they can be planed off. Such splits usually lie along the grain; if they run across it, the wood may well be unsound and should be treated cautiously.

End splitting, like surface splitting, is a trivial fault: the split length can be discarded as waste. However, severe end splitting may run from one face to the opposite side; and though splits can close up, they always remain as structural weak spots.

Honeycombing, or internal splitting, occurs radially (across the growth rings) and along the grain. It cannot be detected until the wood is cut but is often associated with, and develops as a result of, collapse.

Collapse (*top*) can be recognized by undulations in the timber surface, within which there are visible corrugations. The collapsed timber that lies beneath is denser than normal wood and may present dangers in machining.

Warping

 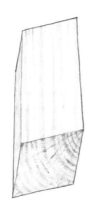

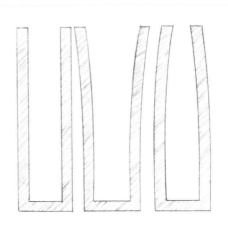

Cupping occurs if a rectangular-sectioned board is sawn through-and-through from an unseasoned log. The board surface that lay farthest from the log's centre shrinks more than the surface nearest to the log's centre.

Diamonding occurs on square sections of timber cut from unseasoned wood. Shrinkage is greater parallel to growth rings than across them.

Prong test for casehardening
If timber has been correctly kiln-dried, the prongs will emerge straight and parallel. If they curve inward, there is casehardening; if they curve outward, the condition has been over-corrected.

 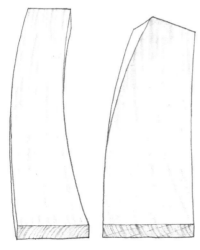

Bow, spring and twist are examples of warping along the grain. With bow, the edges are flat and the face arched. With spring, the face is flat and the edges arched. Twist means neither faces nor edges are flat. Such defects may be caused by cutting boards from unseasoned logs

containing reaction wood, ie, irregular growth with heavy shrinkage along the grain. Alternatively, the defects arise from sawing-out of casehardened boards, whose internal stresses are released on cutting.

Stick stain
Stickers—the timber lengths separating boards during seasoning—are likely to discolour the drying timber if they are of a different species. The stain can penetrate deeply and may be a serious drawback on light-coloured timbers such as sycamore.

Natural defects

What woodworkers regard as natural defects in timber are, from a tree's point of view, not defects at all but essential features of healthy development. Nonetheless, they contribute significantly to making wood the variable material it is.

Most natural defects are easily spotted. **Mineral deposits**, for example, when they are present, can usually be seen on the end grain of timber. Calcium carbonate and silica, two common deposits, rapidly blunt tools. Large deposits, known as **stone**, may be dangerous when machining.

Resin and **gum**—a tree's natural salve for wounds—are produced copiously by some species, pitch pine being a typical example. After conversion and seasoning, resin and gum may still bleed from its surface, making it sticky and, therefore, difficult to finish. Sometimes trees that have been subjected to high winds develop internal splits; these fill with resin or gum, which hardens when the timber is converted to produce **pitch pockets**.

If the outer growth region of a tree is damaged, the adjacent timber will grow around the injured part, resulting eventually in **included bark**.

Some trees last into extreme old age, the central core of heartwood becoming exceptionally brittle and resembling decayed wood: a condition known as **brittle heart**.

The strongest timber has straight grain. Deviant grain takes several forms: **spiral**, **interlock**, and **wavy grain** being common examples. The surface of this timber may be difficult to plane or sand, for in whichever direction the operation is carried out, some areas of grain are likely to lift.

Juvenile, or core, wood (produced nearest the pith) may suffer from **brash fractures**, as opposed to splintery ones.

Knots are areas of considerable grain disorientation and, therefore, weakness. If the timber is load-bearing, consider the position of its knots: near the edge of a board, knots affect strength more than in the centre.

Reaction wood, produced by leaning stems and branches to counteract the force of gravity, has several disadvantages, perhaps the most serious being that they warp during seasoning.

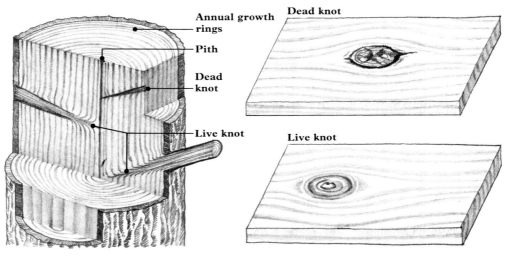

Annual growth rings

Pith

Dead knot

Live knot

Dead knot

Live knot

Knot formation is the result of grain changing direction where a branch sprouts from the trunk: grain in the trunk runs more or less vertically, in a branch, horizontally. In the illustration above, the grain is represented by the annual growth rings, formed each growing season by the addition of a complete new layer of wood over the entire surface of branches and trunk. All knots originate in the centre of the tree trunk.

Live knots are those produced by branches still growing when the tree was felled. They are firmly held in place by the surrounding wood. If a branch dies, the trunk gradually engulfs the dead branch's base. The grain in trunk and branch separate, and wood cut from these regions yields **dead knots**. In seasoning, they shrink, loosen and often drop out.

Hardwoods

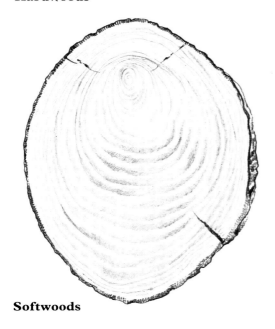

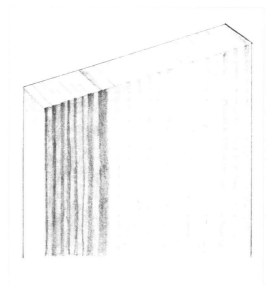

Softwoods

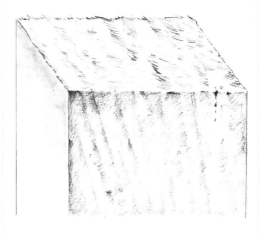

Reaction wood is produced in leaning branches and trees to counteract gravity. The direction of lean is earthward, so the upper surface of a limb is stretched, or under tension, while the lower is squashed, or compressed. Hardwoods produce their reaction wood toward the upper, or tension, side, softwoods toward the lower, or compression, side—hence the terms tension and compression wood. The wood on the opposite side of the limb to the reaction wood is normal.

Compression wood from a softwood tree shows more distinct annual growth rings than normal wood if the condition is slight. It is denser, harder and more brittle. It shrinks considerably (about 5 per cent) along the grain and is likely to warp in seasoning. Tension wood is difficult to distinguish visually, but it may be a little paler than normal wood, with a silvery, lustrous appearance, or it may be quite dull and lifeless. It shrinks badly, both along and across the grain, but is slightly tougher and more tensile than normal wood. In sawing, planing and turning, its fibres tend to be torn from the surface, giving a woolly appearance. Stain may apply patchily.

Fungal and insect decay

Wood, like all living things, is engaged in a cycle of decay and rebirth. In the case of trees, two principal agents encourage this process: fungi and insects.

The fungi which live on wood are broadly classified into moulds and sapstains, as opposed to the true wood rotters. All reproduce by emitting microscopic, air-borne spores. Mould spores, blue-green or sometimes brown or pink, are easily brushed off. Sapstains, a deep blue-black or brown, penetrate deeply, especially along the rays. Both moulds and sapstains commonly occur in timber yards and will grow on wood surfaces not rapidly dried to less than 20 per cent moisture content (MC) after conversion. Suitable fungicides should thus be sprayed on as a precaution.

The wood rotters not only discolour but weaken wood, if not destroy it entirely. Two main varieties exist: the brown rots and the white rots. White rot initially causes localized discoloration, known as pocket rot or white speck: dark zone lines, properly called dote or spalting, may also develop in the early stages.

Brown rot has two common forms, wet and dry rot, both depressingly familiar in buildings. They may be difficult to distinguish. Dry rot shows more surface checking than wet; wet rot may appear as dark-brown strands branching across a surface, while dry manifests itself as white, fluffy growths in wet atmospheres or as a silver-grey, leathery mat in dry atmospheres.

Wood rotters go to work if the MC of wood rises above 20 per cent. Dry infected wood below this level, and decay ceases; allow it to rise again, and the rot will begin again. So never use wood known to be infected, even if it appears sound.

Insects introduce themselves into wood through their eggs. The larvae, or grubs, hatch, eat their way in by burrowing tunnels and later excavate a chamber just below the surface, where they turn into adults. The adults bite their way back to the surface and fly off, leaving a flight hole, which is the first visible indication of infestation. Some wood-inhabiting insects attack only unseasoned material and are deterred by proper drying. The rest must be tackled by fumigation, heat treatment or insecticides.

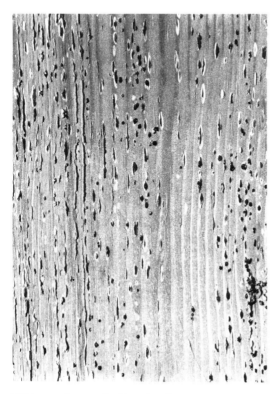

White pocket rot in Douglas fir

Blue stain, a sapstain commonly infecting newly felled timber, does not decay wood nor significantly reduce its strength.

Dote, or spalting, is the early stage of infection by a white rot fungus. If left to develop, it destroys the wood.

Wet rot, or cellar fungus, commonly attacks wet wood wherever persistent water leakage or condensation occurs.

Dry rot is a misnomer: the fungus attacks wet wood, not dry. But the surface checking it causes in advanced stages looks dry.

Pinhole borer, or ambrosia beetle, attacks only unseasoned wood. The insect larvae feed on a fungus that stains.

Massur birch results from insect attack on a living tree. The larvae leave brown flecks that are decorative in veneer.

Wood wasp attacks only unseasoned timber, but, after drying, the larvae may live on for years. Large flight holes are left.

Powder post beetle attacks only hardwoods that have a high starch content and large pores. Much dust is produced.

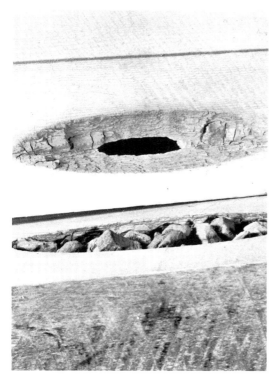

Brown pocket rot in spruce

Blue stain

Insect	Wood attacked	Part attacked	Seasoned/ unseasoned	Flight hole	Frass	Life cycle	Other characteristics
Pinhole borer/ Ambrosia beetle	Mainly hardwoods occasionally softwoods	Sap and heart	Unseasoned only	Round 0.5–3mm	Absent	1–2 years	Straight tunnels; flame-shaped stain around flight hole; wood never powdered
Furniture beetle	Hardwoods 50–60 years	Sap and heart	Well seasoned	Round 1.1–2mm	Present, ellipsoid	1–20 years?	Wood may be reduced to powder
Deathwatch beetle	Hardwoods (soft)	Sap and heart	Unseasoned	Round 2–3mm	Present, coarse	5–10 years or more	Infects partially decayed woods typically in old buildings; makes tapping noise
Powder- post beetle	Hardwoods	Sap	Seasoned & unseasoned	Round 1–2mm	Plenty present	1 year	Attacks large-vesseled timbers with high starch content; sapwood completely powdered
House longhorn beetle	Softwoods (hard)	Sap first, then heart	Seasoned	Oval 5–10mm	Present in tunnels	3–11 years	Dead or dying trees attacked– bark must be present for egg- laying; roof voids usually first place of attack in buildings; wood not powdered
Wood wasp	Softwoods	Sap and heart	Unseasoned	6mm +	Present in tunnels	2–3 years	Adults brightly coloured; does not usually attack healthy trees; wood not powdered

Manufactured board

Quality solid timber is increasingly difficult to obtain and correspondingly expensive. Such is the demand for solid wood that young and, therefore, small trees are being felled, in turn yielding timber of comparatively small dimensions. These facts, and a growing awareness of the commercial possibilities of utilizing previously wasted timber–even the humble shaving–has encouraged the development of manufactured sheet materials.

Advancing technology has made a wide range of such boards available. Their principal advantages over solid timber are cheapness, availability in large, well-prepared sheets, plus stability: shrinkage and expansion are the same in all directions parallel to the surface. Additionally, sheet materials have no natural line of cleavage (splitting) as does solid timber, so splitting is reduced.

It is best to regard manufactured boards as materials in their own right. Problems arise if they are treated as solid timber: joints which are effective with solid timber may not, for example, be so for manufactured board.

There are five main types of laminated manufactured board.

Veneer ply is made up of wood veneers glued together. Looked at in cross-section, the upper half of the board is a mirror image of the lower, construction thereby being 'balanced' and warping greatly reduced. If a decorative veneer is applied to the board by the woodworker, it must be balanced by a similar veneer the other side for stability.

Traditional veneer plywoods consist usually of an odd number of plys–3-ply, 5-ply and multi-ply–the grain of the successive veneers running at 90° to each other for improved strength and stability. Even numbers of plys will also be encountered, and these also have balanced construction, although the grain of the centre veneers will run parallel.

Laminboard, blockboard and **battenboard** are manufactured panels whose cores are made up of strips of wood, which are laid parallel and then surfaced with veneer. The difference between these three types of sheet material is mainly in the size of the wooden strips forming the core. In the USA, they are usually called laminboards of lumberboards.

Composite boards have cores of varying materials, one example being cardboard strips glued together. They can be surfaced with veneers to give ultra-lightweight panels.

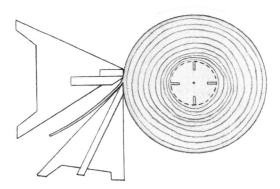

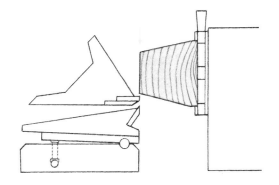

This economical method of cutting veneers requires straight logs, cross-cut into suitable sections and mounted on an enormous lathe, which rotates the log against a stationary blade the length of the log section. It effectively 'unrolls' the veneer in a continuous strip, which is then cross-cut to suitable lengths. The figure, or pattern, so produced is usually loops or arches.

A series of slices is produced by this method. Usually only part of a log is mounted for cutting. If the log is quarter-sawn, for example, each piece, or flitch, can be sliced to give radial veneers, which may show a highly decorative figure or pattern with some species and grain configurations.

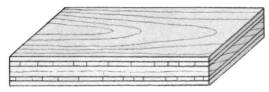

5-ply is the traditional ply construction: an odd number of veneers is laid at 90° to each other, with surface grain parallel.

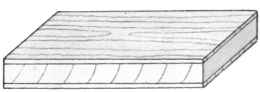

3-ply: the grain of the inner sheet runs at 90° to the outer. The thickness of veneers may be equal or vary, in which event, surface veneers are equal.

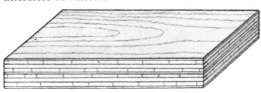

Multi-ply has up to 19 layers, glued with the grain at right angles. It has excellent resistance to distortion and swelling and no natural line of cleavage.

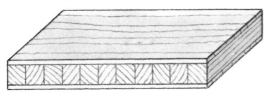

Blockboard: the timber strips are laid parallel, and veneers glued either side, with their grain running crosswise.

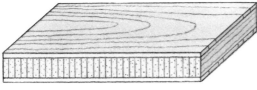

Laminboard: a similar construction to blockboard, but the strips of timber are glued together: a heavier, denser panel.

Plywood grading

Two factors apply: the quality of the face veneers and the type of adhesive used. The latter determines durability, particularly against moisture, and thus whether the plywood may be used indoors or out. The grade of the material is marked on each whole sheet. In the example above, **1**, indicates which grading rules have been applied, here the APA's (American Plywood Association). **2**, is the mill number. **3**, is the grade of the face veneer; AC means the best face is grade A, the poor face grade C. **4**, is the species group number–group 1 has the strongest, stiffest timbers in this system. **5**, is the type–interior or exterior.

Adhesives used in laminated boards

The adhesive used fundamentally affects the board's durability and thus its intended function. By British Standards, the grades of adhesive durability are:

WBP: weather- and boil-proof. Resistant to weather, micro-organisms, cold and boiling water, steam and dry heat. The glue is, in fact, more durable than the wood and the board serves admirably in outdoor and marine use.

BR: boil resistant. The adhesive fails under prolonged exposure to weather, but is resistant to micro-organisms and cold water for many years.

MR: moisture-resistant. The glue can withstand cold water for long periods, hot water for a limited time, but fails under boiling; it is resistant to micro-organisms.

INT: interior. Adhesive grades include mainly animal glues such as blood albumin, casein and soya. Such adhesives should be used where there is no risk of moisture; they are not resistant to micro-organisms.

Particle board

Particle board is a useful term for what most woodworkers think of as chipboard or flakeboard, but which, in fact, covers several different types of board manufactured from a wide variety of woody materials, from peanut shells through sugar cane to wood chips.

Some ingenious recycling of waste wood goes into particle board manufacture. The cores of logs from which veneer has been peeled, and, of course, planer shavings, are both commonplace constituents. Chips obtained from these materials are random-sized, but it is also possible to engineer chips with particular dimensions and shapes. Softwood timbers, for example spruce, larch, fir and pine, are the principal source of chip for particle board, but some hardwoods, for example birch, are also used. Seven principal categories are produced: single-layer (homogenous) board: three-layer board; graded density board; extruded board; orientated strand board (OSB); wafer board and wood cement particle board.

Whatever the category, the wood particles are bonded together with resin, which may be mixed with a variety of additives to enhance particular properties. Cement, for example, is added to create wood cement particle board, which has extra dimensional stability, will not burn and resists fungal attack.

The chips themselves generally lie with their grain parallel to the board surface; however, in extruded board, the chips lie with the grain perpendicular to the plane of the board, giving a material with little tensile strength (resistance to bending) but which can be manufactured to thicknesses greater than in any other type of particle board.

Wafer board contains the largest chips—thin wafers of wood up to 1×1 in/25×25 mm and consequently has the greatest shear strength. Single-layer chipboard consists of chips of similar size lying parallel to the plane of the board, giving a surface of relatively low quality, the shape of the surface chips showing through most surface finishes. Three-layer board consists of both large and smaller chips in a sandwich construction. The core of the material is made up of the large chips and the two surfaces of layers of the finer chips. Graded density board has a similar construction and a smoother surface finish.

Orientated strand board has a high proportion of long, narrow particles laid lengthwise, parallel to the plane of the board. This can produce a two- or three-fold increase in bending strength as compared to randomly orientated material.

Type of board British Standard 5669	Method of bonding 'chips'	Physical properties	Uses
Type I	Urea Formaldehyde (UF)	Basic requirements for bending strength, stiffness and tensile strength perpendicular to plane of board must be met; degree of swelling after one hour in water must be satisfactory.	General-purpose boards, commonly used in furniture.
Type II	UF	Higher performance than Type I, especially in terms of bending stiffness and impact resistance.	Most common in flooring.
Type III	Mixture of UF, melamine formaldehyde (MF) and sometimes phenol formaldehyde (PF).	Strongest and stiffest available; some resistance to moisture.	Typically for flat-roof construction and livestock pens. Type II/III, combining properties of both categories, can be used in kitchens and bathrooms where there are high moisture levels.

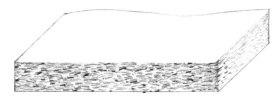

Single-layer chipboard consists of chips of equal size lying parallel to the plane of the board.

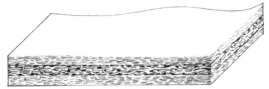

Three-layer chipboard has a sandwich construction. The core is large particles and the two surface layers are finer, smaller particles.

These give a smooth surface for further finishing. The surface layers have a higher density than the core.

Graded density chipboard has a centre made of large chips and surfaces of extremely fine chips. The chips in between show a gradation in size. The smaller the surface chips, the smoother the board surface. The smoothest surfaces are of fine sawdust.

Extruded board accounts for the thickest types of particle board. The chips are of similar sizes and are orientated to lie perpendicular to the plane of the board. Extruded board may have circular holes running internally along its centre to reduce weight.

These boards are not generally resistant to moisture, although their resistance may be improved by the addition of water repellants. More commonly, some resistance may be given by producing a physical barrier between the wood chips and the moisture by painting, varnishing or veneering. Even so, particle board is generally unsuitable for exterior use unless it is a type that is specifically categorized as such because it has been treated with certain chemicals or with certain finishes. The problem is that moisture brings about a deterioration of the resin used to bond the particles. In the majority of these boards, the chips lie with their grain parallel to the surface of the board so that, with the uptake of moisture, the most significant swelling occurs across thickness. On drying out, the board does not return to its original dimensions, so it is essential to ensure that where particle board may get wet the surface, and the edges, are efficiently protected.

Particle board finishes
Standard (usually single-layer type) board is usually supplied ready-surfaced with wood veneer, plastic or some other laminate and is unsuitable for painting.
Fine or superfine boards have smooth surfaces giving minimum show-through of substrata; it is suitable for direct painting or the application of paper foils.
Primed and filled boards have hard, smooth surfaces for subsequent painting.
Paper-faced boards are intended for further finishing. Impregnated paper foils may be used as an alternative to filling prior to painting. Such foils provide a more effective barrier to movement of particles in the underlying core than do filler coats and are, therefore, preferred if damp conditions are likely.
Decorative paper-faced boards are available with a wide range of grain-printed paper foils, some resin-impregnated to increase durability; they may be undercoated for further finishing. Melamine-surfaced boards require no further treatment and are highly durable.
PVC-faced boards are available with white, plain colour or wood-grain effects.
Wood-veneered boards are made in almost limitless different patterns and qualities.

Fibre board

Of all the 'artificial', manufactured wood-working materials, fibre board is made from the smallest 'pieces': wood fibres. It is also the newest of the manufactured boards.

A typical method of producing fibre board is by placing solid wood in a pressure chamber. The pressure of the air inside the chamber is then suddenly reduced to a vacuum, causing the wood literally to explode as the air trapped inside the wood cells expands as a result of the reduced external pressure. Water is usually mixed with the fibres to form 'furnish', and any additives, for example, fungicides, are mixed in at this stage, although none is essential. The furnish is then laid on a wire mesh and pressed with a heated platen. The pressure exerted squeezes the water out through the wire mesh and naturally-occurring substances within the wood bind the fibres together. No resin is necessary, although it may be added to enhance the properties of the board, as it is to MDF.

As a result of pressing, one side of the board is smooth, while the other carries the imprint of the wire mesh. If fibre board needs to be smooth both sides, it can be made that way by a different process. The pressure exerted on the furnish during pressing also determines the density and hence the type of board created: minimum pressure, for example, produces the thickest boards with the lowest densities—the softboards or insulation boards. These are made as sheets, planks or tiles with useful sound- and heat-insulating properties. Water resistance can be induced into the boards by impregnating with bitumen and this extends their range of uses.

A furnish which undergoes higher pressure is properly called hardboard and turns out thinner and denser than softboard. The most common type of hardboard is standard hardboard; its range of uses is wide, from furniture to underlays and panelling. Strength, water- and abrasion-resistance can be improved by impregnation with hot oil or resin to produced tempered hardboard.

Medium hardboard is that with the lowest density. It is sub-divided into three different types: LM (low medium density); HM (high medium density) and MD (medium density). The latter type, properly called MDF, is becoming increasingly popular, since it is more like solid timber than any other board material; but, unlike solid timber, it is of uniform quality and free from defects. It works better than other board materials, and a high standard of cutting, routing, moulding, embossing and finishing can be achieved.

HARDBOARDS

Standard	Tempered
$\frac{1}{16}$–$\frac{1}{2}$ in/1.5–12 mm Wall and ceiling linings, panelling, partitions, joinery, kitchen units, furniture, chalk boards, caravan interiors, floor coverings, underlays, flush-door facings, shop-fitting, display and exhibition work	$\frac{1}{8}$–$\frac{1}{2}$ in/3–12 mm Standard hardboard impregnated with hot oil or resin. Stronger, water resistant abrasion resistant. Interior and exterior wall linings, storage bins, box beams, floor coverings, bench and counter tops

SOFTBOARDS (Insulation Board)

Softboard	Bitumen-impregnated
$\frac{3}{8}$–1 in/9–25 mm Sheet, plank, tile, sound and heat insulation; underlay	$\frac{3}{8}$–1$\frac{3}{16}$ in/9–30 mm 10–30% bitumen. Often water resistant. Heat insulation decking, sheathing, roof sarking

MEDIUM BOARDS

Low density (LM)	High density (HM)	Medium density (MDF)	
$\frac{1}{4}$–$\frac{1}{2}$ in/6–12 mm Wall panelling, ceiling panelling, pinboards	$\frac{1}{4}$–$\frac{1}{2}$ in/6–12 mm Internal wall panelling, partitions, ceilings, sheathing, underlay, shopfitting, sign boards	$\frac{1}{4}$–1$\frac{1}{4}$ in/6–32 mm Fibres bonded by urea formaldehyde resin. Furniture with intricately shaped parts	(chair rails, etc.); needing a smooth surface (billiard tables); or low resonance and stability (hi-fi system cabinets)

Insulation board is the lowest-density fibre board and insulates against both sound and heat. It is produced as sheets, planks or tiles, one side of which may be embossed to give a decorative effect.

Hardboard usually has one side smooth, one side embossed. Here the smooth side is illustrated. Occasionally material with both sides smooth is available.

The rough side or 'mesh-face' of hardboard is created by the imprint of the wire mesh during manufacture.

Peg board, a readily available variation of hardboard, is simply standard hardboard with one side smooth, but with circular holes at regular intervals.

Ribbed board is hardboard with its smooth face moulded to give a decorative effect; it is often used in panelling.

MDF

This material has a wider range of uses and is more versatile than any other manufactured board material. Its advantages are:
• As a sheet material, it can be used like solid wood, but with consistent strength.
• High strength.
• Two smooth surfaces.
• Excellent edge quality that needs no lipping or edge banding.
• Machines well—can be intricately cut.
• Takes finishes well, including stains, lacquers, paints, transfer painting, foils or laminates.
• Low wastage.

Mouldings

The range of mouldings available for the woodworker is nothing if not varied, and most timber merchants or building supply stores carry considerable stocks. It is not hard to find the appropriate material for almost every imaginable architrave, skirting, door or window frame section. If it is impossible to match an existing moulding already in position, don't give up: remove a short length of the moulding and take it to a reputable timber merchant. It is relatively simple to make special cutter blades for the machines that shape moulding; given time, a reputable mill will run off moulding custom-made to individual requirements.

Virtually any timber, softwood or hardwood, may be used for mouldings, but those with finer textures give smoother surfaces for subsequent finishing. The properties of MDF (medium density fibre board) make this new, modern material especially suitable for mouldings that are usually finished by coating or over-wrapping with decorative papers, foils or natural wood veneers.

Timber to be moulded is passed through a machine whose cutters rotate at high speed.

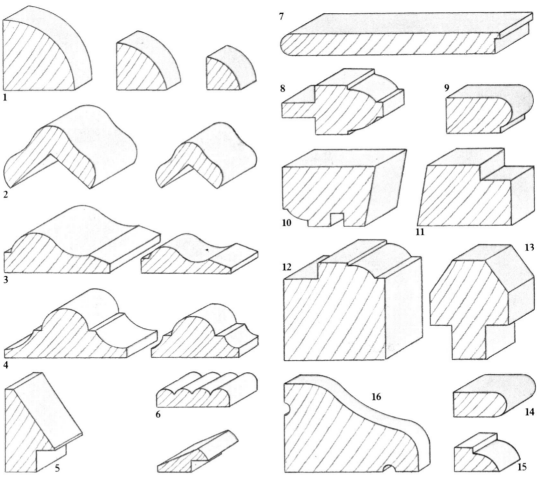

A selection of typical decorative mouldings showing the variety of shapes available: **1**, quadrant beading; **2**, corners; **3**, lambs' tongues; **4**, double astrigal; **5**, ornamental moulding; **6**, lipping for hardboard or plywood.

A selection of window and door sections for use in joinery—usually made from softwoods but also available in hardwood: **7**, window board; **8**, sash bar; **9**, staff bead;

34

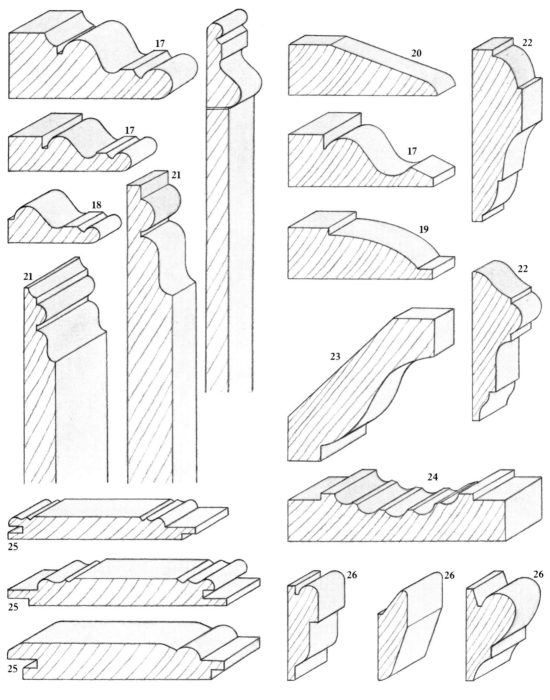

10, bottom sash meeting rail; **11**, sash meeting rail; **12**, bottom rail; **13**, sash bar; **14**, parting bead; **15**, glass bead; **16**, door drip.

A selection of large size decorative mouldings:
17, ogee architrave; **18**, panel moulding; **19**, 'ovolo' architrave; **20**, rounded architrave; **21**, skirtings; **22**, dado rails; **23**, cornice; **24**, fluted architrave; **25**, tongued-and-grooved reed matching.

Varieties of picture rail: 24, 25 and 26.

35

To the woodworker, any workshop, large or small, has its own unique charm, even its own unique smells—the sharp, spicy smells of polish, glue and new-cut timber. It is natural for the craftsman to aspire to a workshop of his own, even a tiny one.

But for most people, a real workshop, away from domestic distractions, where one can concentrate on the job in hand, is unfortunately impossible. The high cost of rent and rates, even in country areas, means that many private professional woodworkers are forced to work in pocket-size home workshops. It is no coincidence, then, that the pages which follow demonstrate ideas for workspaces that will fit into tiny flats, garages and attics. Anyone serious about woodwork needs a working environment at least as good as what is suggested here; no one can do fine work if their expensive tools are kept in a heap under the spare bed.

It is not only the job and the hardware that benefit from workspace organization: those who share their home with the pastime or trade will appreciate less mess and quicker results. A methodical approach to woodwork is, in addition, a safety-conscious approach.

Tools stored in an orderly fashion are easier to keep sharp and rust-free. Moreover, children need protecting from the poisons in paint and polishes.

Paint and varnish stripping is a particularly dangerous pastime and should be kept well way from not only children but animals. Store a few clean sticking plasters in the toolbox or workbench drawer or mount a proper first aid chest on a wall.

Before using power tools, spare a moment or two to check the condition of the plugs and cables. Any sign of damage or excessive wear means that they should be repaired immediately by a professional. Old power tools which are not double-insulated are overdue for replacement: they may appear to be sound mechanically, but any deterioration in the internal wiring can turn the whole tool into a live terminal.

Most commercial activities carried out at home require permission from the appropriate local government department; this is often difficult to obtain, almost certainly time-consuming, if not expensive. Think carefully before launching yourself as a self-employed woodworker.

THE WORKSHOP

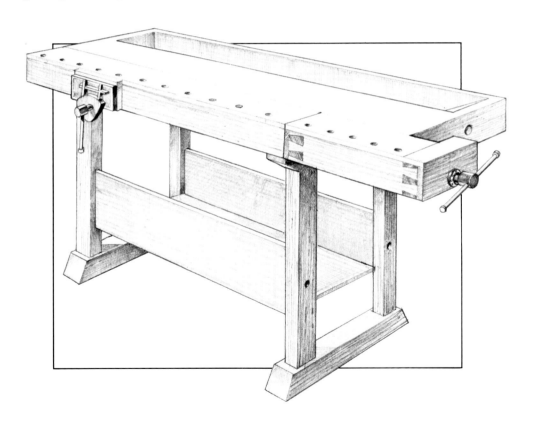

The home workshop

Few are lucky enough to begin woodworking with a fully-equipped workplace, but this does have one advantage in that space can be adapted in line with developing skills.

A variety of areas about the home can make a comfortable, versatile workshop, but the three most usual choices are the garage, the garden shed or a cellar. The garden shed usually has potential only if it is large enough and if it does not, as is likely, suffer from dampness, low headroom and poor light. If a garden shed does happen to be suitable, it can be adapted to the same basic layout as the garage shown opposite. So, too, can a cellar, which shares most of the drawbacks of a garden shed; however its isolation cuts disturbance to family and neighbours.

A garage is generally the best option, allowing large, complex jobs to be stored while work is in progress. Even if a workshop is intended for the construction of small items, it needs adequate light, ventilation and a safe, convenient power supply, plus secure storage for tools and materials. All of these are easiest to obtain in a garage, and if the workshop area is well planned, it will occupy just one end of the parking area.

The garage layout, *opposite*, will prove its worth, especially if power machinery is to be used: free-standing circular saws and the like must be securely attached to the floor for safety, which is not always possible in cramped areas.

A logical layout is essential for safety and to maintain quality of work. Tools and hardware must be kept dry and rust-free and be stored within reach of the main workbench, clear of damp floors or draughty outside doors. Chipboard and other sheet materials should, ideally, be stored flat to minimize warping. Second best, but more practical, is to stand them as near vertical as possible, and to secure them by means of a length of timber fixed to the floor and a safety cord at the top.

Lighting must be bright. To find the correct level, multiply the length of the workshop in feet by its width and double the result. This figure roughly equals the wattage required. If incandescent (tungsten) bulbs are to be used, multiply the floor area by three. This level of lighting is brighter than that needed for most other places in the home, but it is necessary.

Workbenches and storage units opposite are described on the following pages.

'Stirrups' for storing timber

Sheet materials against wall

Power outlets

Bench for dirty work

Length of timber as stop

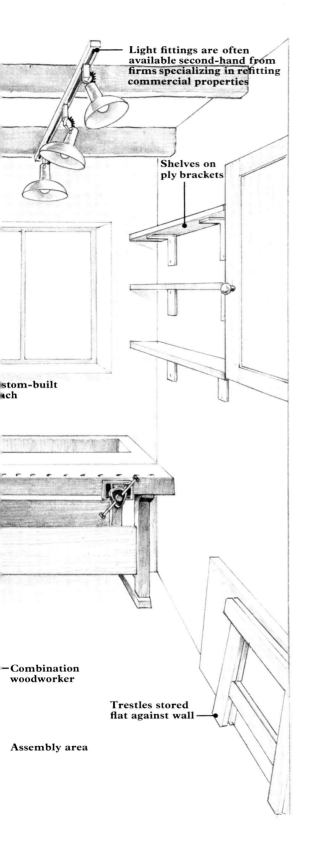

Light fittings are often available second-hand from firms specializing in refitting commercial properties

Shelves on ply brackets

stom-built
ach

Combination woodworker

Assembly area

Trestles stored flat against wall

Safety

Power outlets must be fixed at bench height to minimize danger from trailing cables.

All power outlets and plugs should be earthed and fused.

A master on-off switch is a sensible precaution; fix it high, out of reach of children, and turn it off when leaving.

Stains and polishes should be locked up.

Always return tools to their accustomed storage places.

Planes in particular need careful storage. Traditionally, they are stored on their sides to prevent damage to the blades, but they take up less space if left face- (sole-) down on a piece of unwanted carpet that has been lightly oiled or coated with damp-repellant spray.

Lock the workshop when it is not in use. Install a fire extinguisher near the bench or door and check it regularly to make sure it is in working order.

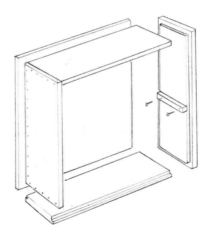

Simple toolbox or cupboard

This toolbox or toolrack is easy to build and can be wall-hung or kept on a suitable horizontal surface. The secret is to construct it first and *then* cut the door (or lid) simply by sawing around the dotted line with a panel saw. Attach the door or lid with hinges and a padlock, add softwood shelves as required and finish with paint or varnish.

The ideal bench

Wood must be held steady if it is to be accurately sawn, chiselled or planed; this is not entirely straightforward if a piece of work is awkwardly shaped. The jaws of a simple woodworking vice operate efficiently only on pieces of timber with two suitably flat, parallel surfaces, and, of course, the size of the piece of work that can be held is limited by the extent to which the vice opens.

For this reason, the cabinet maker's or joiner's workbench incorporates two different types of vice, which operate in conjunction with dogs, or stops, that fit into the top surfaces of their jaws and of the workbench itself. In this way, the vices can hold work of almost any size or shape, though the front vice is generally used for smaller items, while the tail-end vice's unique capability is for clamping and holding firm pieces of timber that need to be supported on the bench's surface along their whole length while work is in progress.

A true professional workbench is made suitably robust and rigid by construction in hardwood, sometimes solid throughout. The top must be thick, flat and level, supported by four heavy-duty legs braced with stretchers.

One of the legs should be a 'deadman', or solid timber post. Work placed directly over it can be hammered at will, since the wood's natural resilience easily absorbs the shocks. Even the strongest of modern metal vices, can, by contrast, withstand relatively little hammering.

The best (most rigid) material for a bench is hardwood; in this example, solid beech throughout.

The tool well should be at least 3 in/7.5 cm deep so that all the usual woodworking tools can lie in it without protruding.

The finish of a top-quality workbench should be 'natural', such as that given by a few coats of Danish oil, which dries to a non-greasy protective layer. If the grain in the top surface runs away from the tail-end vice it is easy to skim the surface clean occasionally.

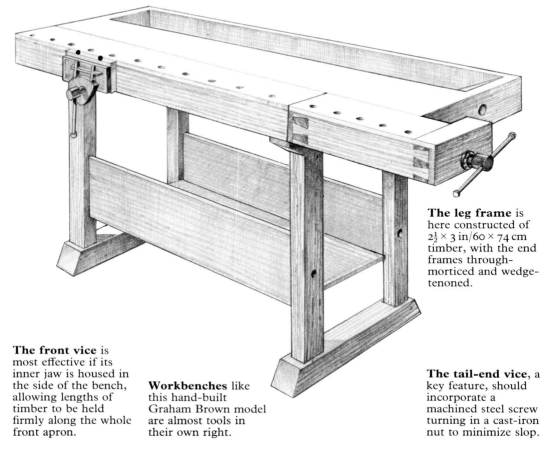

The leg frame is here constructed of $2\frac{1}{2} \times 3$ in/60 $\times$ 74 cm timber, with the end frames through-morticed and wedge-tenoned.

The front vice is most effective if its inner jaw is housed in the side of the bench, allowing lengths of timber to be held firmly along the whole front apron.

Workbenches like this hand-built Graham Brown model are almost tools in their own right.

The tail-end vice, a key feature, should incorporate a machined steel screw turning in a cast-iron nut to minimize slop.

40

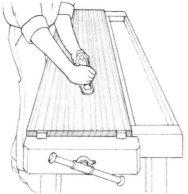

The tail-end vice comes into its own for clamping long boards, for the dogs, or stops, set into the surface of the vice's outer jaws can engage with the end of a board lying on the bench surface. The dogs securing the far end of the board are at the bench's far end.

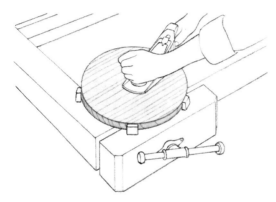

Clamping awkwardly or irregularly shaped work is the unique capability of the dog, or stop, set into the upper surface of a vice and working with others set into the surface of the bench.

Hammering strains a workbench unless one of the legs is a 'deadman'—a solid timber post. Work placed over this can be hammered at will.

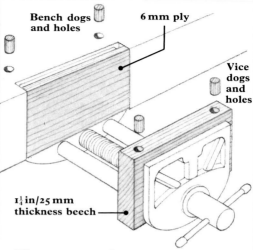

Bench dogs and holes

6 mm ply

Vice dogs and holes

$1\frac{1}{4}$ in/25 mm thickness beech

Vice construction

The Record vice, most commonly fitted as the front vice on a craftsman's workbench, has metal jaws to which wooden cheeks are fitted to protect work from damage. The outer jaw needs a sturdier cheek than the inner one does.

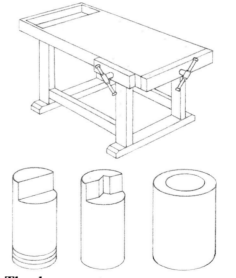

The dogs, or stops

Round bench and vice dogs have proved more versatile than the traditional rectangular ones; they are just as strong and accept oddly angled work more easily. Notched or drilled in various ways, dogs can be adapted to almost any purpose. Extra dog holes can be drilled at will. Home-made dogs should have a flat surface planed on one side so that they can be held in place with hardwood wedges.

Home-made bench

The workbench below is made mainly of discarded off-cuts bought cheaply from a timberyard, but it will prove perfectly sturdy with several years of use.

Begin by planing the five best pieces flat on one face and square on both edges. Dowel them together to form the worktop; to find the positions for the dowels, arrange the timbers together on edge and mark four pencil lines square across them—one line 2 in/5 cm in from each end, the other two spaced equidistant between them. Next gauge a line on each piece of timber. It should be half the timber's thickness and should cross the pencil line. Turn each timber and repeat on the opposite side. Now mark the best faces—easy recognition pays later. Then accurately bore the dowel holes (10 mm di-ameter, 1 in/25 mm deep) at each intersection of gauge and pencil lines. Next cut and plane the side or apron pieces.

Now glue the worktop pieces together with their dowels. Plane and rub with abrasive paper until level and smooth. Finish the top part of the bench by gluing and screwing the apron pieces on edgeways. The legs, like the worktop, are made of $4 \times 1\frac{1}{2}$ in/100×35 mm stock, joined as shown below.

For stiffening, runners are bolted to the legs at floor level. The space between the runners can be boarded over to provide extra strength and space to store tools. Additional tool storage can be created by constructing an open-topped box from four pieces of the $4 \times 1\frac{1}{2}$ in/100×35 mm timber plus a ply base. Glue and screw it to the bench end.

To complete the bench, add a tail-end vice and a front vice. The first can be improvised from a light-duty woodworking vice with the jaws faced with hardwood, each piece drilled to accept dogs. The second should be a heavy-duty vice, again faced with hardwood. Drill the work surface as required for dogs.

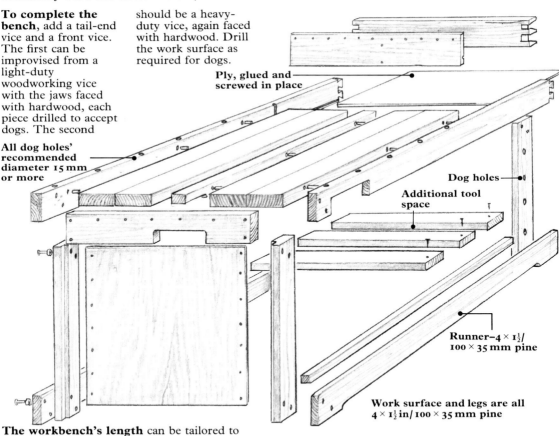

Ply, glued and screwed in place

All dog holes' recommended diameter 15 mm or more

Dog holes

Additional tool space

Runner–$4 \times 1\frac{1}{2}$/ 100×35 mm pine

Work surface and legs are all $4 \times 1\frac{1}{2}$ in/ 100×35 mm pine

The workbench's length can be tailored to suit workspace available, but a minimum extent is about 50 in/120 cm. The most comfortable working height, especially for those with back problems, is 39 in/99 cm, and this governs the leg height. Drill dog holes in the bench surface as required for varying work shapes and line them with copper piping. It is soft enough not to damage tools in the event of their slipping.

The bench's width is dictated by the width of the surface timbers, here making a total of about $22\frac{1}{2}$ in/ 575 mm

The Black and Decker Workmate is advertised as a workshop in itself—quite a fair claim. It is also a versatile adjunct to an existing workshop, for the large vice jaws can hold outsize work, and the structure is so sure-footed that it unbalances only under heavy pressure. It is especially useful for holding house doors while they are being fitted.

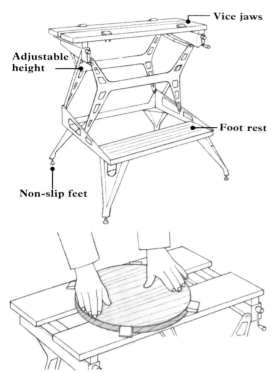

Vice jaws

Adjustable height

Foot rest

Non-slip feet

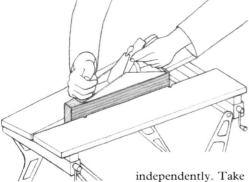

Holding awkwardly shaped work is possible with a Workmate: it is supplied with plastic pegs that fit into the vice surfaces.

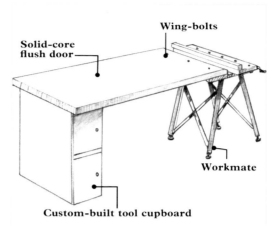

Wing-bolts

Solid-core flush door

Workmate

Custom-built tool cupboard

Pack-away workbench

A useful pack-away workbench can be made from a Black and Decker Workmate, a solid-core flush door and a custom-built tool cupboard. Simply bolt one end of the door to the Workmate, the other to the cupboard. The outer Workmate vice jaw should be left free so that a length of $1\frac{1}{2}$ in/35 mm timber bolted to it can act as a tail-end vice.

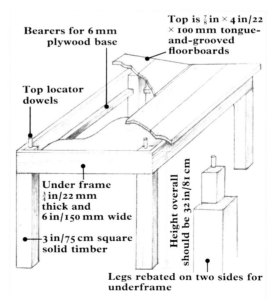

Bearers for 6 mm plywood base

Top is $\frac{7}{8}$ in × 4 in/22 × 100 mm tongue-and-grooved floorboards

Top locator dowels

Under frame $\frac{3}{4}$ in/22 mm thick and 6 in/150 mm wide

Height overall should be 32 in/81 cm

3 in/75 cm square solid timber

Legs rebated on two sides for underframe

Wedge-shaped work can be gripped in a Workmate's vice jaws because each end can be tightened independently. Take care not to mark work by excess pressure. Pad surfaces with scrap wood for protection.

Kitchen table workbench

The top of this table is secured by a dowel at each corner so that it can be lifted off and turned over, one side being plain for wood-working, the other finished for everyday household use.

Workshop accessories

A well-made workbench is an extremely versatile piece of equipment–almost a tool in its own right; but it cannot support every piece of work in the manner required. Cutting up large sheets of ply, for example, is best done on trestles; and, of course, there are the numerous occasions when work has to be carried out on location, away from the workshop. Sooner or later, some means of carrying tools about, and of supporting work without the luxury of a bench, becomes essential.

In and out of the workshop, nails and screws need storing tidily; the only way to achieve this is with a purpose-built nail box or a series of carefully labelled drawers or containers in which they will remain dry and rust-free. Being able to locate the required size of nail or screw without hunting through a heap of oddments saves time and frustration, enabling woodworking operations to procede in a continuous, smooth sequence.

Many woodworkers find a square and mitre cutting-box as essential as the nail box. It is inexpensive to buy (or easily made in the workshop) and allows swift rough-cutting of square ends or mitres, accurate enough for joinery. If the cutting-box is to be made in the

workshop, use an off-cut of hard timber–beech or oak are the best.

For the extra finish and accuracy required in cabinet-making, where fine furniture or picture framing is the end result, make a shooting board. This is the accessory that enabled cabinet-makers to cut superbly close-fitting joints before the advent of machine tools. It is especially useful for reducing the length of a piece of timber by a small amount, as anyone will appreciate who has attempted to remove, say, $\frac{1}{16}$ in/1.5 mm from the end of a length of wood with a saw. The knack of using a shooting board is essential to fine woodworking; remember it can be tailor-made for a left- or right-handed person.

All these accessories should be constructed to the highest possible standard. People judge a woodworker by the items that lie around the workshop. If they are well made, they will also be a pleasure to use, besides lasting a lifetime. A saw horse, in particular, will be pressed into service for all manner of jobs, from wallpaper hanging to doubling as a childrens' climbing frame. Make it at least strong enough to stand on and heavy enough not to tip over easily.

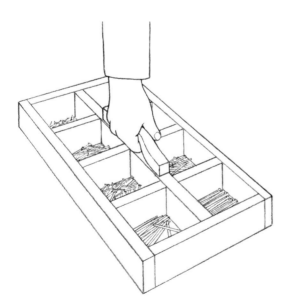

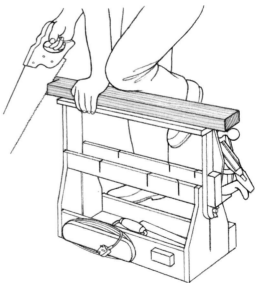

Nail box with compartments: pin together the two sides with the ends between them. Cut the centre piece to 4 in/100 mm wide at the ends, and

shape a handle in the middle. Glue and pin in place. Glue and pin the ply bottom in place. Cut quadrant beading and pin it into place.

Tote box or portable workshop: make the internal partitions of $\frac{1}{4}$ in/ 6 mm ply, glued and pinned. The top rail is cut from 2 × 2 in/

50 × 50 mm stuff, well glued, and each end is fastened through the box sides with three $1\frac{1}{4}$ in/32 mm No 6 screws.

44

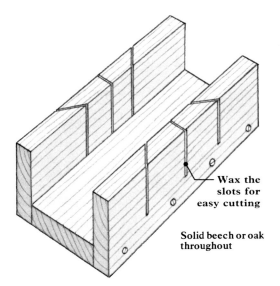

Wax the slots for easy cutting

Solid beech or oak throughout

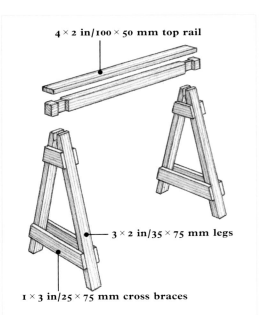

4 × 2 in/100 × 50 mm top rail

3 × 2 in/35 × 75 mm legs

1 × 3 in/25 × 75 mm cross braces

Mitre and square cutting box: make to any desired size up to 24 × 8 × 4 in/ 600 × 200 × 100 mm internally, or as small as 6 × 1 × $\frac{5}{8}$ in/ 150 × 25 × 15 mm for beading work. For general use try 12 × 3 × 2 in/ 300 × 75 × 50 mm. Glue and screw the three pieces together; carefully mark and saw the slots.

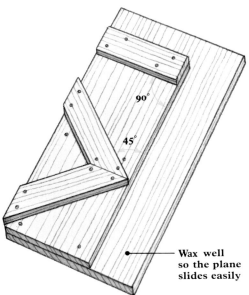

90°

45°

Wax well so the plane slides easily

Steel nail plates

Shooting board: glue and screw together, taking great care to make accurate angles. To use, sharpen plane and set the blade for fine shavings. Firmly squeeze the timber up against the chosen rail with the left hand, with about 1 mm protruding over the bed. Lie plane flat, pressed against base and bed; slide it along.

Saw horses
The simple saw horse, *top*, will pack neatly away. It could also be made with hingeing legs and cross-braces of nylon rope. A sturdier version, *above*, makes use of the angled nail plates normally employed to join roof trusses. Be safety-conscious when constructing or using a saw horse. Insurers may decline to pay claims arising from accidents incurred through rickety equipment.

The tool box

Different tasks demand different tools: obvious perhaps in the context of different woodworking trades, but not so clear to the newcomer to woodworking. Carpentry, which is the construction of wooden-frame buildings, roofs and floors, needs sturdy and powerful tools. Joinery, the art of making domestic fittings, doors, windows and so on, demands greater accuracy and consequently tools capable of giving a better finish on exposed surfaces. The cabinet-maker or restorer works to the highest standards of all and needs special tools.

The chart lists tools suited to these three distinct categories of work. As might be expected, carpentry tools are fewest in number. They are less versatile than other types in that some are suitable only for rough cutting. The best all-round tool kit is probably the joiner's, for many joiner's tools are strong enough for heavy work but still suited to cabinet-making. One can build up to the furniture-making or cabinet-making tool kit by adding the tools listed in columns two and three to the basic set given in column one.

Tools are heavy, so take trouble organizing the tool kit in advance of a job away from the workshop. Items such as drills, wall plugs and an extension lead are useful.

Toolbag and workshop tips
A plumber's toolbag, made from canvas, is useful for carrying tools around. The bag opens out flat so that all the tools are on view. Keep a **candle stub** in the tool kit; it is useful for lubricating tools or screws, and a smear of wax will often help when hammering nails into hard timber. A **spare pencil**, and a couple of **sticky plasters** in a clean envelope will save lost time. Professionals keep a **pencil** behind an ear; it is harder to lose that way. A piece of **fine cord** takes up no space in the kit but can be used as a plumb line for checking verticals or as a straight edge. It also comes in handy for holding long lengths of wood while fixing them. If jobs are spread across many sites, make a **totebox**. This will be useful as a support for sawing and other operations besides helping to keep small tools together. **Sawdust and shavings** have their place in the workshop: they soak up atmospheric moisture and so help to keep tools free from damp. A **water-repellant spray** such as WD40 is also useful for this purpose.

BASIC CARPENTRY
(Fences, roofs, floors)

CUTTING AND MARKING

Panel saw or rip-saw: 24 in/61 cm
Tenon saw: 12 in/30.5 cm
Carpenter's square: 9 in/23 cm
Steel tape: 10 ft/3 m
Pencil
Marking gauge
Firmer chisels: $1\frac{1}{2}$, 1, $\frac{1}{2}$in/
    4, 2.5 cm, 12 mm

FASTENING

Masonry drills: $\frac{3}{16}$, $\frac{1}{4}$in/5.5, 6 mm
Small screwdriver
Large screwdriver
Claw hammer: 16–22 oz/450–625 g
Bradawl
Power drill (hammer)
Twist drills: $\frac{1}{8}$, $\frac{1}{4}$, $\frac{3}{8}$in/
    3, 6, 9 mm
Flat bits: $\frac{1}{2}$, $\frac{9}{16}$, $\frac{3}{4}$in/12, 15, 19 mm
Countersink
Pincers

FINISHING

Surform block plane
Jackplane: No $5\frac{1}{2}$
Sanding block
80 and 120 grit abrasive
Paint, polyurethane, creosote,
    Cuprinol

JOINERY (Doors and windows)	FURNITURE-MAKING AND RESTORING
Panel saw: 22 in/56 cm Hacksaw Steel rule: 12 in/300 mm Bevel-edge chisels: $\frac{1}{4}$, $\frac{3}{4}$ in/6, 19 mm Mortise chisel: $\frac{1}{4}$ in/6 mm Marking knife Awl	Dovetail saw Mitre square Sliding bevel Bevel-edge chisel: $\frac{1}{8}$ in/3 mm Paring chisel: $\frac{5}{8}$ in/ 16 mm Cutting gauge
Yankee spring Ratchet screwdriver Twist drills: $\frac{3}{16}$, $\frac{3}{8}$, $\frac{5}{8}$ in/ 4.5, 9, 16 mm	Warrington hammer (cross pein) 8 oz/225 g Mallet (size to suit)
Smoothing plane: No 4 Shoulder plane Rasp	Cabinet scrapers Rebate (rabbet) plane French polish Scratch stock Router Low-angle block plane

If a woodworking operation flows in an uninterrupted, orderly sequence, time is saved, frustration is minimized, and the quality of the finished article will undoubtedly be enhanced. The only way to ensure this smooth flow is by organization in advance.

As a first step, before attempting to mark up, check that all sheet materials and solid timber have the grain direction and appearance required. Plywood, laminated board and other manufactured panel materials should, in particular, be free from faults in the core material such as overlapping veneers, voids, and loose or irregularly shaped core strips. The surface(s) should be checked for ripples, splits, holes or blisters. Tapping a surface with the fingernails will usually reveal blisters or areas that have been inadequately glued to the core: they make a hollow sound.

Solid wood should be free from sapwood, wild grain, surface checks, end splits and knots, which could weaken the structure or show up unattractively when finished.

Prior to marking-out, it is also advisable to recheck that planed timber has been prepared to the width and thickness required and that the edges are square.

Marking-out, cutting and shaping are most easily carried out in bright, natural light. If this is not available, then bright, artificial light is essential, preferably soft, fluorescent lighting carefully positioned so that it casts no hard shadows.

When marking-out is complete, double-check that it is accurate; 'check twice, cut once' should be the rule. Little is more soul-destroying than having to replace a component because it has been incorrectly marked out and cut, particularly if the timber is rare or exotic and, therefore, expensive.

Before starting any process, check that all tools and equipment are to hand and that cutting-edges are sharp. If jigs or similar aids are required, this is the moment to make them or to check that they do not require any modification.

If the process to be worked through is unfamiliar or complicated, it pays to list the various stages in a logical sequence.

Adopt the habit of returning tools to their alloted places. They are then less likely to be damaged or to cause injury, they will last longer and they will not be mislaid nor clutter the bench top.

If power tools are to be used, observe the safety rules:
● Never adjust a tool that is not isolated from the main power supply.
● Never perform an operation outside the scope of the equipment.
● Adjust all guards correctly.
● Clamp the work to the bench top securely.
● Inspect power tools regularly for damage to cables and plugs. Check that plugs are properly attached to cables.
● Wear protective goggles when using a portable electric router or a lathe.

MARKING, MEASURING, CUTTING

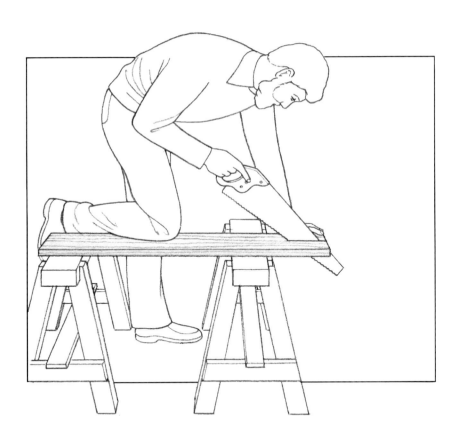

Marking up and measuring

Timber cannot be accurately marked out for cutting into the shapes or lengths required for a piece of work unless it has first been painstakingly prepared with flat faces and square, parallel edges. Assuming this has been done correctly, the marking-up tools then come into their own, not only for creating the necessary guide lines for chiselling and sawing but for testing the results. These are the most useful types:

Try square: used only for marking lines square to the edge against which it is held; this is one of the basic marking-up tools. Traditionally the try square is made with a rosewood stock and a steel blade. (The stock is the mount that holds the blade.) The modern plastic variety is, however, more stable, unaffected by atmospheric changes.

Combination square: used for marking lines square to the edge of the work and for 45° mitres. Because of its versatility, it is sometimes bought instead of a try square.

Sliding bevel: the blade can be adjusted to any angle required.

Mitre square: the blade is set permanently at 45° to the stock and is used for marking out mitres.

Marking knife: this is purpose-made for producing cut lines across the surface of the grain before chiselling or sawing; the sharp blade severs the wood's surface fibres without tearing.

Steel rule (straightedge): the metal retains a truly straight edge, despite the knocks it receives in the workshop. A 12 in/300 mm straightedge is long enough for most purposes.

Flexible steel tape measure: highly convenient for measuring out specific lengths, it rolls up neatly inside the compact container. The most useful varieties are marked with both Imperial and metric scales.

It is useful, in addition, to be aware of the basic professional terms used in measuring: the *length* of wood is always taken *along* the grain. The *width* of the material is the distance from edge to edge *across* the grain. The *thickness* is the distance *between the faces*.

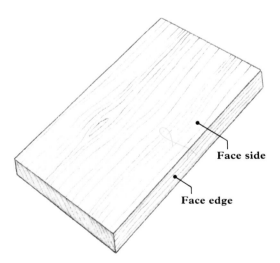

Face side

Face edge

Professional squiggles are the means of easily identifying the face side and the face edge of wood, no matter how it lies on the bench. They also indicate that the two adjacent surfaces are true—square to each other. The face-side mark is a simple, looped character, extended to touch the face edge. The face edge is indicated by a V, its apex pointing toward the face side.

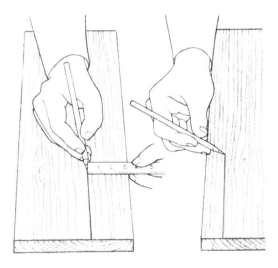

To mark out lines parallel to edges quickly, especially when accuracy is not essential, hold the pencil against the end of a rule while the other hand grips the rule firmly between thumb and first finger, the knuckle of which is held as a stop against the edge of the wood. If working close to the edge, dispense with the rule—but take care not to get splinters under your fingernails.

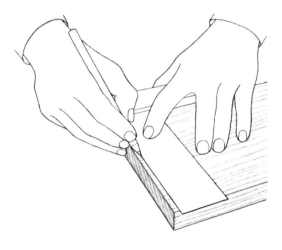

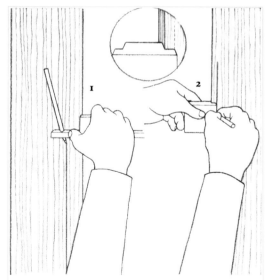

To use a try square, simply rest the blade flat on the timber, pressing the stock firmly against the edge. Mark out against the outside edge of the blade and reserve the inner edge for testing. Use a carpenter's pencil for the preliminary marking, then a knife to sever the surface fibres of the wood.

Pencil gauges and scribing
To mark accurate lines parallel to an edge, use a marking gauge drilled to accept a pencil, **1**. If the line is close to the edge, as for instance when marking a bevel, use a simple plywood gauge, **2**, with a rebate of the desired size worked along one edge.

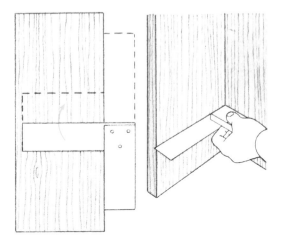

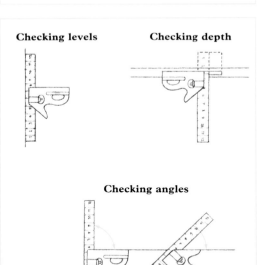

Checking levels   **Checking depth**

Checking angles

To test a try square's trueness, place it against an edge known to be straight and mark a line. Then turn the square over: any inaccuracy will show as a divergence of the line and the blade.

Checking internal angles of 90° is simple with a try square: just hold blade and stock square to the work. For checking angles other than 90°, use a sliding bevel.

The combination square
This tool is useful for checking the depths and squareness of housings, rebates (rabbets) and mortises. With a spirit level incorporated, it may also be used for aligning vertical and horizontal edges. Before use, check that the screw securing blade to stock is tight.

51

Using gauges

Marking off widths or thicknesses and setting out joints are key operations in woodwork. It is usually essential, and particularly important in the case of joints, for the cutting lines to be not only accurate but parallel to an adjacent edge. Gauges are the surest way of marking such lines. Better-quality gauges have brass facing strips on the working face of the stock to minimize wear.

Four types of gauge are used regularly:

The marking gauge is fitted with a simple spur, or spike, for marking *with* the grain. Because the spur would tear the surface fibres, it is not used for marking across the grain, except in the case of end grain.

A cutting gauge carries a blade instead of a spur and can thus cut a clean line *across* grain; it is also used for cutting thin wood and for trimming grooves and rebates (rabbets).

The mortise gauge is essential for marking out the parallel lines that act as guides for cutting tenon and mortise joints. Two spurs are fitted to this type of gauge, the inner one being adjustable.

Panel gauges are for marking exceptionally wide boards. They can be made in the workshop with stems as long as 30 in/760 mm and have special design features.

Of the other measuring and marking aids, pinch rods are perhaps the most used. Checking internal dimensions is not easily or accurately done with a tape or rule. Pinch-rods—simple, overlapping lengths of timber—are the solution.

The tips are just butted up against the internal surfaces, and the amount of overlap carefully marked. With the rods removed, the internal measurement is re-established by putting the rods back together so that the markings indicating the overlap coincide as before.

Marking arcs, a more specialized operation, is usually done with compasses, but they are also easy to improvise with a sprung lath—a flexible length of timber. Different radii are marked just by bending or straightening the lath so that its effective reach decreases or increases.

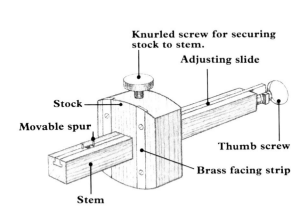

Knurled screw for securing stock to stem.

Adjusting slide

Stock

Movable spur

Thumb screw

Brass facing strip

Stem

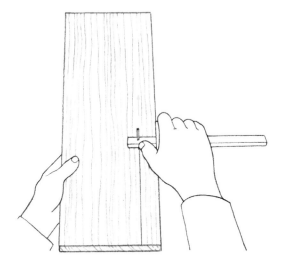

A mortise gauge is designed so that the chisel used for chopping the mortise can determine the width between the spurs. The blade is placed between the two pins and the movable pin then adjusted for a snug fit. Before doing this, slacken the screw that secures stock to stem—it also bears on the adjusting slide for the movable spur. Retighten the knurled screw before using the gauge.

Correct grip on a gauge contributes greatly to accurate marking out and makes successful operation much easier for the inexperienced. The thumb is located close to the spur and pushes the stem forward. The index finger lies over the top of the stock, pressing down lightly, and controls the gauge's tilt. The other fingers hold the stem and press the stock against the work. Thus the marking gauge's spur is *trailed*, giving extra control and less chance of it digging erratically into the wood.

1 Rounded blade (general work)

2 Pointed blade (slitting, trimming)

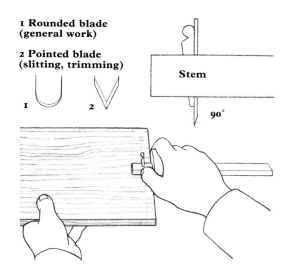

A cutting gauge's blade should stand at right angles to the stem but, viewed in plan, may be angled slightly to prevent it 'running out'— following irregular grain. It is sharpened on one side only, the bevel facing the stock. For general work, a rounded blade is best, but for slitting or trimming an existing edge the blade cuts better if sharpened to a point.

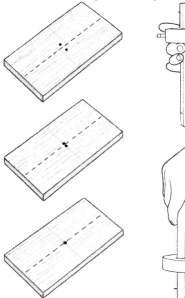

To centre the spur on a board, adjust the stock so that the spur lies close to the centre line. Mark a line in from each edge of the board. Readjust stock so that the spur lies equidistant between the two marks. Check from each edge of the work. Fine adjustments can be made to the stock, even when it is secured, by tapping the stem firmly on the top of the bench.

Dividing into equal parts

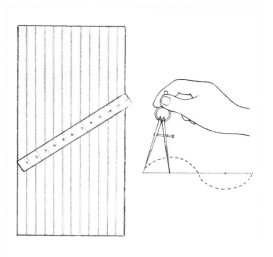

To divide timber into equal parts, place a rule diagonally across it, adjusting the rule to give the number of strips required. Mark off with a pencil, then cut with a marking gauge. Or use dividers, adjusted so they mark off equal intervals when stepped.

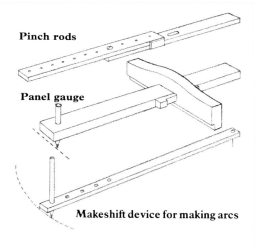

Caption: Pinch rods / Panel gauge / Makeshift device for making arcs

Internal and other measuring aids

Improvised pinch rods serve their purpose, but a more permanent device, with greater accuracy, can be made by drilling one rod at regular intervals and slotting the other. The two are then clamped together with a bolt and wing-nut. The panel gauge, for marking wide boards, has the lower edge of the stock rebated to locate on the edge of the board being marked, and is secured to the stem with a wedge.

Saws

A bewildering variety of saws is available to the woodworker, but for simplicity they can be considered as three main groups.

Handsaws are used for preliminary cutting and take three different forms: the rip-saw, the cross-cut saw and the panel saw. A rip-saw is 26 in/66 cm long, with four to six teeth per inch (TPI), and is generally used only for sawing with the grain. A cross-cut is 24 in/61 cm long, with seven to eight TPI and is generally used for cutting across the grain. A panel saw is 22 in/56 cm long, with 10 to 12 TPI and is generally used for sawing across the grain of sheet materials or thin wood. Cross-cut and panel saws may be used to saw with the grain, but a rip-saw is faster.

Back saws are for bench work. The top edge of the blade is stiffened with a steel or brass back, and there are three varieties. The tenon saw, 10 to 12 in/25.5 to 30.5 cm long, with 12 to 14 TPI, is for general bench work. The dovetail saw, 8 to 10 in/20 to 25.5 cm long, with 18 to 22 TPI, is for fine work. The bead saw, 4 to 10 in/10 to 25.5 cm long, with 32 TPI, is for the finest work, including cutting small mouldings, and is sometimes called the 'gent's saw'. As the very fine teeth are difficult to sharpen, the saw is discarded when blunt, though some types have replacement blades. It is useful to have two tenon saws, one with bevelled teeth for sawing across the grain and the other with sharp teeth left square across their faces, like a rip-saw, for sawing with the grain. Bevelling fine teeth is difficult, so dovetail and bead saws usually have teeth left square across their faces.

The third and final group of saws is for cutting curves and can be divided into two subgroups. First, frame saws, including bow-saws, coping saws and fret-saws, in which the blades are held in tension by the frame. Second, miscellaneous saws, consisting of compass-, pad- and hole-saws.

One common factor unites all the different saw types: in the long run it pays to buy those made by reputable manufacturers.

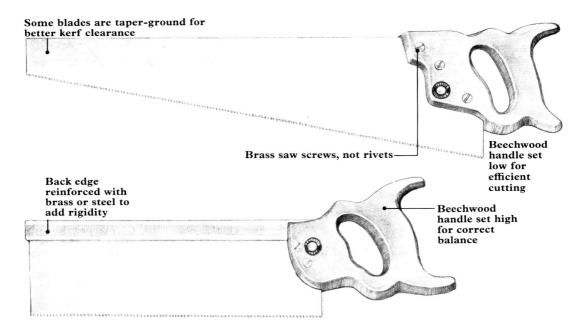

Some blades are taper-ground for better kerf clearance

Brass saw screws, not rivets

Beechwood handle set low for efficient cutting

Back edge reinforced with brass or steel to add rigidity

Beechwood handle set high for correct balance

Choosing saws
Ensure the blade is straight, the teeth sharp, evenly spaced and set. Check metal quality in a handsaw by a sharp tap of the knuckle on the blade: this should produce a ringing sound, not a dull thud. If a handsaw is bent into a U shape and released, it should straighten naturally. The back of a tenon or dovetail saw should fit tightly on the blade.

Caring for saws
Protect the teeth with a guard; hang up when not in use, lightly smearing the blade with oil to prevent it rusting, since pitting reduces efficiency. Don't cut reclaimed timber that may contain screws or nails.

Cross-cut saw   **Rip-saw**

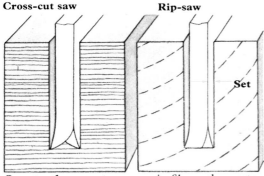

Set

Saw teeth are set (bent) outward so the cut (kerf) gives blade clearance. Cross-cut teeth are angled and bevelled to fine outer points, which score across the grain fibres; the waste between crumbles away, creating the kerf. The squared teeth of a rip-saw cut with a chiselling action.

10 teeth per inch (TPI)

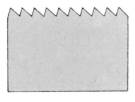

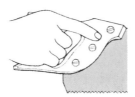

The more teeth per inch (TPI), the finer, though slower, the cut. On some handsaws the TPI is stamped near the heel.

Grip the saw handle lightly but securely, with the index finger and thumb lying parallel against opposite sides of the handle. This gives maximum control when cutting.

Knee

Thumb as guide

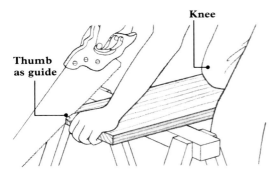

Starting a saw cut: draw the blade backward a few times, using a steep cutting angle and short strokes until the saw runs true. Continue the cut, using the full blade length. Downward pressure should always be light, and the cutting angle comfortable.

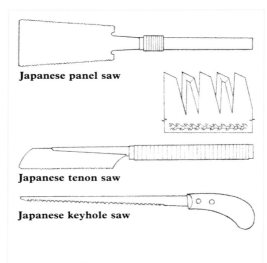

Japanese panel saw

Japanese tenon saw

Japanese keyhole saw

Japanese Saws
The special feature of these saws, which are increasing in popularity for special work, is that they cut on the draw stroke only, giving fine control. The long teeth are prone to damage. Sharpening is difficult, requiring purpose-made files.

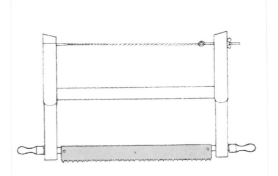

The continental bow-saw or scroll bow-saw
This is more versatile than the standard bow-saw, and is used almost exclusively by some craftsmen for ripping, cross-cutting and general cabinet work because a variety of coarse, fine, rip and cross-cut blades is interchangeable within the one frame. The cheeks pivot on each end of the spreader, and tension is applied by twisting a string or tightening a nut.

55

Sawing

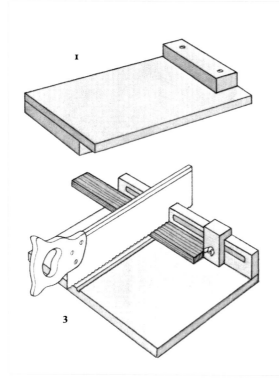

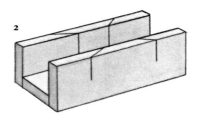

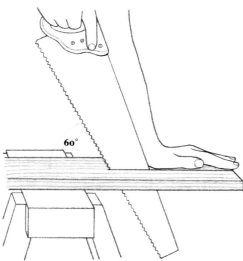

Sawing Aids

1 The bench hook, which butts conveniently against the front of the bench, is standard for holding timber steady when cutting across the grain. A convenient size is 10×7 in/250×178 mm. Recommended construction: $\frac{3}{4}$ in/19 mm beech.

2 A mitre block is also best made from $\frac{3}{4}$ in/19 mm beech. Its main use is for mitring small mouldings.

3 It is simple to construct a device with an adjustable stop that assists accurate repeat cutting of lengths. The wood or metal stop is secured with a wing-nut.

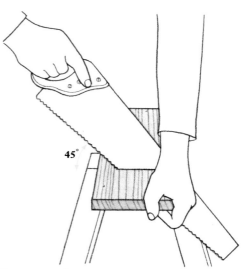

Ripping

To make a cut along the grain rather than across it, use a rip-saw, whose teeth are designed for the job. Hold the wood firmly on a bench or trestles. Use the saw at a low angle to start the cut and continue at about 60°, using the full blade length. If pinching occurs, hammer in a wedge and lubricate the blade with candle wax.

Cross-cutting

Never use a rip-saw to cut across the grain, splintering results. The correct tool is a cross-cut saw, whose teeth are shaped for the purpose. To get the best from a cross-cut saw, hold it at about 45° and firmly support the waste, or overhanging end. When finishing a cut, use gentle strokes to prevent tearing.

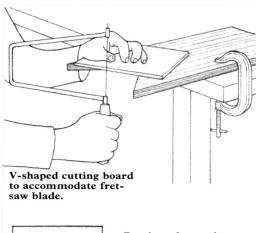

V-shaped cutting board to accommodate fret-saw blade.

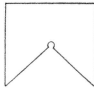

Cutting shapes in thin materials
Use a fret-saw, and hold the work flat on a cutting table, or on a board cut with a V-shape. The teeth should face the handle. Cut on the *downward* stroke. If possible, sit while working.

Two trestles or similar supports are needed to rip a long or wide piece of timber efficiently. Begin at one end, continuing the cut between the trestles and complete the cut beyond the second trestle or by sawing from the uncut end. Add extra support for thin materials by laying battens between the trestles.

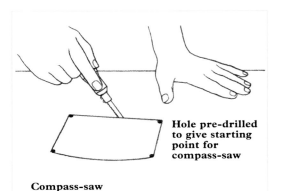

Hole pre-drilled to give starting point for compass-saw

Compass-saw

Hole-saw attachment for power drill

Cutting circles
The simplest way to cut a circular hole in timber is to fit a hole-saw to a power drill. Irregular hole sizes or complex curved shapes require marking out, pre-drilling to give a starting point, and cutting with a compass-saw.

Narrow boards can be conveniently cross-cut on a single trestle; hold steady by clamping, or with a knee or foot. If this stance is difficult to adopt, try overhand cross-cutting, that is, sawing with the blade held upright and the teeth facing away from you.

Sharpening saws

To cut efficiently, a saw must be not only sharp but well set; 'set' meaning the amount by which the teeth are alternately bent out of the perpendicular in order to create a cut, or kerf, which is wider than the blade, so giving the blade clearance. With practice, and the right equipment, both operations can be satisfactorily carried out in the home workshop, so eliminating the waste of time and money entailed in professional sharpening.

The basic equipment and technique for sharpening and setting are similar for all types of saw. The actual sharpening tool is a purpose-made triangular saw file, which must be the right size for the saw to be sharpened. To set the teeth, a special, adjustable tool, known as a saw set, is required. And to hold saws steady while sharpening, it is essential to have devices for clamping blades firmly along the entire length, close to the teeth. For back saws, the most convenient is a chop—a simple clamp secured by wing-nuts, easily made by the woodworker. For handsaws, stiff, hardwood jaws, shaped at one end to fit around the handle, are the usual method. The whole assembly—saw plus clamping device—is then held in a vice so that filing can be carried out with no vibration.

Practise sharpening saws with large teeth. The sharpening and bevel angles that are shown below are those most suited to general work, and every effort should be made to maintain them. Sharpen panel saws and tenon saws for general bench work in the same way as cross-cut saws.

Cross-cut saws

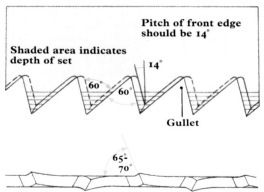

Pitch of front edge should be 14°

Shaded area indicates depth of set

14°

60° 60°

Gullet

65°–70°

Inverted plan of teeth showing required angle of bevel on front face of tooth: 65° for softwoods, 70° for hardwoods and general use.

Rip-saw

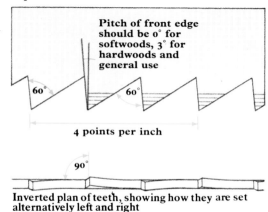

Pitch of front edge should be 0° for softwoods, 3° for hardwoods and general use

60° 60°

4 points per inch

90°

Inverted plan of teeth, showing how they are set alternatively left and right

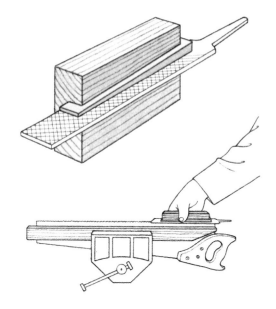

1 Topping is the first step in sharpening any saw. The tips of the teeth must all be level; this is achieved by running a flat file lightly along them. Hold the file square to the saw blade, and to make this simple (also to protect the fingers), wedge the file into a block of wood grooved to receive it. Remove just enough metal from the teeth to make the longer ones the same height as the shorter, and to produce a 'shiner'—a newly filed surface on each and every tip.

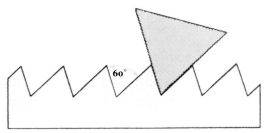

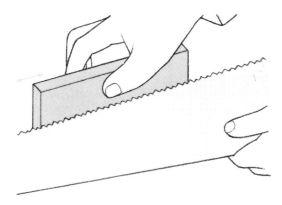

2 Reshaping the teeth is necessary for all saws. Start from the handle end on the *front* face of the first tooth bent *away* from you. Hold the file horizontal, at the required angle (*see opposite*). Press it into the gullet and file across at right angles to the blade, removing half the shiner produced, **1**, when topping. Repeat in alternate gullets, then reverse the saw and repeat in gullets not yet filed, removing the remaining halves of the shiners; they should just disappear. All teeth should finish the same size and shape. A rip-saw is now ready for setting; a cross-cut requires more work.

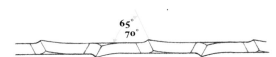

3 Putting a cutting edge on cross-cut teeth is usually described as a separate stage, but in practice it is done in conjunction with reshaping. Having reshaped the tooth as in **2**, the bevel on a cross-cut tooth will be blunted and the shiner removed. So re-create a small shiner on the top of each tooth, then, file held at 65 to 70°, file the bevel until the shiner just disappears. Putting a bevel back on the front face of a tooth also puts one on the back face of the adjacent tooth. Work in alternate gullets and repeat with the saw turned around.

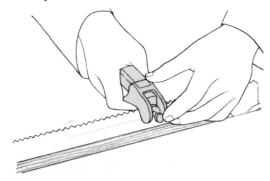

4 Setting the teeth is essential for all saws: no more than half the tooth should be bent over, and the set should be the minimum for blade clearance. Check the number of teeth per inch on the saw and adjust the saw-set accordingly. Place the set over the blade and squeeze the handles firmly; reverse the saw to set the remaining teeth.

5 Side dressing, the final stage of sharpening, is essential for removing burrs and ensuring all teeth are evenly set. Lay the saw flat on a bench and draw a medium grade oilstone lightly along the teeth on each side.

Sharpening miscellaneous saws
Trying to sharpen small saws, such as coping saws or keyhole saws, is a waste of time: replacement blades are cheap. Chain saw and band-saw blades are best sharpened by specialists with the expertise to inspect them for wear that could make further use dangerous. Circular saws that *do not* have tungsten carbide tips on the teeth may be sharpened by using millsaw files. For correct sharpening and bevel angles, consult the manufacturer's instructions.

The right size of file
A file too small for the gullet will leave part of the tooth face unsharpened; one that is too large will round out the gullet and diminish the size of the tooth. As a rule of thumb, the saw tooth should rise about half-way across the file face.

Saw Type	Teeth per inch	File length
Dovetail	18–22	6 in/15 cm
Tenon	12–14	7 in/18 cm
Panel	10–12	8 in/20 cm
Cross-cut	7–8	9 in/23 cm
Rip	4½–6	10 in/25.5 cm

The jigsaw

The jigsaw provides a simple and inexpensive introduction to power sawing. Versatile and compact, it has neither the speed nor the accuracy of the circular saw, but makes up for these shortcomings in other ways.

Jigsaws vary widely in price and quality, so, before purchasing, consider the workload and the use expected of the tool. For most woodworkers, a model from the middle or the lower half of the price range will be adequate, but if considerable use is anticipated, it may be worth investing a little extra in a pendulum model.

Even low-powered jigsaws will cut quite thick softwood (up to 2 in/5 cm). However, correct choice of blade is crucial, especially when working on thick material. Fitted with the appropriate blade, a jigsaw will cut metal or perspex (plexiglass); if the tool offers variable speeds, select the slowest one possible when working on these materials.

Most jigsaws have a metal sole plate that can be angled to make cuts at up to 45° to the surface of the material, but this does decrease the maximum thickness that can be cut.

When a new blade is fitted, check that it is at 90° to the sole plate by using a try square. If a used blade persists in wandering out of line, discard it and fit a new one. (This fault is often caused by poor quality-control during manufacture.) Quality jigsaw blades are expensive, but the best often last three to six times longer than cheap ones.

Since a jigsaw actually cuts on the upstroke, it leaves the smoothest cut on the underside of the work. Bear this in mind when marking out, putting cutting lines on the side of the workpiece that will eventually be out of view.

Always ensure that the work is firmly held when using a jigsaw. Excessive vibration will cause slow, wavy cutting and may damage the saw or blade. Check that the blade is projecting below the bottom of the workpiece, and take care not to cut into the support being used.

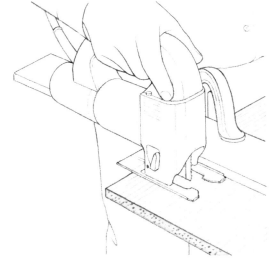

To cut straight lines or bevels, clamp an off-cut of straight timber to the work and use it to guide the jigsaw sole plate. Select extra-sharp blades for cuts along the grain and at 45° to it; this reduces wandering. Before cutting, rub the blade with candle wax. Cut solid wood with, not against, the grain. Use a jigsaw to make bevels only if the material is ¾ in/19 mm thick or less. (Note that cutting accuracy is limited. Adjust the sole plate to the bevel angle required.)

Plunge cutting is the simplest way to start an 'inside' cut on thin materials. Hold the jigsaw firmly in both hands, with the 'nose' of the sole plate on the wood surface on the waste side of the line. Switch on and lower the saw gently into the work. When it has broken through the underside of the work, switch off, insert the saw through the hole and use normally. On thick material or fine work, drill a hole in the waste and put the saw through before switching on.

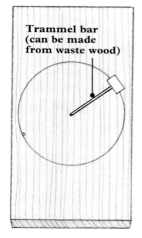

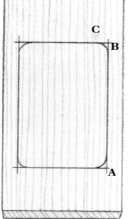

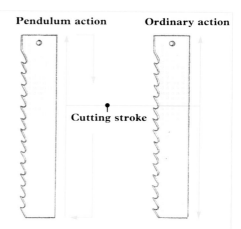

Pendulum jigsaws are relatively expensive, costing up to twice as much as similar models without pendulum action. Instead of moving only up and down, like the ordinary jigsaw, the pendulum jigsaw blade moves back on the non-cutting downstroke and forward on the cutting upstroke. This improves the finish of the cut surface, reduces blade heating and makes it easier to feed the blade through the work.

To cut a round or curved hole, use a circle-cutting jig or a trammel bar, which describes an arc for the jigsaw blade to follow. Cut in one continuous action.

To cut a square hole, first cut straight from **A** to **B**. Go back toward **A** and cut curve to **C**. Then cut from **C** to meet the first cut at the corner **B**.

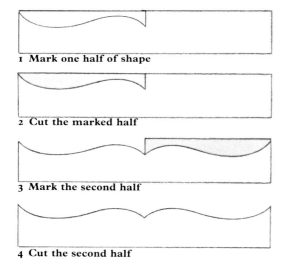

1 Mark one half of shape

2 Cut the marked half

3 Mark the second half

4 Cut the second half

Cut symmetrical shapes by first marking out just one half of the shape. Cut out the marked half and use it as a template to mark up the second half, prior to cutting it. Clean up the edges with a spokeshave and abrasive paper. The result should be a perfectly symmetrical shape, even if there has been slight deviation from the cutting line on the first half-section.

Hardwood

Softwood

Curve cutting

Plastics/metal

Many different grades and types of jigsaw blade are available. In general, the finer the tooth, the harder the material the blade will cut. Large teeth are best for softwood, cross-cutting and ripping. Manufacturers claim that blades with an abrasive strip bonded to the front edge, instead of teeth, combine long life with exceptionally clean cutting.

The bandsaw

Bandsaws are efficient, versatile machines, whose principal uses are shape-cutting and handling large quantities of hardwood. They can cut to considerable thicknesses, the thin blades causing little waste, and for this reason are also used for log-cutting by the timber trade. Even small bandsaws can 'deep cut': a modestly priced machine will saw through up to 6 in/150 mm of hardwood. A circular saw with that sort of capacity would weigh at least a quarter of a ton and cost four times as much.

A bandsaw is also ideal for cutting complex outside shapes. However, it cannot, like the jigsaw, cut holes or inside shapes without also sawing through the surround.

Another drawback of the bandsaw is its inability to cut a truly straight line; the fences or guides for this purpose are generally unhelpful. For best results, follow a pencil line on the work.

Bandsaws are all of similar design except that some have two wheels and some three, a variation which does not affect efficiency. The main limiting factor is throat depth—the distance between the blade and the rear casting of the machine—which restricts width-cutting capacity. A small, three-wheel bandsaw of 13 in/33 cm throat depth is the best all-round machine for the home or small workshop.

A larger second-hand bandsaw is often a worthwhile buy. Check the wheel bearings for 'slop', and the condition of the rubber tyres on which the blade actually runs. The small guides on the blade are easily replaced, but wheel bearings and tyres are not so readily available and are more expensive. Start up a second-hand machine and listen to it. A healthy bandsaw should be quiet.

Before using a bandsaw, always check that the blade is correctly fitted. Should it be 'inside out', twist it firmly around with both hands to position the teeth so they point down toward the table. Double-check the tension. The blade should just hum rather than rattle when plucked. Finally, ensure the doors of the saw are properly closed before switching on.

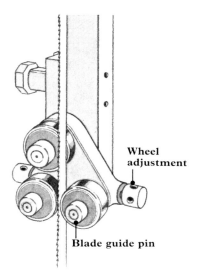

Wheel adjustment

Blade guide pin

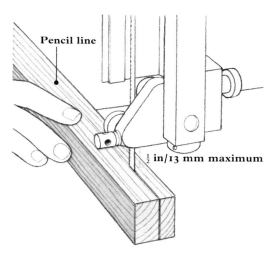

Pencil line

½ in/13 mm maximum

To fit a new blade, lower the top wheel. Slip the new blade on to the top and bottom wheels so the teeth point downward on the cutting side. Thread the blade through the guide blocks; then raise the top wheel again. Check the tension. If the blade is not tracking properly, use the appropriate control to tilt the top wheel. Adjust the guide blocks until they just cuddle the wheel behind the teeth. Set the thrust wheel until it barely touches the back of the blade.

When cutting without a fence, lower the guard and guide blocks to just above the workpiece. This improves safety and accuracy. Practise cutting straight lines on waste wood. Steer the blade along a line by moving the work. For shape-cutting, use a narrow blade and feed slowly, twisting and turning the work firmly.

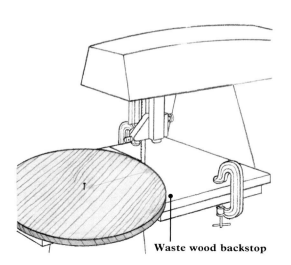

Waste wood backstop

Large circles, such as circular table tops of almost any size, can be cut on a bandsaw. Fix a 'false' bed of chipboard or plywood to the machine.

Attach the circle blank to it with a panel pin or a small nail. Starting at one edge of the blank, feed the work steadily through the saw.

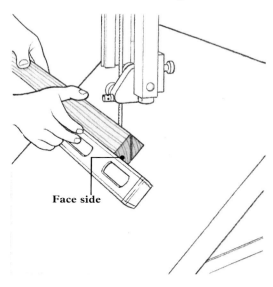

Face side

Bevelled cuts as steep as 45° to the vertical can be made on many bandsaws. Wood is more difficult to control on a steeply sloping tilt table, so take extra care and use sharp blades. When cutting angled curves, rotate

the work correctly to avoid cutting bevels the 'wrong' way. Set the tilt table at a slight angle to cut 'weathering' slopes on window sills and door frames.

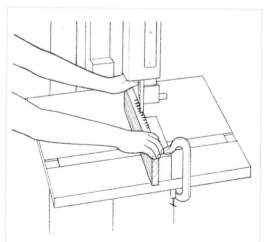

Kerfs—shallow grooves—can be conveniently cut with a bandsaw on the unseen side of moulding which needs to be curved: the grooves allow the wood to expand or contract along the curve. Space kerfs regularly, about $\frac{3}{8}$ in/10 mm apart, and use a backstop to keep depths constant. Pencil a guide mark $\frac{3}{8}$ in/10 mm from the blade.

Narrow blade for tight curves; has a wavy set, like a hacksaw

Alternate set

Skip and hook teeth suitable for clearing waste sawdust

Cutting-blades for curved shapes and thin wood should be narrow; those for thick wood and straight lines, wide. Fine teeth are for hardwoods and coarse teeth for softer materials. Use a super-hard, steel-tipped blade for abrasive material such as chipboard. For thick wood, a five- or six-point rip-tooth blade is suitable. To ease sticky cuts, apply candlewax sparingly to the blade.

The circular saw

Hand-sawing long lengths of timber is slow, hard work. A power saw, even a small one, saves time and labour which can be put into other aspects of a job. Circular saws are, for this reason, the choice of the professional woodworker for much straight-cutting. The extra width of the blade, compared to that of a band-saw or jigsaw, helps to keep the saw running true, even on materials which are wavy-grained or contain knots. Two basic types of saw are available: hand-held saw units, often called skilsaws, and free-standing machines, often called table saws.

Space and cost considerations make the hand-held saw the popular choice for small users. This popularity has led to manufacturers offering a range of machines, with cutting capacities varying from 1 in/2.5 cm to 3 in/7.5 cm or more. The smaller machines are fine for most furniture work, but construction joinery or heavy, solid oak furniture require the more powerful models.

To gain an impression of a machine's power, look at the rating figure for the motor in the maker's handbook, usually given in watts. Five hundred watts is satisfactory for light work, but for prolonged use and deep cutting, look for 1,250 watts or more. For more information on power ratings, see p. 67.

Hand-held saws are best suited to cutting up large sheets of material. The most comfortable, efficient way to work is with the material supported on trestles. Small pieces and narrow strips can be awkward to cut with a hand-held saw, a problem that can be overcome by purchasing a saw-table. This converts the saw into a bench-mounted model and leaves both hands free to control the workpiece.

Most manufacturers now offer a dust bag with their saw units. This is a worthwhile extra, especially useful when cutting large amounts of chipboard (flakeboard) or ply, which contain a high proportion of glue and other chemicals that are irritating and dangerous when inhaled excessively.

Asbestolux and similar asbestos cement sheets must on no account be cut on a circular saw, since even small amounts of their dust can be hazardous to health.

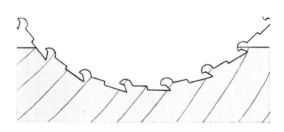

Set the depth of cut to give the minimum projection of the blade: $\frac{1}{16}$ in/1.5 mm is adequate. When cutting a groove, remember that the sawdust will be trapped in the cut and it may be necessary to clear it manually. A saw of this type cuts with the blade moving upward, which means that the clean-cut edges will be on the underside. So mark out and cut on the side that will be out of sight.

The guide fence is used to make cuts parallel to the edge of a board. The fence will only follow a straight edge: any bumps or curves will make the saw jam. Make sure the workpiece cannot slide around during cutting, and keep the power cord well away from the blade. The width of cut possible with the fence is limited, and wider sections require the aid of a straight length of timber.

Saw blades

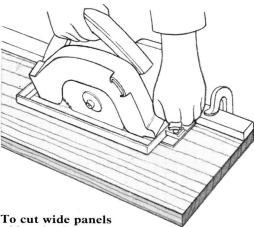

Gullet or combination type blades are suitable for most general timber cutting; they may not last long on man-made materials but are easy to sharpen with a round-edge mill file.

To cut wide panels with a circular saw, use a guide piece of 2 × 1 in/50 × 25 mm softwood. Clamp it firmly to the work and simply slide the saw along it. Measure up carefully: errors are easy to make with this method.

Angled cuts are achieved by tilting the saw baseplate, which is variable between 0 and 45°. A sharp blade and a firm grip on the saw make angled cutting easier to control.

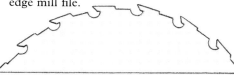

Tungsten (carbide)-tipped blades are expensive to buy and sharpen, but give a clean finish and have a long 'edge life'; they are used by most professionals. Handle with care—the teeth can chip.

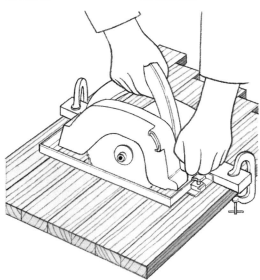

Hollow ground or planer blades put a planed finish on solid woods. They are hard to obtain and maintain, so are best reserved for the table saw and used on timber.

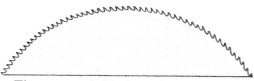

The peg-tooth blade, available in a variety of patterns, is ideal for cross-cutting hard or soft timber and for cutting up plywood sheets.

Pieces all the same length are a common requirement, and the easiest way of producing them is on a saw-table with a cross-cut fence. To do this with a hand-held saw, clamp the timbers together with ends aligned and use a guide piece to trim off the required lengths. Check and double-check the setting out with a tape and try square before cutting: this is potentially the quickest way of spoiling large quantities of wood.

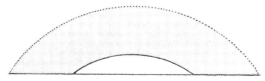

The abrasive disc is a builder's tool, capable of sawing through stone, concrete, and tiles. Use a mask, for the dust produced contains many abrasive particles. To prolong the life of the saw, clean thoroughly after use.

The table saw

Noisy, and producing copious quantities of dust, table saws should really only be used in a garage or other self-contained workplace away from the house. Properly housed and set up, they are invaluable for producing accurately sawn work at speed. Many different types are available, but all worthwhile ones have these basic features:

The saw table should be at least 15 × 15 in/ 37 × 37 cm, sturdily constructed and smooth to the touch.

The rip fence, used for guiding timber past the saw blade, must, for accurate cutting work, be parallel to the saw blade or very slightly 'toed-out'. It should be easy to adjust and should lock securely in any position.

The riving, or split, knife, a crucial part of the saw, should be made from a strong piece of steel and be bolted to the machine exactly in line with the blade. Its function is to keep fingers away from the back of the blade and to prevent 'curly' wood from pinching the back of the blade and consequently jamming.

The crown guard should be made from thick, tough plastic at least, preferably from a more substantial material. The guard's function is to keep hands clear of the saw and to help prevent the saw kicking back.

Rise and fall control determines the depth of cut. The adjustment should not be too stiff and should lock firmly. It is infuriating if the blade sinks half-way through a cut.

Some machines also have **blade tilt control**, a somewhat overrated feature, not often used in practice. Where it exists, check that the 90° blade-upright position is accurately marked.

Many new saws are sold with **blades** of inferior quality. Study the 'Box' on page 65 and budget to buy at least one appropriate blade. Most dealers run a saw-sharpening service, or know where one is to be found.

Be extra-conscious of safety when using a circular-saw, and remain alert at all times. Don't work on power saws when drowsy or in a hurry or when likely to be distracted.

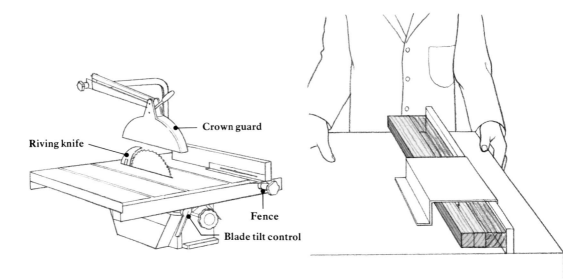

Riving knife

Crown guard

Fence

Blade tilt control

Sound basic technique with a table saw starts with ensuring there is a clear space both sides of the saw in which to handle a workpiece. Then set the fence carefully, measuring from the fence to the right-hand side of the teeth and allow an extra $\frac{1}{8}$ in/3 mm for planing off the saw-marks. Ensure all adjustments are locked before switching on. Press the workpiece lightly against the fence, and feed it in steadily.

Modern safety standards demand the use of a tunnel guard when cutting grooves, rebates (rabbets) or any other job where the crown guard and riving knife have to be removed. If a purpose-made tunnel guard is not available for a table saw, make one from thick aluminium or steel sheeting, folded to the shape illustrated above. Bolt it to the back of the fence and, when cutting, pass the timber underneath it.

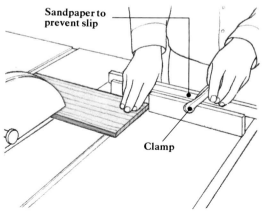

Sandpaper to prevent slip

Clamp

A cross-cut fence
fitted to a table saw
makes it easy to cut
several pieces of
timber to exactly the
same length at once.
Make sure the fence
slides easily in its
groove and is at
exactly 90° to the
blade. If desired,
improvise a stop block
from a piece of wood
and a small clamp.
Move the main rip-
fence out of the way
during this operation,
since off-cuts trapped
between this fence
and the saw can jam
the blade.

17 in/450 mm

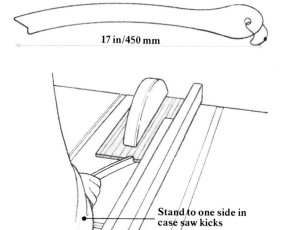

Stand to one side in
case saw kicks

Push sticks are a
vital safety aid in the
power workshop.
Make a couple from
lengths of hardwood
and fit a short loop of
twine at the handling
end, so the implement
can be hung up near
the saw. A little
awkward to use at
first, a push stick soon
seems like an
extension of the hand.
Always use one for
pushing work past the
saw when ripping, for
flicking away off-cuts
and for finishing cuts.

Power requirements

Rating in watts	Blade size	Uses
Under 500	Under 6 in/ 15.5 cm	Light work only
500–750	Around 7 in/ 18 cm	Furniture and light construction
750–1,250	Around 8 in/ 20.5 cm	Domestic joinery
1,250–2,000	8–10 in/ 20.5– 25.5 cm	Intermittent heavy use
2,000+	10–12 in/ 25.5– 30.5 cm	Any small workshop task

This is a rough guide to the power ratings
required for various tasks. Hard and fast
rules cannot be applied. Manufacturers
tend to exaggerate the work capacity of their
tools. Try not to overwork power tools.

Keep workspace clean and tidy.
Ensure there is room in which to
manoeuvre.

Never use an unguarded saw.

Use a push stick whenever possible.
Keep hands 12 in/30.5 cm from blade.

Keep sawblades sharp and clean: never
force work through the machine.

Always switch off and disconnect the
power supply before making adjustments.

Keep power cords away from the saw.

**Never leave a saw unattended and
running**.

Be alert for danger at all times—keep
children and pets away.

Avoid dust and splinters: wear a mask
and goggles.

The radial arm saw

Radial arm saws have made a major impact on home woodworking and small workshop practice in recent years. Essentially, they consist of a motor unit with a saw blade attached to it, all mounted on rollers on an overhead beam. Beam and motor unit have adjustments which enable the saw blade or other attachment to be rotated to almost any position. This makes the saw highly versatile: it can be used for cross-cutting, mitring or ripping, using only a standard sawblade. Attachments are available which enable the tool to be used, in addition, for moulding and rebating (rabbeting), sanding, jigsawing and drilling.

When shopping for a radial arm saw, keep an eye open for special offers. The market for small machines is highly competitive, and patience can well be rewarded with a bargain. Don't be taken in by smartly painted models or a large range of accessories, many of which will never be used. Look for sturdy construction (generally the arm should be cast metal) and ease of adjustment for the various head positions.

If using the saw for the first time, follow the setting-up instructions carefully. With every adjustment at zero, the saw blade should be truly at a 90° angle to the bed and to the fence. The arm should also be at 90° to the fence, and this can be tested by pressing the handle of a large square against the fence, with the edge of the blade just touching the saw teeth. Pull the saw unit forward, checking that the saw teeth brush lightly along the square for the whole length of travel.

Like all woodworking machines, the radial arm saw should be treated with respect. Always use a sharp blade and check that adjusters are locked tight before use. When using the radial arm as a rip-saw, take great care to set the hold-down and kick-back guards, and always use a push stick (not fingers) to feed the saw, since the tool will give the occasional violent kick-back when used carelessly for ripping work.

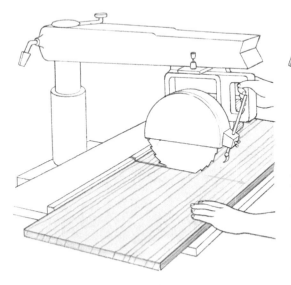

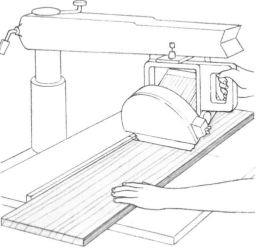

Cross-cutting wide boards can present problems with a radial arm. The most popular radial arm saw has, for example, a maximum cross-cutting capacity of about 17 in/43.5 cm. The solution is to cut half-way across the board, push the saw back, switch it off, turn the board round and complete the cut from the other side.

The level cross-cut facility is useful for constructing mitred boxes and long mitre joints. Set the saw angle carefully. Really sharp saw blades are important for clean, level cuts. Bevel or straight cross-cutting to length can be done accurately by cramping a small wooden stop block to the fence.

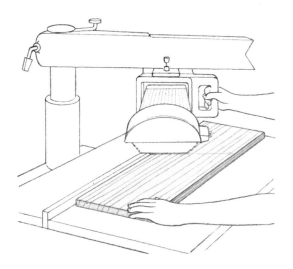

**Moulding
blocks**

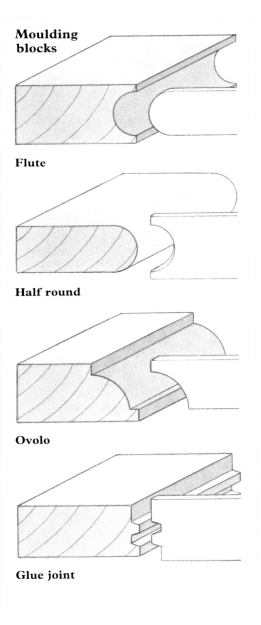

Flute

Half round

Ovolo

Glue joint

Mitre cutting for picture and door frames can be done accurately on a radial arm saw; but, for safety, work against a false fence fixed to the machine fence. The false fence supports the wanted moulding only. The waste piece must be given room to move away from the spinning saw blade. Its wedge shape makes it prone to jamming in the gap between blade and fence—potentially hazardous.

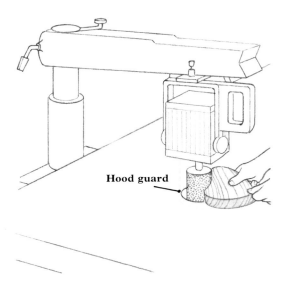

Hood guard

Sanding, boring or drilling are possible with a chuck attachment. If drilling, clamp the work to the saw bench. If the hole is deep (1 in/2.5 cm or more), extract the drill half way through to clear away dust.

At least one make of radial arm saw can be fitted with a moulding block or head which, with its set of matched cutters, can produce a wide variety of different mouldings. Mouldings made in this way have a finish that is comparable with, or better than, commercial finishes, but the cutters do have to be sharp. Always follow the manufacturer's instructions on setting up, and double-check that cutters and guards are firmly fixed in place. Small beadings are best made by moulding the edge of a wide board and then sawing off the moulded edge.

69

The router

The router is an inexpensive, versatile addition to the workshop. It consists basically of a high-speed electric motor in a simple plastic or metal casing with handles attached. On the end of the motor shaft is fitted a collett chuck, which can take a wide variety of special cutters for grooving, rebating (rabbeting) or moulding. Only cutters designed for the router may be used, since the high rotation speed (up to 24,000 rpm) may cause breakage of incorrect cutter types, with dangerous results.

The casing of the router usually carries a simple locking-clamp to determine the depth of cut in the wood; alternatively, there may be a plunge-type depth setting. Once the clamp is tightened, the cutter is fixed in position. The plunge-depth control is, by contrast, fixed to a spring-loaded slide, which enables the operator to plunge the router cutter down to a pre-set maximum depth. This is a useful facility, since it enables deep cuts to be achieved in a number of passes without resetting the depth stop. It also makes it possible to make neat stopped grooves without the problems caused by inserting and removing a router running at speed.

Small hand routers can be used freehand when light cuts are being made—especially in signwriting work, for which a V-pointed veining cutter should always be used.

A worthwhile accessory for the router is the router table, which enables the machine to be used in the inverted position and to carry out many of the functions of the spindle moulder.

Remember not to overload a router. This will make the speed drop too low for clean cutting and will shorten the working life of the machine considerably. A common cause of overloading is attempting to remove too much material in one pass; so deep cuts should be made in several passes. As a rule, do not attempt to remove more than $\frac{3}{8}$ in/ 9 mm deep by $\frac{3}{8}$ in/9 mm wide at one time.

Another cause of overloading is using blunt cutters. Both man and machine are protected if cutters are really sharp. In addition, sharp cutters have a longer life, so careful maintenance can save money.

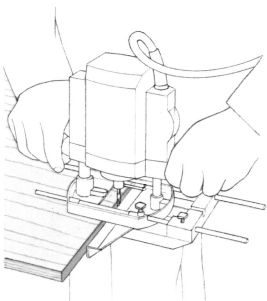

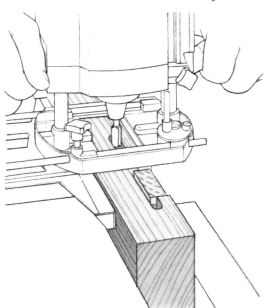

Guide fences are standard on most routers, enabling the machine to work parallel with a straight edge. Improvise a fence by clamping a length of timber to the work and sliding the router along it. Set the position of the cut by measuring the distance between the edge of the batten and the cutting edge of the router bit.

If grooving a narrow strip of timber, cramp it into a pre-cut notch to give a wide, solid surface along which to slide the router. The high-speed cutting action of the router gives a clean cross-grain cut. Use single flute cutters for best results. Construct a simple jig for making tenons.

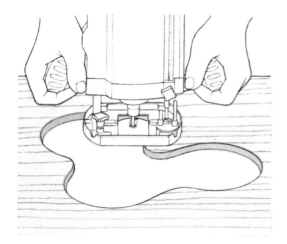

Cutting curved shapes and mouldings is possible with a router because the bit is made with a pilot nose: this part of the bit has no cutting edge and will run along a curved surface or follow a template.

Make templates from 6 or 9 mm ply and pin on top of work. Set router depth so that the cutter pierces the work and the pilot nose runs around the template. Simple, sweeping curves give best results.

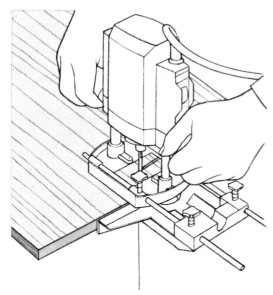

Cutting moulding is facilitated by rubbing a candle or piece of hard soap along the edge to be moulded. This reduces friction and prevents surface

burning. Clamp the workpiece firmly to the edge of the bench or in a Workmate for added safety and speed of working.

Router bits

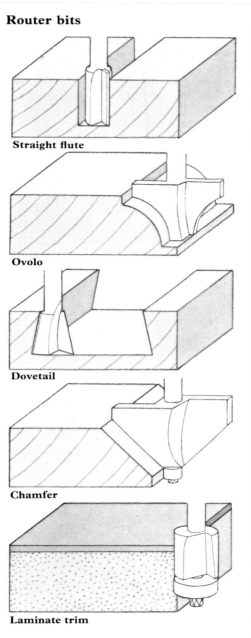

Straight flute

Ovolo

Dovetail

Chamfer

Laminate trim

Trenching or grooving bits are for use with a guide fence. **Pilot-nosed beading cutters** produce edge moulding and decorative finishes. **The dovetail cutter** makes housing joints where strength is vital. **Chamfering cutters** provide simple 'stopped chamfer' decoration, used on exposed corners of chests to reduce the chance of splintering from accidental blows. Various **flute cutters** are available for trimming off overhanging laminates.

The combination machine

Small combination machines, or tables, offer most of the facilities found in a professional's machine shop, and can, therefore, prove invaluable to the committed woodworker, especially one with limited space.

A small combination machine comprises saw, planer-thicknesser and spindle moulder driven by a single motor unit. Other attachments, such as a slot mortiser, are available.

Good combination machines are normally constructed of cast iron or cast aluminium. Cast-metal machines are more rigid than folded sheet steel and generally give more accurate and reliable results.

The circular saw has a maximum capacity of 3 in/7.5 cm. It is fitted with accurate cross-cutting and ripping fences.

The planer-thicknesser generally has a maximum width of 8 to 10 in/20.5 to 25.5 cm and a table length of 39 in/1 m. This is sufficient to process most timber sizes required in the small workshop.

The spindle moulder is extremely versatile. It can, for example, make dovetails, tenons and mouldings. Its grooving saw is ideal for fitting panels and cutting small rebates. Small-diameter, tipped grooving saws are available in widths up to $\frac{5}{8}$ in/15 mm.

A slot-mortiser attachment is relatively simple to use. It will give good results and enormously speed up all operations. Always use best-quality cutters.

All woodworking machines are potentially lethal, but a spindle moulder can be particularly dangerous. Always follow the manufacturer's instructions about cutter sizes, and be alert at all times. Check and double-check cramps and adjustments before use. Always disconnect the power supply before carrying out adjustments.

Take extra care to feed the work into the spindle in the correct direction. For example, if the spindle rotates anticlockwise, as is usual, feed in the work from right to left. Feeding work the wrong way can cause a serious accident.

Wherever possible, use simple, sturdy home-made jigs to hold the workpiece, and never use the spindle without correct guarding.

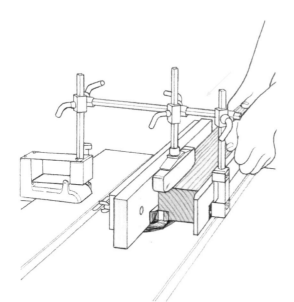

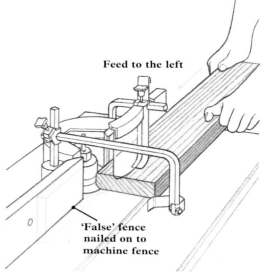

Feed to the left

'False' fence nailed on to machine fence

To make a tenon, fit a 'false' fence. Fit a rebating (rabbeting) block on the spindle. Push back the 'false' fence. Make a jig with a groove lined with abrasive paper. Set the hold-down.

Tighten up all the adjustments. Start the machine. Feed the jig and work through, pressing against the fence. When one side has been cut, turn the work over. Fit the jig. Cut the other side.

To use a grooving saw, nail a $\frac{3}{8}$ in/10 mm ply 'false' fence to the machine fence. Bolt the saw on to the spindle. Set the saw height. Gripping both machine fences, push back until the saw breaks through the 'false' fence. Stop the spindle. Tighten all adjustments. Fit the hold-down. Feed work through with a push stick. For extra safety fit a metal or plywood front spring.

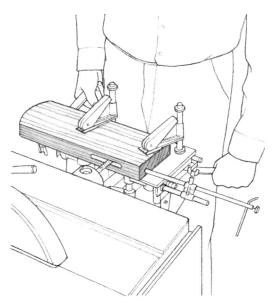

When using an orbital or belt sander always try to avoid cross-grain working. Do not dub over the edges of the work. Many belt sanders can be inverted to smooth the edges of straight or shaped work. Always use garnet abrasive papers: 120 grit is a useful all-round grade.

The slot mortiser has a fixed chuck with a two-flute cutter and operates rather like a horizontal boring drill. Clamp the work firmly to the table. Feed the work slowly on to the cutter, moving the table forward and from side to side. Pull back regularly to avoid wood chips accumulating in the mortise. If forced through wood, the cutters will snap.

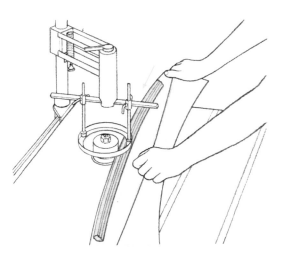

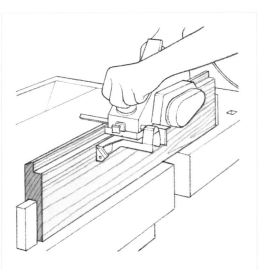

Use the ring moulder to cut circular or straight mouldings. From $\frac{1}{2}$ in/ 13 mm ply, make a jig or template to the plan of the moulded section. Put a 3 in/ 7.5 cm lead-in on the jig. Screw the jig to the work. Use a French cutter or a moulding block. Lower the helmet guard. Feed the work on to the cutter; hold it down firmly and make light cuts.

The hand-held electric planer uses a small rotating cutter block with two disposable or resharpenable blades. Use for re-claiming old timber and for other heavy cutting jobs such as fitting doors and worktops. Do not use it when a fine surface finish is required. The planer produces vast quantities of fine shavings and dust, so use all dust bag if possible. Most planers have a fence for rebating (rabbeting) and for planing thin edges.

Choosing planes

The first efficient planes were probably made of wood and bronze by the Egyptians. Further developed by the Romans, they were rediscovered in Britain during the Middle Ages. Mass-produced metal planes, almost identical to the ones now used in Britain and the United States, have been available since World War I. Craftsmen in Europe have, by contrast, had much more use for the wooden plane. Many types exist, some of exceptional quality, but in Britain and the USA, they tend to be available only from specialist tool dealers. Some craftsmen prefer wooden planes for their superior slip over the wood, but they need more care and attention than the more rugged metal types.

When it comes to buying a plane, opt for one with a reputable brand name. Since woodwork has become a growth area, some 'look-alike' planes of generally inferior quality have appeared on the market.

The same general principle holds good when buying any tools: a few quality tools are more use than a whole box of poor ones, and, as a bonus, they will probably last into, and be enjoyed by, the next couple of generations.

Some worthwhile disposable-blade planes are available, but most professionals prefer the traditional type of resharpenable blade.

If buying the resharpenable type for the first time, an oilstone for sharpening, should be purchased as well. The India brand combination stone is best: the fine brown side is used for routine honing and the coarse side for occasional regrinding of the main bevel. Either car engine oil, mixed in equal parts with paraffin, or brake fluid makes an excellent oilstone lubricant.

The Bailey, or bench, plane has, over the years, proved its efficiency and ruggedness. Pre-World War II examples are sometimes available and can be a good buy, since most parts are still available.

Different types of plane are required for different jobs. The Bailey, or bench, plane comes in four sizes: the smallest, the smoothing plane, is best for short lengths of wood and for final cleaning up; the longest, the try-plane is designed to remove bumps and hollows from long stuff. The most useful compromise, and most sensible first purchase, is a jack-plane about 15 in/38 cm long. Used for heavier cleaning-up, most find it easier to handle than a smoother. Well sharpened, it will be almost as efficient as a smaller plane for finer types of work.

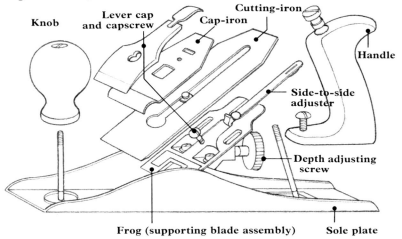

Knob · Lever cap and capscrew · Cap-iron · Cutting-iron · Handle · Side-to-side adjuster · Depth adjusting screw · Frog (supporting blade assembly) · Sole plate

Smoothing plane

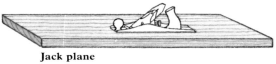

Jack plane

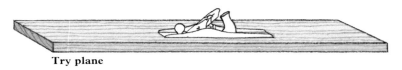

Try plane

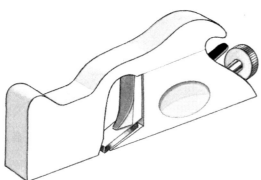

The shoulder plane is used for cleaning up the shoulders of tenon joints. The blade is set at a low angle and extends the full width of the sole plate, features which make it ideal for working across the grain or in rebates (rabbets) and grooves.

The block plane is a simpler version of the bench plane and is available in standard or low-angle versions. Low-angle blades are best for fine cross-grain trimming and plastic laminate trimming.

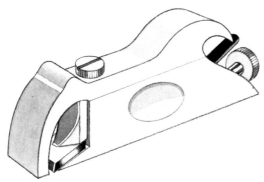

The rebate, or rabbet, plane has a full-width blade with two mounting positions at the front so it can work close into awkward corners. It is fitted with a guide fence and a depth stop. The tiny removable spur near the sole is to sever the wood in front of the blade and should be used across the grain.

Wooden planes
Old English wooden planes are now highly prized by tool collectors and appreciate in value yearly. The most expensive modern wooden planes, manufactured in France and Germany, are made from extremely hardwearing timbers such as hornbeam and lignum vitae. The drawbacks of the old wooden plane are its lack of any positive means of adjustment and its tendency to warp. Modern wooden planes have cutter adjustment and are relatively stable.

Router planes
Also called the 'hag's tooth', the router plane has a crude appearance which belies its functionality. The blades come in a variety of widths, and depth of cut is adjustable. The smaller sizes are the most useful since the 'bull nose' cutter permits cleaning out a groove or housing right against a cabinet side or other obstacle. The big two-handed router is at its best with wide grooves and harder woods. A small oilstone is required to sharpen this plane.

Using planes

A plane will work well only when the blade is sharp. This may seem obvious, but it really does mean that when working on tough woods, such as elm or teak, the blade needs sharpening every few strokes. Old-time craftsmen used to hang up half-a-dozen ready-honed blades by their benches, ready to change the moment a blade lost any of its incisiveness.

The blade of a plane is in two parts, the cutting iron and the cap iron, held tightly together by a slot-headed bolt. The cap iron helps to control the size of the shaving taken off, and when buying a new plane it is sensible to check that the cap iron beds down close to the blade. If not, it will need reshaping, for even a tiny gap will make the plane clog. When planing, stand in a comfortable position, with the wood firmly secured on the bench. Hold the plane positively, put its 'nose' down on the wood and, pressing lightly, slide the plane over the wood. If the plane has been properly sharpened and set, it should take off a fine, continuous shaving. Planing should not be backbreaking work: if it is, the setting is probably wrong.

Do not forget to lubricate the sole of a plane with a little candle wax or soap occasionally; and, if reworking old timber, watch out for panel pins and rock-hard paint or putty which may chip the blade.

A new plane is an expensive investment, costing as much as a cassette player or wristwatch. Treat it with the same care.

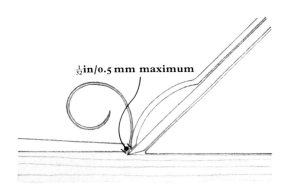

$\frac{1}{32}$ in/0.5 mm maximum

The distance between the cap iron and the cutting edge of the blade is important: $\frac{1}{16}$–$\frac{1}{8}$ in/ 1.5–3 mm is the right clearance for most woods.

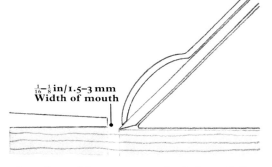

$\frac{1}{16}$–$\frac{1}{8}$ in/1.5–3 mm
Width of mouth

An adjustable mouth is a feature of quality block planes. Closing it up assists working with short- grain timbers. Bailey, or bench, planes have an adjustable frog for moving the blade assembly forward.

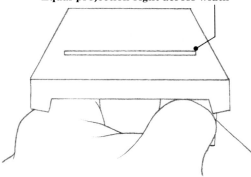

Equal projection right across width

To set depth of cut, hold the plane up and sight along the sole plate. Turn the blade adjuster until the blade just shows— $\frac{1}{32}$ in/0.5 mm is the maximum projection. Try planing, and readjust to give a transparent shaving.

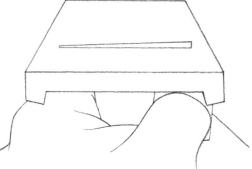

To set the blade level, sight along the sole plate, checking that the blade projects equally right across the mouth. To adjust, rock the side-to-side control lever.

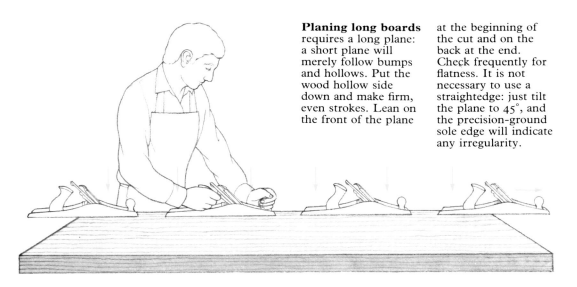

Planing long boards requires a long plane: a short plane will merely follow bumps and hollows. Put the wood hollow side down and make firm, even strokes. Lean on the front of the plane at the beginning of the cut and on the back at the end. Check frequently for flatness. It is not necessary to use a straightedge: just tilt the plane to 45°, and the precision-ground sole edge will indicate any irregularity.

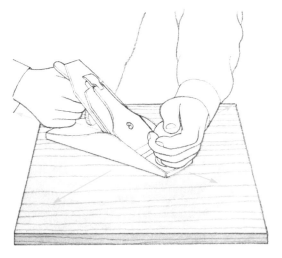

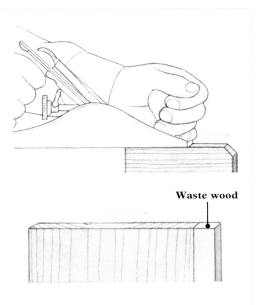

Waste wood

For planing large surface areas, use a plane blade with a slightly curved edge to reduce corner tracks on the surface. Work in all directions, being careful not to take too much off the corners. The blade should be extra-sharp to prevent tearing when working across the grain.

Edges are difficult to plane at first: try curling a finger under the sole at the front to assist steerage.

Planing end grain

A simple way to avoid splintering the vulnerable end grain at corners is to trim off the corner and then plane toward it. This works well on many timbers and has the advantage of speed. With precious or brittle timbers, clamp a piece of waste wood behind the corner so that any splitting occurs on the scrap piece. Some professionals can plane from both ends toward the middle and avoid splintering—a difficult art. The shooting board can be invaluable for preventing splitting—see page 45.

77

Special planes

Before the introduction of machinery for preparing and moulding wood, joiners and cabinet-makers used a wide range of special planes. Some, like the Bismarck plane for making heavy cuts on rough timber, have vanished. Others have proved so useful that they are still mass produced.

If speed is a secondary consideration, just one or two special planes will do most of the tasks involved in joinery or cabinet-work. Some of the most useful are shown below. Bear in mind that, of these, only the scratch-stock and the compass plane are easy to master; patience and preseverance is needed for the others, and particularly for the combination plane. This is typically used for rebating (rabbeting) and grooving, fancy moulding on edges, reeding and tongue-and-groove jointing of boards. It has a wide range of adjustments with which to control the depth and the position of cut.

The woodworker who discovers a particular use, or indeed a liking, for any of the special planes could do well to look in the woodworking press for a second-hand Record 405 Multi-Plane. These magnificent tools, which have not been manufactured since 1982, combine a bewildering variety of operations carried out by special planes and may well be an appreciating investment.

Many of the general points made about planes on previous pages hold good for special planes. Particularly important is sharpening: these tools will give results only with really sharp cutters, and specially shaped oilstones—slip-stones—are in many instances essential to maintain the oddly-shaped and curved blades.

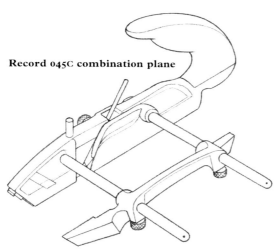

Record 045C combination plane

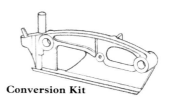

Conversion Kit

Various combination plane blades

The combination plane is essentially a composite tool, useful for many functions, ideal for none. Always start by checking that the chosen cutter is sharp. New cutters are supplied ready-ground but need honing with a fine oilstone. A typical use of the plane is for making grooves. In this, as in all instances, set the plane up carefully, ensuring that the depth stop is correctly adjusted and that the fence is at the correct position. Make sure that the fence is parallel to the body of the plane, otherwise the groove may go off course. The cut is started at the far end of the piece, and the plane worked gradually back toward the operator. Lift the plane clear of the wood on the backstroke when making mouldings to avoid scoring the surface. It sometimes helps to stop 'chattering' if the depth stop is initially set to rub gently on the surface, then raised gradually until the required depth is reached.

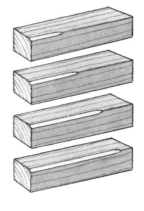

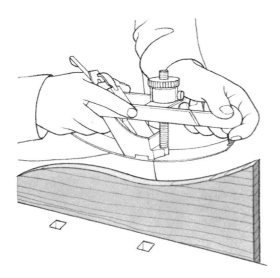

Flat-bottomed spokeshave

Chamfer spokeshave

Round-bottomed spokeshave

Stand at a comfortable height; blade drawn *toward* user

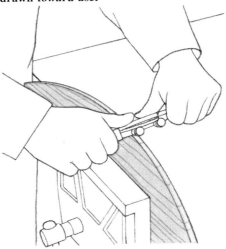

The compass, or circular, plane is the tool for smoothing rough-sawn curves. The blade assembly is like that of the Bailey or bench plane, but the sole plate is made from a strip of flexible steel. An adjusting screw allows the sole to be curved to fit against a concave or convex curve. Set the curve by means of a template.

Hardwood waste timber

The wooden moulding plane is fitted with a blade specially shaped to cut a moulding pattern. By using various combinations of moulding plane, together with a rebate (rabbet) plane, almost any size or shape of moulding can be made. Wipe the sole with linseed oil before use, and work on straight-grained timber until well practised. Cut the workpiece longer than needed. The ends are most difficult to get right. It may be necessary to clamp on a guide-piece.

Spokeshaves

Spokeshaves of many patterns are available, but the most useful types for general wood-working are the flat-bottomed, the round-bottomed, and the chamfer cutter. The flat-bottomed spokeshave is like a plane with a wide and extremely short sole. The handles make it easy to keep square when balancing it on a narrow edge, and the short sole helps to keep the blade in contact with the wood when working on curved surfaces. This tool will only work on flat surfaces or convex curves. Inside curves are best worked with the round-bottom shave. The chamfer spokeshave is most useful for applying simple decoration.

Sharpening planes/chisels

Like many crafts, woodworking requires some knowledge of related skills—for example metalwork, glazing, painting, polishing and, perhaps most useful of all, sharpening. Being able to resharpen planes and chisels is as important as being able to use them properly. The main topic here is sharpening planes though the information applies also to chisels. Additional information on sharpening chisels appears on pages 86–87.

The equipment required is simple. A flat oilstone about 8 × 2 in/20 cm × 5 cm is the basic essential; a combination stone, with both medium and fine surfaces is the best buy. To this add a fine slipstone (a wedge-shaped oilstone), and, of course, a little fine oil, and sharpening can begin.

If possible, make a wooden case for the oilstone. This is best constructed from a single piece of timber, hollowed out in the middle. One piece of wood is used because the oil used on the stone will perish any glued joint; take the bulk of the waste out with an electric drill. Fit a hinged lid to the case to protect the fragile stone from damage, and, most important, to prevent its surface from clogging with dust.

Oilstones can be lubricated with oil or water. Oil is the general choice since it causes fewer problems with rust and binds the fine dust from sharpening into a grubby sludge which can easily be wiped away. The light oil sold in small cans for domestic use is ideal. Never use a stone dry—the metal will overheat, losing its temper (strength), and the stone will become glazed and useless.

A water-repellent lubricating spray will clean up a grubby or clogged oilstone.

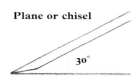

Plane or chisel

30°

Honed edge or cutting angle 30°

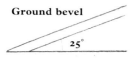

Ground bevel

25°

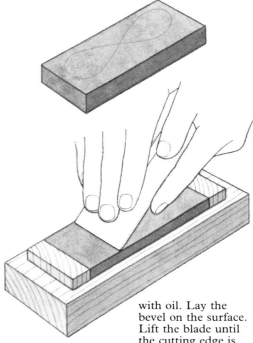

The cutting angle is the angle at the 'sharp end' of the blade. If it is too steep, penetration is difficult. If it is too fine, the cutting edge will be too thin, and liable to snap. The ideal cutting angle for all general woodworking is 30°; many people unnecessarily complicate the issue by using different angles for different blades and woods. The ground bevel—usually put on by the manufacturer—should by contrast be 25°.

Sharpening is simple. Put the oilstone in its box and secure the box in a vice. If the blade is completely blunt, use the coarse, gritty side of the stone first, followed by the fine side. Routine honing is done on the fine side. Wet the surface with oil. Lay the bevel on the surface. Lift the blade until the cutting edge is parallel to the stone. Press gently; move the blade in a figure of eight pattern, keeping the angle constant. When a burr appears on the back of the cutting edge, turn the blade over, lay it *flat* on its back and rub gently to remove the burr. Wipe clean.

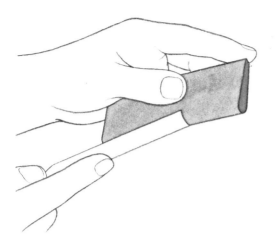

Gouges need to be sharpened on a fine slip-stone. With an outside gouge, roll the bevel backward and forward on the stone to sharpen it. Try to maintain a constant 30° angle. Finish by removing the burr from the inside with the slip. With an inside bevel (in-cannel) gouge, rub the slip to and fro inside it. Take the burr off the outside, again with the slip.

Honing guides
Honing guides are a sound investment for those unsure of their ability with the oilstone: the guide helps keep the edge at a constant angle of 30° to the stone when honing. Several makes are available; ideally buy one made from metal that will hold planes and chisels. Most come with instructions on how to set the angle.

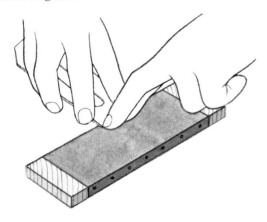

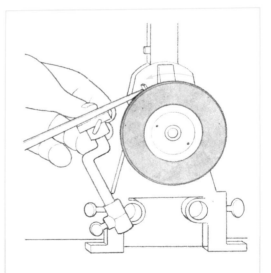

Some problematic timbers easily splinter and tear when cut with a plane or chisel. The solution is to make a leather strop to give tools an edge as sharp as a cut-throat razor's, capable of gliding through the wildest grain. Obtain a small off-cut of shoe leather from a cobbler: tell him what it is for, and he will provide the right leather. Tack it to a board and spread some valve-grinding paste on it. Then use it in the same way as an oilstone to produce a super-sharp edge.

Regrinding
Always protect the eyes with goggles or visor and be aware of safety regulations for abrasive tools. Set the tool rest so that the blade meets the wheel surface at about 25°. Start the machine, and with the blade resting gently on the stone, grind the new bevel. Work slowly, frequently checking that the blade is not overheating; if it is, dip it in water before continuing.

Files, rasps and scrapers

The **rasp** is a long-toothed file for the rapid removal of waste wood, particularly in those areas where another tool would be awkward or unsuitable, for example, close to nails or metal fittings. Wood-carvers often use a small rasp, called a riffler, for pierced carving work. Rasps should be used only for the initial rough work, since, as well as removing the surface wood, the long teeth will score the work deeply.

Files can also be used to good effect on wood and give a finer finish. Many musical instrument and model makers use them for this reason. If the file teeth clog up with dust, wetting the tool will clear them immediately. Don't forget to dry the file thoroughly each time you wet it.

Safety precautions must be observed with files, as with all tools. The ultra-hard steel from which most files are made is extremely brittle, and any attempt to use a file for hammering or as a lever may cause it to shatter violently and without warning.

Scrapers, often dubbed 'cabinet scrapers', are simple and inexpensive tools, often overlooked by amateur woodworkers. Once the sharpening process is mastered, a scraper can be used to prepare the surface almost completely. A wide variety of shapes and sizes is available designed especially for use on flat or curved surfaces and on problematic woods. A sharp scraper is often the best tool with which to remove old paint and polish from furniture, prior to renovation.

Old files can be given a new lease of life by dipping them in *dilute* sulphuric acid. Avoid splashes, wear gloves and rinse with copious fresh water.

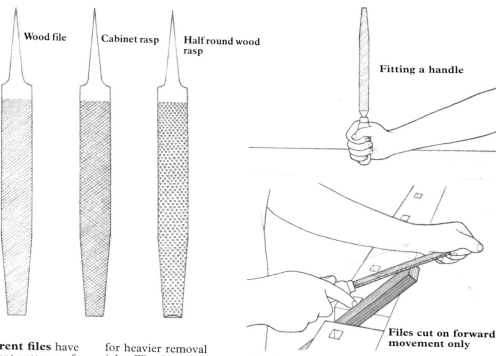

Wood file   Cabinet rasp   Half round wood rasp

Fitting a handle

Files cut on forward movement only

Different files have different patterns of teeth etched into their working surfaces. First-cut files have surfaces suitable for fine work and particularly for sharpening saws and other jobs where a keen finish is essential.

Second-cut files are for heavier removal jobs. Wood rasps have individual, raised teeth, which assist rapid removal and reduce clogging. They are available in bastard—very rough—and second-cut, or cabinet, types. For general workshop use, three files (*above*) cover most jobs.

File handles can be purchased separately to suit most sizes of file and should be fitted for safety. Put the file into the handle, grip the handle firmly, bang it on the bench to bed the handle securely. For the most permanent bond, use a resin glue.

File teeth are shaped so that they cut only in one direction, like a saw, so press down lightly on the forward stroke and ease up on the return. Metal filings can be removed with a wire brush.

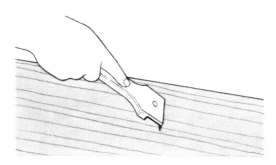

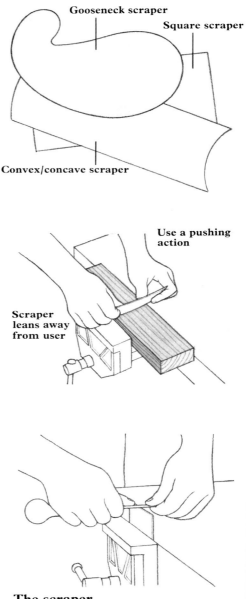

Gooseneck scraper

Square scraper

Convex/concave scraper

Skarsten scrapers are handy, disposable-blade tools, excellent for removing old paint or varnish from furniture and joinery. They also lighten the task of removing surface scars from old and new work. For best results, change blades frequently.

Use a pushing action

Scraper leans away from user

Surform tools, with their replaceable blades made from perforated, hardened steel, take quite a substantial cut from the timber and, like rasps, give a rough finish. However, they are excellent on chipboard, and on aluminium, which would soon destroy other tools.

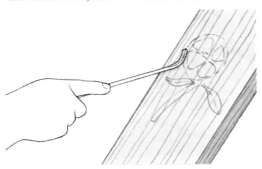

The scraper
Designed to largely replace sandpaper, the scraper is a cheap, renewable resource for finishing furniture. It depends for its cutting action on a minute, hook-like burr to remove tiny shavings from the surface. If the scraper removes only dust, it is blunt and needs resharpening. This is done by first honing the edge square to the face on an oilstone and then, with the scraper held firmly upright in a vice, 'turning' the edge with a proper burnishing tool, which resembles a toothless file. A bradawl (awl) shaft makes a fair substitute.

Rifflers are often invaluable for removing small quantities of waste from the recesses of intricate carvings. They are usually double-ended, the centre part being left smooth for holding. The round and knife-section types are the most useful first buys.

Choosing chisels

A chisel blade has to be made from highest quality steel; the handle is normally of ash, beech, boxwood or plastic, and, to prevent splitting, should be fitted with a brass ferrule. As a further precaution against splitting, a leather washer is often inserted between the edge of the handle and the shoulder of the tang. High-impact plastic handles are common: they are tough, capable of withstanding blows from a hammer, provided its flat face strikes the end of the chisel handle. (A bench mallet is of course the preferred implement for hammering a chisel.)

Most chisel blades are fastened to their handles by either a tang or a socket. Preferences for one or the other are personal—both are perfectly efficient.

There are many different kinds of chisel, all varying in size and shape according to the work they have to do. The five main types in general use are: square-edged firmer chisels, bevel-edged firmer chisels, mortise sash chisels, bevel-edged paring chisels and gouges. The commonest of them is the square-edged firmer chisel, which is fairly strong, unlike the bevel-edged firmer chisel.

The sectional design of the mortise sash chisels makes them stronger than firmer or paring chisels. They sometimes have a ferruled handle to withstand mallet blows. Bevel-edged paring chisels have very long blades, which are generally thinner than those on firmer chisels. Gouges have curved blades, and two types are available: those with inside ground blades, and those with outside ground blades. Firmer gouges have the bevel edge on the back of the blade, whereas scribing gouges have one on the blade front.

Chisels are expensive, so buy only a few to start with. A sound first investment would be a set of four bevel-edged firmer chisels with plastic handles and blade widths of $\frac{1}{4}, \frac{1}{2}, \frac{3}{4}$ and 1 in/6, 13, 19 and 25 mm.

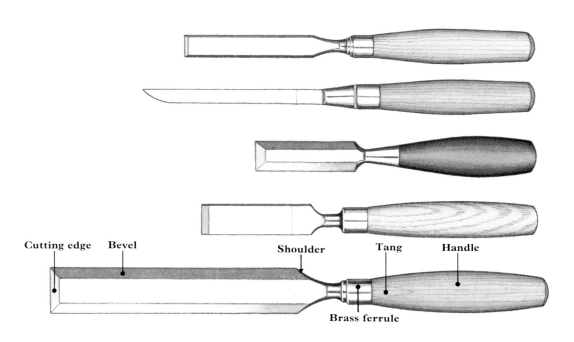

Cutting edge Bevel Shoulder Tang Handle

Brass ferrule

Square-edged firmer chisel: blade $\frac{1}{8}$–$1\frac{1}{2}$ in/3–38 mm wide. For roughing off, paring and mortising.

Bevel-edged firmer chisel: blade $\frac{1}{8}$–$1\frac{1}{2}$ in/3–38 mm wide. For chopping out dovetail sockets and reaching into awkward corners.

Mortise sash chisel: blade $\frac{1}{4}$–$1\frac{1}{2}$ in/6–38 mm wide. For chopping out mortises and slots.

Bevel-edged paring chisel: blade $\frac{3}{16}$–$1\frac{1}{2}$ in/5–38 mm wide. For paring long surfaces and housings.

84

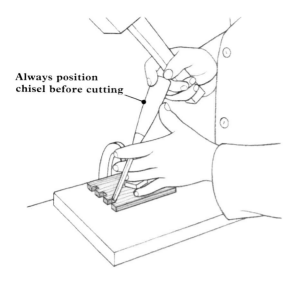

Always position
chisel before cutting

Take great care when using chisels: incorrectly positioned, they cause more accidents than any other hand tool used in woodworking.
• Always secure the work to the vice or bench. To protect surfaces, place a piece of waste wood between the work and the bench or between a cramp and the work.
• Use the correct chisel for the job.

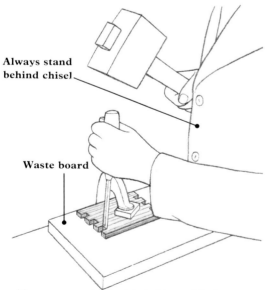

Always stand
behind chisel

Waste board

• Always use a sharp chisel; blunt chisels cause accidents.
• Always position the chisel carefully and try to cut either with the grain or straight across.
• Keep both hands behind the chisel.
• Chop out a little wood at a time.
• Remember, chisels can snap.

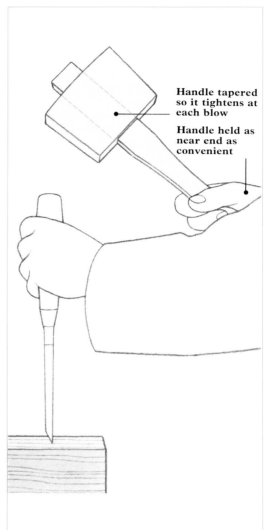

Handle tapered
so it tightens at
each blow

Handle held as
near end as
convenient

A bench mallet must be used with a chisel for some types of work, typically when chopping out a mortise with the mortise chisel. A bench mallet is essentially a wooden-headed hammer and should be used in preference to a metal-faced hammer to prevent the chisel handle splitting. The mallet is normally made of beech or ash, its handle ideally of ash. The slot or mortise in the head is tapered, widening at the thickest part of the head. The handle is also tapered, and passes through the mortise, tightening on itself. The striking faces of the mallet head are bevelled so that they hit the chisel straight. When using a mallet and chisel, carefully position the chisel, then holding the mallet handle as near its end as convenient, use a wrist action to produce well-controlled, even blows.

Using and sharpening chisels

To serve any useful purpose, a chisel must be sharp; and to be sharp it must undergo first, grinding on a groundstone, then honing on an oilstone. A chisel blade thus has two angles: the ground bevel of 25° and the honed one of 30°. A new chisel is supplied with the ground bevel only.

An oilstone is, therefore, the essential adjunct to a set of chisels. A convenient size is $8 \times 2 \times 1$ in/20.5 $\times$ 5 $\times$ 2.5 cm, and it is possible to buy combination stones with both medium and fine surfaces. Use the medium grit face if the chisel is very blunt, followed by the fine grit to achieve a truly incisive edge; use the fine grit alone for routine honing. Before use, oil the stone slightly: this keeps the pores of the stone from becoming clogged with the finely ground steel; it also lubricates so that the blade is prevented from heating and, thereby, losing its temper or strength. Store the oilstone in a purpose-built hardwood box—it is surprisingly brittle.

Chisels should only need regrinding to their original bevel angle of 25° when the cutting edge is nicked or when a sufficiently sharp cutting edge can no longer be achieved on the oilstone. The best type of groundstone has constant lubrication on the blade either by water, oil or a combination of both. The grindstone wheel is generally revolved downward, toward operator and cutting edge.

Grinding chisels properly is not easy. Make sure all guards are in position on the grindstone and wear eye protectors. Set the tool rest at the desired angle and apply the blade lightly against the rim of the wheel. If too much pressure is applied, the cutting edge will overheat, turn blue and lose its temper. In this condition it is impossible to sharpen; keep it cool by dipping it in water.

If a grindstone wheel is not available, a chisel blade can be reground to its original 25° bevel using an oilstone with a coarse surface. Then hone on a medium and fine-surfaced oilstone in the usual way.

Clearly chisels should be kept sharp, and to assist this they are normally supplied with plastic edge protectors; a canvas hold-all provides convenient additional protection during storage. Further information on sharpening, particularly on sharpening plane blades, is given on pages 80–1.

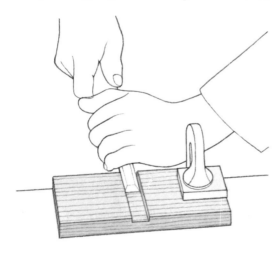

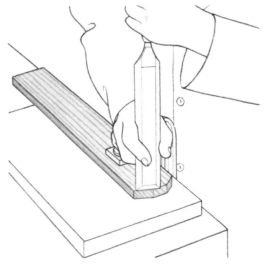

To cut a slot, use a bevel-edged chisel. Ensure the work is secured to the bench. Chisel half-way through, taking a little wood off at a time until the desired depth is reached. Then turn the wood around and complete the slot from the other side. If the slot is large, use a mallet. On wide slots, make additional saw cuts in the waste. Always chisel from both sides: if a slot is chiselled from one side only, the corner of the other side may break off.

To pare a corner, lay the workpiece flat on a piece of waste. Secure both to the bench. Always try to chisel with the grain, otherwise the chisel will dig in and split the wood. Work inward toward the centre of the piece. (If a corner is chiselled by working outward, splitting may occur.) Keep the chisel vertical, with both arms behind it and the right hand on top, the thumb giving downward pressure. Pare off a little wood at a time.

Cutting a mortise

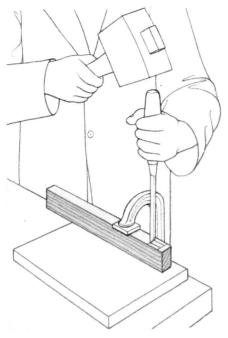

1 Secure the work to the bench. Place the chisel in the centre of the mortise. Hold the chisel vertical with its bevel facing outward.

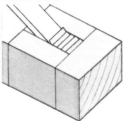

2 Make shallow cuts, moving the chisel backward a little at a time. Stop $\frac{1}{8}$ in/3 mm from mortise end.

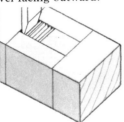

3 Reverse the chisel. From the centre, chop toward the other end, stopping $\frac{1}{8}$ in/3 mm from the mark.

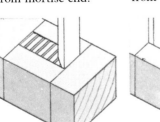

4 Repeat this process, driving the chisel into the mortise. Remove the waste.

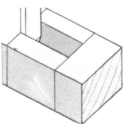

5 Pare the two mortise ends clean once the desired depth is reached.

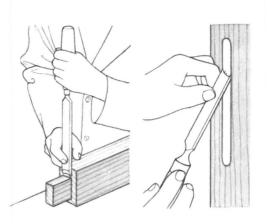

Cutting with a gouge requires the same technique as using a chisel. Use a scribing gouge for internal curved work such as the end of a chair rail. This gouge is more convenient to use than a firmer gouge but more difficult to sharpen. The bevel on the back of the firmer gouge is for cutting external surfaces such as finger grips.

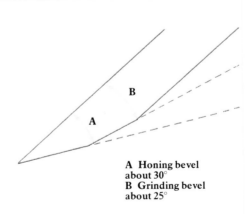

A Honing bevel
about 30°
B Grinding bevel
about 25°

Honing a chisel
Hold the blade at an angle of 30° to the oilstone. Move the chisel backward and forward over the full length and width of the stone until a burr is formed on the flat side of the blade. The burr can be felt by rubbing lightly with a finger tip. Turn the blade over and hold it perfectly flat on the stone. Rub from side to side until the burr has disappeared completely. The chisel is sharp.

The lathe

Wood turning is the process of forming rounded objects on a lathe.

Perhaps the most basic of the techniques required is the preliminary one of selecting the right speed for the job in hand. Most lathes have four speeds from which to choose: the larger the diameter of the work, the slower the speed required. Typical choices are: for work up to 1 in/2.5 cm in diameter, 2,250 rpm; 1 to 4 in/2.5 to 10 cm in diameter, 1,330 rpm; 4 to 8 in/10 to 20.5 cm in diameter, 790 rpm; above 8 in/20.5 cm in diameter, 425 rpm—which is normally the slowest speed available.

There are two principal types of turning: turning between centres and faceplate turning, the first giving cylindrical-shaped work, the second disc- or bowl-shaped work.

Few tools are used at the lathe compared with the bench: a gouge, skew chisel, parting tool and scraper serve most purposes. All require long handles in order to provide leverage on the tool rest sufficient to resist the turning force of the wood. Sharp blades are essential, and time spent properly grinding and honing tools is never wasted. Never attempt to use the tools without a proper support, correctly positioned. The work revolves toward the operator, and the downward pressure so exerted on the cutting edge is more than can be resisted by the hands alone. Height of the rest varies according to the work in hand, but it should always be as close to the work as possible without touching it. If the rest is too far back, leverage increases to dangerous levels.

In turning between centres, the cut is made across the grain; in faceplate turning, the grain runs across the diameter of the wood; as in bench work, cutting against the grain should generally be avoided.

When buying turning tools, look for strong handles 10–12 in/25–30 cm long, with blades of quality metal.

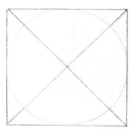

1 To prepare wood for cylindrical turning, first saw it square and free of defects. Determine the centre of each end and mark it with a bradawl (awl). Make saw cuts at one end to take the centre of the driving fork.

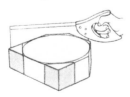

2 Cut wood to an octagonal shape to facilitate the final smoothing.

3 Plane off surplus corners. This prevents chisel whip and flying splinters.

A lathe, *below,* consists of four basic parts: the head stock, which supports one end of the material and rotates it; the tail stock, which simply supports the other end of the material; the bed of the lathe and the tool rest. In cylindrical turning, the work is held by both head stock and tail stock—the first is fitted with a fork centre, the second a cone. In faceplate turning, which gives disc-shaped work, attachment is to a metal faceplate that screws on to the lathe's mandrel (the drive shaft). Before switching on a lathe, select the correct speed and revolve the wood by hand to check the tool rest clearance.

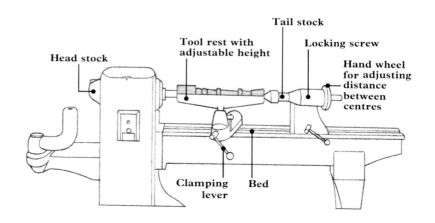

Head stock

Tool rest with adjustable height

Tail stock

Locking screw

Hand wheel for adjusting distance between centres

Clamping lever

Bed

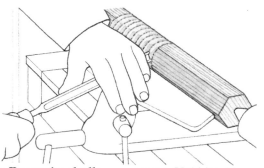

1 Removing bulk waste is the first step in cutting down or turning a cylinder. The ideal tool is a $\frac{3}{4}$ in/20 mm half-round roughing gouge, ground straight across. Hold it with the right hand on the handle, the left across the blade close to the cutting edge. Obtain the cut by raising the right hand, not by pushing the gouge.

2 To finish a cylinder, use a skew chisel. Used correctly, it gives a planing cut and thus a smooth finish. Set the rest just above centre. Don't start the cut at one end—end grain can cause chisel whip. Begin, say, 1 in/2.5 cm in from the end and cut the residue by working outward toward the end. Cut with the bottom half of the chisel. Digging-in occurs if the top half is used.

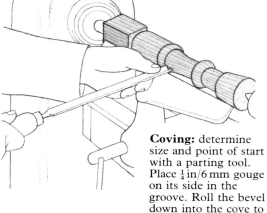

Coving: determine size and point of start with a parting tool. Place $\frac{1}{4}$ in/6 mm gouge on its side in the groove. Roll the bevel down into the cove to the desired depth. Repeat the process on the other side.

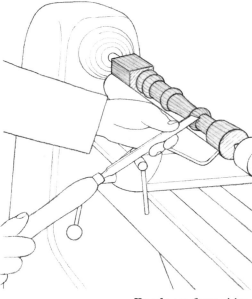

Beads are formed by using a skew chisel. Work outward from the desired centre line of the bead, rolling the bevel sideways to the base of the bead.

Lathe safety

Turning material must be defect-free.
Never use blunt or badly worn tools.
Trim corners off large material.
Oil the tail-stock end of the material if the tail stock is the static variety.
Centre stocks accurately.
Keep tool rest close to the material; if faceplate turning, position the rest a little above centre. Keep readjusting the rest as cutting progresses.
Hold cutting tools correctly.
Beware of 'whipping' when the tail stock is extended to hold long material.
Keep fingers away from moving parts.
Never run the lathe with the drive pulleys exposed.
Do not tamper with micro switches.
After running material, retighten the tail stock centre.

Turning on a faceplate

To fashion disc- or bowl-shaped items on a lathe requires a different set of techniques from those used in producing cylindrical work. Instead of turning between centres (ie, between the lathe's head and tail stocks) the material to be shaped, usually known as the blank, is fixed to a faceplate. This in turn is fixed to the head stock mandrel (driving shaft) and all subsequent operations, from turning through sanding to polishing, are carried out with the wood secured to the faceplate or other holding device.

Once the blank has been roughly prepared for turning, the faceplate is detached from the mandrel and the blank securely screwed in place; take special care to centre it precisely. This assembly is then screwed to the mandrel and the lathe started.

Before any complex shaping takes place, the blank must be brought to a true circle, for which a $\frac{3}{8}$ in/10 mm gouge is recommended. Next, assuming a bowl shape is the object, the outside of the blank is shaped; again the $\frac{3}{8}$ in gouge is recommended. The technique for using the tool for this purpose is similar to that for turning between centres. If performed correctly, little finishing needs to be done with abrasive paper. When the outside shape and finish are satisfactory, clean the work by buffing it with a clean cloth; then give it a final polish.

To gouge out the inside of a bowl, the partly turned blank must be removed from the faceplate and reversed so that what is to be the bottom of the bowl can be reattached. With the lathe restarted, a parting tool is applied to define what will be the rim of the bowl and to mark a starting point. Removal of the inside can then begin, once again using the $\frac{3}{8}$ in gouge provided the bowl is up to 8 in/ 20 cm in diameter.

The shape of a gouge is quite critical when hollowing because digging-in will occur unless the corners are ground well back. The 'nose' of the gouge should be shaped like a little finger.

A step-by-step account of hollowing out a bowl shape continues on the next two pages.

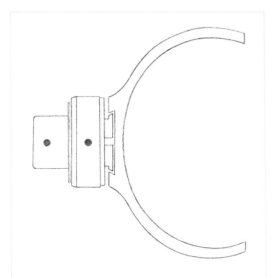

The six-in-one chuck
This versatile device enables different sizes and shapes of blank to be mounted in appropriate chucks, thus eliminating unsightly screw holes. A bowl, for instance, is secured in the expanding collet chuck, which fits tightly into a small recess hollowed in the material's base.

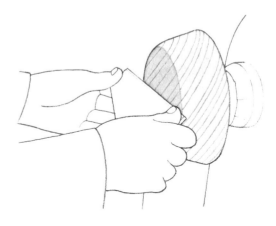

To prepare a blank for faceplate turning, saw it square and free of defects. Then remove the corners and, preferably, cut it roughly round with a band-saw. Next draw concentric circles on the blank to assist in placing it dead centre on the faceplate or other holding device. Large-diameter work is turned on the outer faceplate because the inner faceplate is limited in size by the proximity of the lathe bed. A felt washer between the faceplate and mandrel helps prevent seizing. Position the tool rest across the bowl, a little above centre.

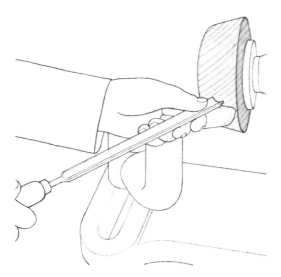

Tool sharpening
Turning tools are supplied singly or in sets, ground to shape but in need of final sharpening.

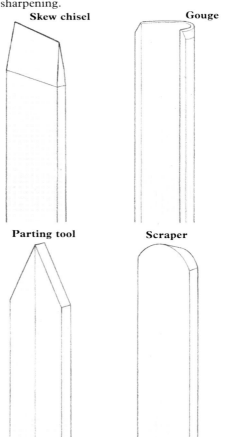

Turning the outside: before starting, check clearance with the tool rest by manually revolving the blank. Select the appropriate turning speed, then, using a $\frac{3}{8}$ in/10 mm gouge, bring the outside of the blank to a true circle. Continue shaping as desired, still with the $\frac{3}{8}$ in gouge. Ensure the bevel rubs on the work; keep adjusting the tool rest so that is is close to the cutting edge. Raise the right hand to determine the thickness of the cut; do not push the gouge into the material.

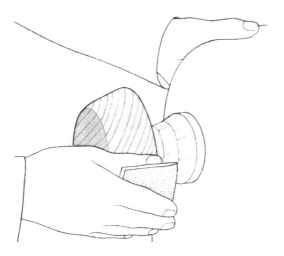

Finish the turned surface by manual application of abrasive paper. No 4 garnet paper, followed by No 6, with a damping-down between to raise any whiskers, is a useful combination.

Skew chisels are sharpened on both bevels with an angle of 30° between them sharpen the factory-ground bevel itself. **Gouges** should also be sharpened on the ground bevel; the nose may be square for spindle-turning, but for bowl-turning it must be ground well back. Move it to and fro in a figure-of-eight pattern along the length of the grindstone, rolling it from edge to edge. Always keep the bevel in contact with the stone. Complete the operation by placing the gouge sideways on the stone and rolling it from edge to edge while rubbing. **Parting tools** should be sharpened on both ground faces with an angle of 30° between them. **Scrapers** are sharpened at an angle of 80°, also on the ground bevel. Remove the burr and keep the face of the scraper perfectly flat on the stone. Finally, develop the scraping edge with a burnisher, working along the sharpened edge so that it is turned, or bent over, at an angle of about 10°.

Turning on a faceplate /2

Having mounted the workpiece properly on the faceplate, the possibility of turning bowl-shaped work is now open. To the novice this may seem a daunting undertaking, but it is, in reality, surprisingly easy and—not so surprising—extremely enjoyable.

Much of the satisfaction of turning bowl-shapes is in revealing the decorative figure or pattern of the chosen wood. The table (*right*) lists woods generally accepted as best for turning decorative objects; whichever the choice, it is usually worth keeping the material to be worked, turned roughly to size, in the workshop for a week before the turning session. Turning exposes inner layers of timber which may not have fully seasoned, and this breathing period may well enhance the stability of the material.

Useful woods for turning

Coarse hardwoods, and softwoods generally, are the least satisfactory timbers for turning because they tend to disintegrate if shaped to tight curves. Some of the timbers below are selected for their figure, others for their fine grain and ease of working.

Sycamore	African mahogany
Maple	Yew
Birch	Teak
Ebony	Lime
Beech	Elm
Ash	
American black walnut	

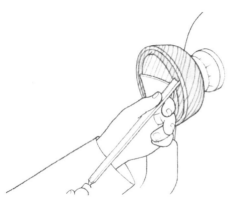

1 When content with the outside shape of the bowl, use a parting tool to create a point of start for hollowing out the inside. Work from this point to the centre with a gouge.

2 Using a $\frac{3}{8}$ in/10 mm gouge or a rounded scraper, work in toward the centre as usual, taking care to adjust the tool rest correctly, to keep the bevel in contact with the wood and to determine the cut by moving the hand outward.

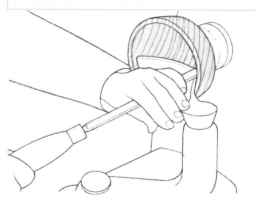

3 Before cutting deep into the bowl, return to the inner rim and clean it up.

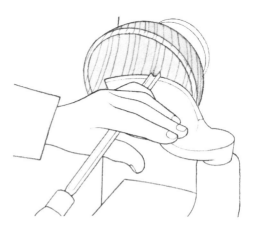

4 As the cut advances deep into the material, a specially shaped tool rest becomes increasingly helpful for keeping the point of support for the tool as close as possible to the cutting point.

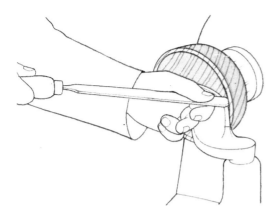

5 Awkward or specially shaped recesses in a bowl may be most easily tackled with a rounded scraper.

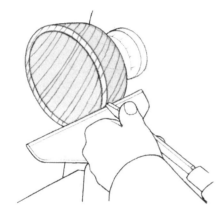

6 Final adjustments to the outside rim often need to be added at this stage; a parting tool is suitable for the purpose.

7 Apply the chosen finish. If the bowl is to be used for salads or other foodstuffs, olive oil is recommended. Wax polish gives a more decorative effect. Build up to the desired finish by alternate application and buffing.

Measuring instruments for different purposes in lathe work

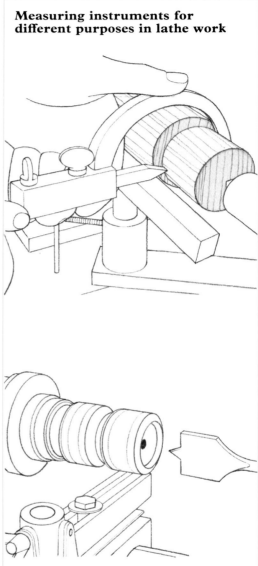

Boring on a lathe

For boring into end grain, without the support of the trail stock, secure the material in a suitable chuck. The six-in-one chuck with its various attachments can be useful; a metal cup chuck will hold small pieces. First turn the wood between centres so that it fits the chosen chuck. Then select the boring tool, mounted in a suitable boring attachment. Locate the brad point of the drill bit dead centre in the place to be bored, select a suitable speed and switch on. Occasionally remove the bit from the hole and clear it of shavings. Watch for overheating. Hole-boring augers can be obtained to drill holes in excess of 24 in/61 cm deep.

Chucking systems

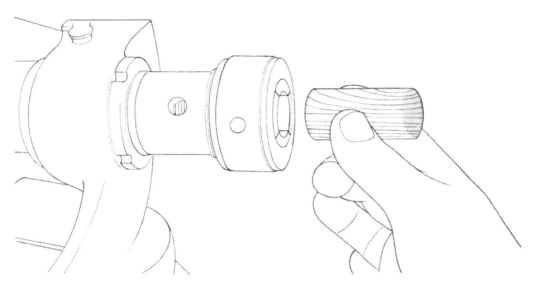

Various types of chuck are available that will conveniently hold unusually shaped or small pieces of material securely for turning on a lathe. The collett chuck, for example, can grip short, round pieces of timber between $\frac{3}{8}$ in and $1\frac{1}{2}$ in/10 mm and 38 mm in diameter. This means that items such as egg cups can be turned and finished entirely on the lathe; even detaching the finished, shaped item from the timber cylinder out of which it was shaped is done with the lathe still revolving. Another useful attachment, similar in function to the collett chuck, is the metal cup chuck.

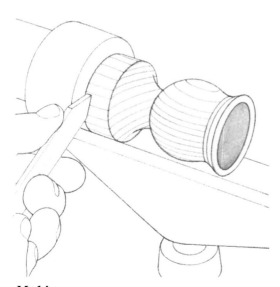

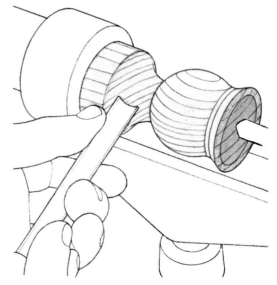

Making an egg cup

1 Turn a piece of square timber between centres to produce a cylinder; narrow one end into a spigot to fit the chosen chuck.

Make a scratch mould from nails driven through ply; mark out the desired curvature by applying it to the revolving piece.

2 Hollow out the bowl with a spindle gouge, then work the shape of the outside curvature. Detach by applying a parting

tool or a saw, taking care to prevent the finished piece from falling to the floor.

94

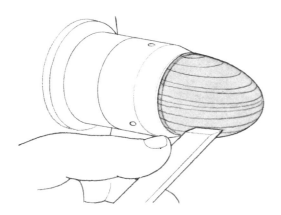

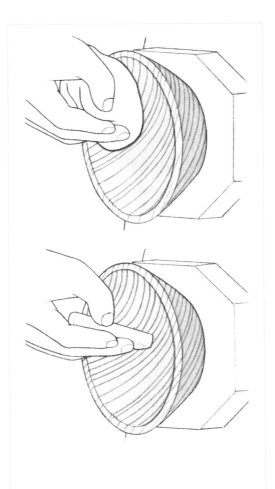

Turning an egg shape

1 Select a hardwood off-cut about $4 \times 2\frac{1}{4} \times 2\frac{1}{4}$ in/ 100 mm × 57 mm × 57 mm. Between centres turn to a cylinder slightly oversize to the finished egg. Shape one end to fit the chuck securely; here it is a metal cup chuck.

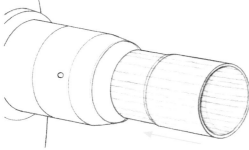

2 Attach cup chuck to lathe head stock. Shape, buff and polish most of the egg shape. Then, turning between centres, make a custom-made wooden cup chuck to receive the finished part of the egg shape. One end of the wooden chuck should be shaped to fit the metal cup.

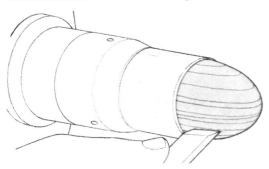

3 With the unturned part held in the wooden cup chuck, shape, buff, polish and detach the egg.

Finishing on a lathe

Preparation is essential. With the lathe stopped, check the work for rough areas and make good. Remove tool rest. Select a suitable abrasive, for example No 4/0 garnet paper, and start the lathe at a medium speed. Keep the abrasive moving across the work or scratches will result. Moisten the surface with a damp cloth to raise loose fibres. When dry, smooth with No 6/0 garnet paper. Remove dust. The final finish may now be applied. A simple quick finish is given by wax—proprietary brands are suitable. Apply with a soft cloth, burnishing with a clean cloth and repeating until the desired degree of finish is obtained. Alternatively, apply the wax with a carnauba stick, then burnish as before. An oil finish is equally simple: apply linseed oil or button polish (beeswax and methylated spirit) with a pad, recharging it frequently to give a substantial build-up, then leave to dry.

Excavations of Bronze Age boats (from around 1500 BC) in England reveal that their oak planks were joined by being sewn, or lashed, together, with twisted stems of yew threaded through holes in the edges of the boards. Although nails were clearly not in use in northern Europe at this time for boat-building, the problem of fastening wood had to this extent been solved. A tool for boring holes was, of course, the essential prerequisite, and the Bronze Age boat-builders probably used the Celtic drill, or auger, which is referred to in Roman writings at the time of Julius Caesar's invasion of Britain in 54 BC. This auger, developments of which are still in use today, would have consisted of a wrought-iron bar about 24 in/61 cm long, with a shell or spoon-shaped cutting end, which was rotated by a cross-handle to cut through the wood.

It was not until early in the fifteenth century that the carpenters's brace, initially fitted with a fixed bit, began to be used in Europe, and not until the nineteenth century that the hand drill was invented.

The Romans, by contrast with the barbarians of northern Europe, used wrought-iron nails extensively. They had to be individually and laboriously hand forged and hence were expensive items, but they were also strong, and wrought iron is highly rust resistant. There is plenty of evidence to show that the same nails were used over and over again. Because nails were so costly, the alternative was to use hard wooden pegs driven through holes in joints. These pegs are sometimes referred to as trenails—tree, or wooden, nails. It was not until the nineteenth century that machinery was developed to make the mass-produced nails known today.

There are many early illustrations of carpenters using hammers to drive in nails. These early hammers had a square-section head and either a wedge-shaped pein or a claw—similar to those used today.

Screws are a much later development in the history of fastening. They first appeared in the seventeenth century and, like nails, were handmade. Making a screw was a time-consuming process—the spiral threads had to be cut by hand using a file. Threads were uneven and rounded, rather than sharp; screws had no points, and the slot in the top was shallow and frequently off-centre. They were clearly expensive to produce and would only have been used in the best work. Screwdrivers, originally called turn-screws, appeared at the same time as screws. The first mass-produced, pointed screws, were made in the nineteenth century.

FASTENING

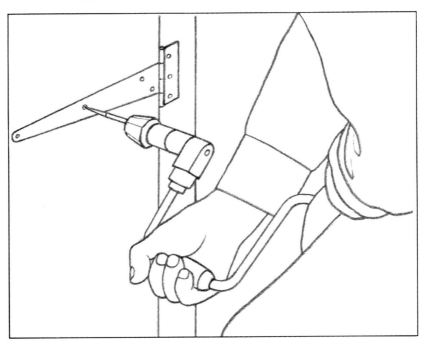

Nails

Nailing is the quick, simple way of forming a joint between two pieces of wood, but the woodworker must always bear in mind its limitations.

In general, nailing is least efficient when the two pieces tend to be pulled apart, and more efficient when they tend to slide over each other. As a nail is driven into the wood, it pushes the fibres apart, and it is the grip of these fibres on the shank of the nail that provides the holding power. Nails that are not round are less likely to split the wood, but they should be driven in with the long axis parallel to the grain.

The efficiency of nailed joints can be as low as 15 per cent, compared with 100 per cent in the case of a strong adhesive. For maximum strength and efficiency, choose a nail of the correct type, length, gauge and finish. For example, when driving into end grain, which has a naturally poor hold, use a nail with a roughened shank or one with annular rings to improve the grip. Always drive in a nail with care so that hammer marks do not show on

the wood and the joint does not look crude.

Nailing is not satisfactory if, for some reason, the joint may need to be taken apart and reassembled at a later date.

Nails have a head, a shank and a point, and they are usually made of mild steel wire. Different finishes are available; for example, galvanized nails for outdoor use. Check that the finish is appropriate. Mild steel nails will, for instance, stain oak.

The size of a nail is usually expressed in terms of its length. Nail thickness, that is the diameter of the shank, is measured in terms of the Standard Wire Gauge (SWG). The more common varieties are available in different sizes of gauge.

If a nail starts to bend when driven in, take it out and, using a new nail, start again in a slightly different place. Extract nails either with the claw of a claw hammer or with a pair of pincers. Before levering, place a piece of waste wood under the head of the hammer or pincer jaws to prevent damage to the surface of the work.

Select a nail that is between 2½ and 3 times longer than the thickness of the top piece of wood being nailed.

Dovetail nailing grips better than straight nailing, particularly in end grain. Drive in pairs of nails towards each other, at a similar angle to a dovetail.

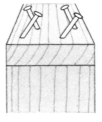

Use skew nailing when two pieces of wood are to be joined at right angles. When driving the nails home, take care not to damage the wood surface.

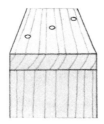

Stagger the spacing of the nails across the width of the wood. This will greatly reduce the risk of splitting.

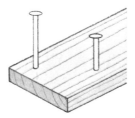

To eliminate splitting, blunt the nail point by filing or by tapping it against metal before driving it into wood.

Near edges, start the nail hole with a drill or a bradawl slightly smaller than the nail size to avoid splitting the wood.

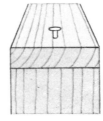

To avoid bruising the wood, stop driving the nail when just above the surface, and finish off with a nail punch.

Hold very small pins in position with card. Hammer the pin through the card and tear away before the pin is driven home.

Most nails and pins are finished in bright mild steel; however, those required for outdoor use are available in rustproof finishes. They are usually sold by weight, but popular types and sizes are also available in prepackaged boxes and packets. Nail and pin types most commonly used for woodworking are:

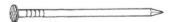

Round wire nail, or French nail The round shank and flat chequered head make this nail suitable for joinery. *Sizes ½–6 in/13–150 mm.*

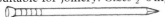

Oval wire nail This nail's shape ensures that it can easily be driven below the wood surface. *Sizes ½–6 in/13–150 mm.*

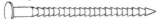

Annular ringed nail Use this corrosion-resistant nail for fixing into plywood. *Sizes ¾–3 in/19–75 mm.*

Panel pin For general cabinet-work, such as fixing ply or mouldings; it can be punched below the surface. *Sizes ½–2 in/13–50 mm.*

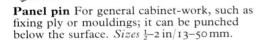

Veneer pin For holding veneers in position until the glue has set. *Sizes ⅜–1½ in/10–38 mm.*

Hardboard pin For fixing hardboard or thin ply; sometimes has a square-sectioned shank. *Sizes ½–1½ in/13–38 mm.*

Sprig For holding materials such as glass in picture frames; will not grip if driven in too far. *Sizes ½–¾ in/13–19 mm.*

Escutcheon pin Use this brass pin for fastening small metal items such as escutcheon plates. *Sizes ⅝ or ¾ in/15 or 19 mm.*

Staple Use with a staple gun for quickly fixing upholstery and other thin materials. Made with both round and square tops.

Gimp pin Solid brass, this small panel pin is rust resistant; it is used in upholstery. *Sizes ⅜–¾ in/10–19 mm.*

Cut tack For upholstery and for laying carpets. Rust-resistant finish available. *Sizes ¼–1 in/6–25 mm.*

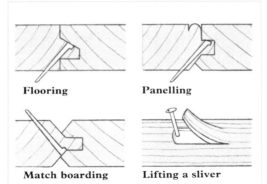

Flooring Panelling

Match boarding Lifting a sliver

Secret nailing

When fixing tongue-and-groove boards for floors and panelling, lost-head nails are driven through the tongue at an angle to force the boards more closely together. The groove of the succeeding board effectively hides the nail head. For general nailing, a sliver of wood can be lifted with a chisel or gouge and the nail driven into the recess. The head of the nail is concealed when the sliver is glued back down.

Using hammers The Warrington, or cross-pein hammer, with its tapered end opposite the face, is preferred by cabinet-makers to the claw hammer, which is better suited to heavy work. Cross-peins are obtainable in various weights, the smallest of which is known as a pin, or tack, hammer. Use a cross-pein to start off short pins by tapping gently with the tapered end before driving in with the hammer face. Driving nails accurately requires care. Keep an eye on the nail and constantly monitor the angle at which it enters the wood. At the moment of impact, the handle of the hammer should be at a right angle to the nail. Ensure the face is kept clean at all times, polishing it if necessary with fine abrasive paper. A dirty hammer face tends to bend nails.

Boring/drilling tools

Drills for woodworking fall into two distinct categories: twist drills and drill bits. The first are for making relatively small holes, the second for larger.

Twist drills are made of carbon steel or, alternatively, of high-speed steel, which stays sharper longer and can drill in metal. Twist drills are normally 'jobber' length, that is, they can drill holes up to ten times their diameter. For deeper holes, extra-length drills are available.

Use twist drills in a hand drill or an electric drill. Most hand drills have a double-pinion drive system—essentially a group of gear wheels (enclosed on some models) powered by turning a handle. To grasp the twist drill itself firmly, there is an adjustable chuck, usually accepting twist drills up to $\frac{5}{16}$in/8 mm. An electric drill does the same job as a hand drill, but more easily.

For small holes, say up to $\frac{1}{4}$in/6 mm in diameter, a twist drill in a hand or electric drill is the correct equipment. To make holes from $\frac{1}{4}$in/6 mm up to about 2 in/50 mm diameter, use an auger bit or centre bit in a hand brace. This is essentially a cranked shaft, which, when turned directly, revolves the chuck. Most braces have a ratchet mechanism, essential for working in confined spaces, and most have alligator jaws in the chuck, designed for holding only square-section shanked bits. Braces with universal jaws hold both square-section and circular shanked twist drill bits.

Larger holes can also be made with a flat bit, which is specially designed for use with an electric drill.

To make a hole with a diameter of more than 2 in/50 mm, use an expanding bit or a hole saw. These cut holes up to 3 in/75 mm diameter.

Bits and drills will not cut properly unless they are kept sharp. The golden rules to observe in sharpening are always to keep the original angles on the various cutting surfaces and to remove as little metal as is necessary.

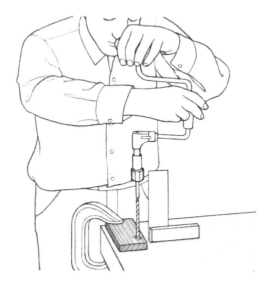

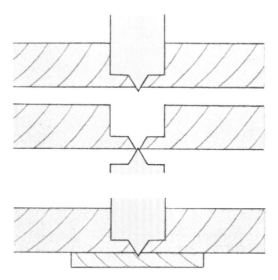

Drilling accurately is difficult. Make a starting hole with a bradawl (awl) or a centre punch: twist drills do not have sharp points. Ensure that the bit enters the work squarely by placing a try-square alongside the hole to act as a guide. If boring into the end of a leg, clamp a strip of wood on each side of the leg to guide the position of the brace and bit.

To avoid splitting the workface on the far side of the hole, clamp a block of waste wood to the far side of the work and drill right through. The block will prevent the bit splitting the work. Alternatively, drill through until the point of the bit just appears. Then turn the work over. Place the point of the bit in the small hole that has appeared and complete the operation.

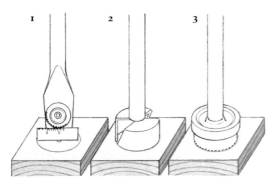

Sharpening drills

Jennings-pattern bit: using a fine file, sharpen the spurs on the inside only—the outside of the bit must never be touched, for this would alter its diameter. Then sharpen the cutting surfaces of the cutters, taking care not to damage the threads in the centre.

Special bits: To bore holes of varying diameters in softwood, use an expanding bit, **1**. Two sizes are available: ¾–1½ in/19–32 mm, and ⅞–3 in/22–75 mm. The Forstner bit, **2**, drills an accurate, flat-bottomed hole. Use the hole saw, **3**, in thin wood and manufactured boards. Mount circular saw blades of different diameters on the central arbour of the twist drill.

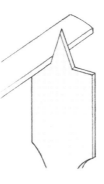

Flat spade bit: use a small sharpening stone or a very smooth file. Sharpen the forward cutting edges, never the sides. Keep the original cutting angle and ensure the surfaces are flat. Take off the same amount each side.

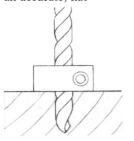

Fit a depth stop to the bit when boring holes to the same depth. Plastic or metal stops are available.

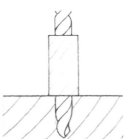

Make a wooden depth stop by pre-drilling a piece of softwood.

Brad point drill: sharpen the spurs and cutters with a small stone or a small triangular saw file. File only on the inside of the spurs and keep both pairs of cutters and spurs level.

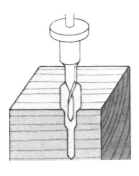

A combination drill bit makes the pilot hole, clearance hole for the screw shank and the countersink.

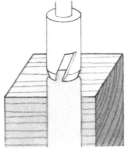

A plug cutter forms wood plugs for concealing counter-drilled screws.

Equal / 118°

Twist drill: sharpen on a grindstone. Considerable practice is needed both to maintain the correct cutting angles and to keep the point in the centre. It is probably best to buy a jig to help do this correctly.

Screws

It may not be entirely obvious to the inexperienced woodworker how much better screws are than nails for making strong joints between timber components and for joining metal fittings, such as hinges, to wood.

Screws have much more gripping power than nails because, as a screw is tightened, with its head 'seated' on the timber surface, it draws the two pieces together in a clamping action. Nails, by contrast, rely solely on friction for their holding power.

The other great advantage of screws is, of course, that they may be readily taken out and reinserted without damage to the surrounding timber surface.

A screw consists of a head (available in a number of shapes) and a shank–the threaded part. The diameter of the shank is described as the gauge.

Most screws are made from mild (unstrengthened) steel, but brass, silicon bronze, aluminium and stainless steel are also used. A range of different finishes is generally available, either for decorative purposes or for their resistance to corrosion; they include cadmium plating sherardizing, bright zinc-plating, black japanning and antique bronzing.

When ordering screws, always specify gauge, length, material, head style and type of finish that you require.

So although a screw may seem a straightforward item, choosing the right type for the work in hand can be complicated. It is not, for example, good practice to use steel screws in oak: the acid in the wood corrodes the steel and stains the wood; brass may seem more suitable, but brass is soft and oak is tough, and the danger of breakage quite real. The solution is, therefore, to drive steel screws into the oak; then, having made satisfactory threaded holes, to remove the steel screws and replace them with brass. Alternatively, use brass-plated steel screws.

A final complicating factor is the advent of the Twinfast screw: its special double-threaded design makes it particularly suitable for use with manufactured boards.

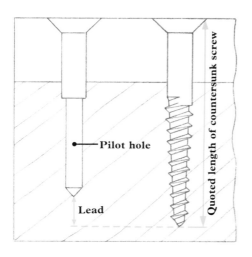

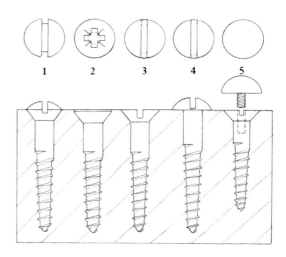

To eliminate splitting, drill a clearance hole in the piece to be attached, and a pilot hole in the piece to which attachment is made. Different diameters of pilot hole are required (see chart opposite) for both hard and softwoods. The pilot hole is never drilled to the full depth of the screw; the undrilled depth is called the lead. If a screw has a countersunk head, fit a countersinking bit to the drill and with it make an appropriate depression to contain the head.

1 Raised countersunk head: for highly finished fittings which need occasional removal; raised head prevents possible damage to wood. **2 Pozidrive**: many screws are now made with the Pozidrive star-head that minimizes slipping. **3 Flat countersunk head**: wood to wood, metal fittings to wood; flush finish. **4 Round head**: for metal fittings where a flush finish is not needed. **5 Dome-top mirror screws**: chromium-plated brass dome screws into threaded hole on countersunk head screw.

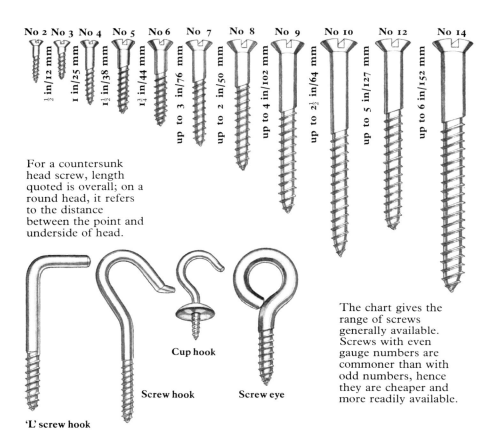

No 2 No 3 No 4 No 5 No 6 No 7 No 8 No 9 No 10 No 12 No 14

$\frac{1}{2}$ in/12 mm   1 in/25 mm   1$\frac{1}{2}$ in/38 mm   1$\frac{3}{4}$ in/44 mm   up to 3 in/76 mm   up to 2 in/50 mm   up to 4 in/102 mm   up to 2$\frac{1}{2}$ in/64 mm   up to 5 in/127 mm   up to 6 in/152 mm

For a countersunk head screw, length quoted is overall; on a round head, it refers to the distance between the point and underside of head.

'L' screw hook

Cup hook

Screw hook   Screw eye

The chart gives the range of screws generally available. Screws with even gauge numbers are commoner than with odd numbers, hence they are cheaper and more readily available.

Screw Gauge	Clearance Hole		Lead		Pilot Hole *Hardwood*		Pilot Hole *Softwood*	
	in	mm	in	mm	in	mm	in	mm
2	$\frac{3}{32}$	2.5	$\frac{1}{16}$	1.5	bradawl		bradawl/awl	
3	$\frac{3}{32}$	2.5	$\frac{1}{8}$	3.0	$\frac{1}{16}$	1.5	bradawl/awl	
4	$\frac{1}{8}$	3.0	$\frac{1}{8}$	3.0	$\frac{1}{16}$	1.5	bradawl/awl	
5	$\frac{1}{8}$	3.0	$\frac{5}{32}$	4.0	$\frac{1}{16}$	1.5	bradawl/awl	
6	$\frac{5}{32}$	4.0	$\frac{5}{32}$	4.0	$\frac{5}{64}$	2.0	$\frac{1}{16}$	1.5
7	$\frac{5}{32}$	4.0	$\frac{3}{16}$	4.5	$\frac{3}{32}$	2.5	$\frac{1}{16}$	1.5
8	$\frac{3}{16}$	4.5	$\frac{7}{32}$	5.0	$\frac{3}{32}$	2.5	$\frac{5}{64}$	2.0
9	$\frac{3}{16}$	4.5	$\frac{1}{4}$	6.0	$\frac{3}{32}$	2.5	$\frac{5}{64}$	2.0
10	$\frac{13}{64}$	5.0	$\frac{1}{4}$	6.5	$\frac{7}{64}$	2.75	$\frac{5}{64}$	2.0
12	$\frac{15}{64}$	6.0	$\frac{5}{16}$	8	$\frac{1}{8}$	3.0	$\frac{3}{32}$	2.5
14	$\frac{1}{4}$	6.5	$\frac{11}{32}$	9	$\frac{9}{64}$	3.5	$\frac{7}{64}$	2.75

Screwdrivers

The techniques of joining woodwork components become increasingly complex with the development of new materials. As new methods, requiring new types of screw, come into use, so new types of screwdriver take their place alongside the traditional ones.

To try to make do with one antique screwdriver, which has a rounded, worn tip, for all the dozens of sizes and types of screw is to court disaster. Even with conventional screws, at least three sizes of screwdriver are required: first, a large one for driving 12 to 16 gauge screws, the handle say 10 to 12 in/25 to 30 cm long; then, a medium-sized one for use with screws of around gauge 8, the handle 8 to 10 in/20 to 25 cm in length; and finally, a screwdriver for the small gauges—3, 4 and 5—one of the long, thin electrician's screwdrivers being perfectly suitable.

Additional types of screwdriver should be acquired *as needed*, and will probably include the short, stubby-handled and angled varieties for use in awkward places, together with one of the special types designed for use with cross-head screws.

There are a good many cheap screwdrivers on the market, and it is worth remembering that, as well has having to cope with quite considerable forces in regular use, screwdrivers are often misused, for example, to lever open paint tins. It pays to buy a screwdriver of superior quality: the point is less likely to break than that of a cheap one or the shaft to bend with repeated hard use.

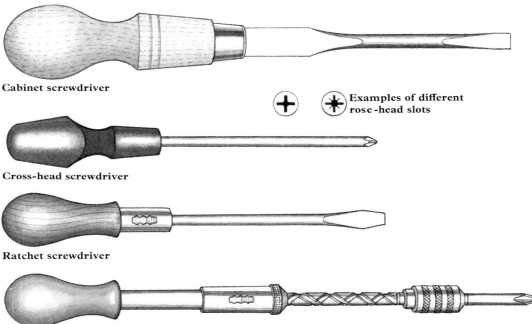

Cabinet screwdriver

Examples of different rose-head slots

Cross-head screwdriver

Ratchet screwdriver

Spiral ratchet, or Yankee, screwdriver— pumping action

The traditional cabinet screwdriver has a rounded, wooden handle which is pleasant to hold and gives a sound, comfortable grip. The London pattern screwdriver is similar, but the blade is flat instead of round, and the handle has flat faces which afford improved grip.

Different cross-head screwdrivers are, in theory, required for the different brands of cross-headed screws. In practice, however, the Phillips type will work quite well for all brands. But, as with regular, slotted-head screwdrivers, different sizes are needed for different screws.

The ratchet screwdriver is useful because it can be used with one hand; there is no need to release the grip on the handle, so the other hand can be used to hold or support the work. It is also useful for driving in screws in awkward places.

The long, spiral ratchet, or Yankee, screwdriver eliminates the need to turn the handle to drive in a screw. If there is a large number of screws to drive in, it is, without doubt, worth having because operation is fast and relatively effortless. Interchangeable bits are available.

104

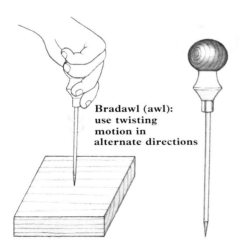

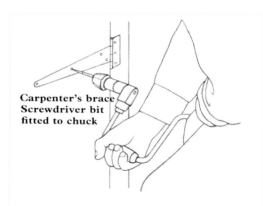

Carpenter's brace
Screwdriver bit
fitted to chuck

Removing stubborn screws

Ensure adequate grip in the screw head by removing foreign matter from the slot. Use the right-sized screwdriver, keep the tip square in the slot and apply even pressure. It may help to heat the screw with the tip of a soldering iron. Extra leverage can be applied by spanner or wrench on the flat faces of the screwdriver handle or blade, but a brace or auger gives the best leverage.

Always make a starting hole for a screw. A bradawl or awl can be used for the smaller sizes; for the larger, a hole must be drilled (*see table on page 103*). The awl or bradawl point may be flat (insert it across the grain to avoid splitting); or it can have a tapered, square section, giving more accurate location for small screws.

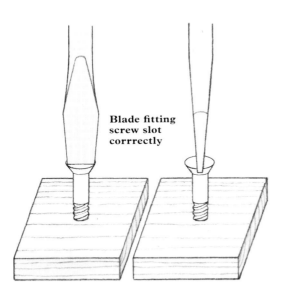

Blade fitting
screw slot
corrrectly

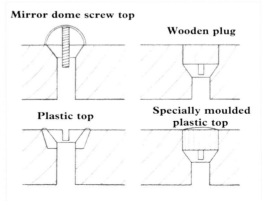

Mirror dome screw top

Wooden plug

Plastic top

Specially moulded
plastic top

Concealing screwheads

If the screwhead must be concealed, there are several options. **Mirror dome screw tops** are chrome-plated brass domes, screwed into a threaded hole in the screw head. **Plastic tops** (in a range of colours) press on to a retaining washer under the screw head. **Wooden plugs** are cut with a special cutter from matching wood; the screw hole is counter-drilled and the plug glued in place. **Wood filler** is the final option, usually only suitable on a surface that is to be painted.

Selecting the right screwdriver is a matter of closely matching the width of the blade to that of the slot in the head of the screw. If the blade is too small, it will twist or chip. If too large, it will tend to slip out, and, when the screw is driven almost home, the protruding edges will start scoring the surrounding timber surface. A screwdriver should always have clean faces and a square blade edge.

Joints

The earliest form of joint seems likely to have been a simple notch at one end of an unsawn log of wood. The end of another log placed in it at right angles was thereby locked into place; subsequent logs held in similar notches formed the walls of primitive log cabins. The lap joint, a refined form of notch, could well have been the next development. Construction of domestic artefacts in the great early civilizations—those of the Indus Basin, ancient Egypt and, later, Greece and Rome—probably accounted for the next refinements of the joint; certainly some early tables from these cultures were made with simple mortise and tenon joints.

The joint may have its roots in prehistory, but from the decline of the classical world until the late fifteenth century, its development was slow. Furniture was a rare commodity in the Dark Ages and, significantly, the word joiner is first recorded in the English language in 1483. Carpenter, by contrast, comes from a much older Latin word. Until the fifteenth century, tools and craftsmanship were not refined enough for joinery, or joint-making, to exist as a separate craft. Once it did, the development of different types of joint was rapid.

New developments included reinforcing frames with dowels and holding panels in grooves to leave them free to move if shrinkage occurred. Then, in the mid- to late seventeenth century, Chippendale, Sheraton and numerous other craftsmen in England and France began to specialize in cabinet-making. They invented, or adapted to their special needs, a whole range of joints, including dove-tailing, mitring and secret joints. The third principal category in the woodworking trade had come into being.

Carpenter, joiner and cabinet-maker all use joints, but it is the differences between these joints that mainly distinguish the craftsmen. The carpenter makes joints that will bear loads. The joiner's province is doors, windows, cupboards and decorative trim: appearance, resistance to shrinkage and minimum of exposure of end grain to the weather are his main concerns. The cabinet-maker, by contrast, creates joints which are suitable for three-dimensional—'carcase'—constructions, box constructions, flat frame work, for example, picture frames, and leg and rail work such as that which appears in tables and stools.

Tongued and mitred corner joint

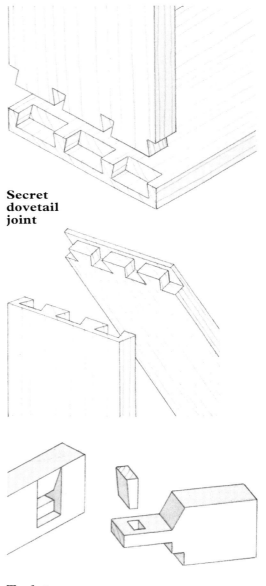

Secret dovetail joint

Tusk tenon

Dovetail joint

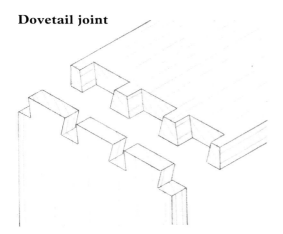

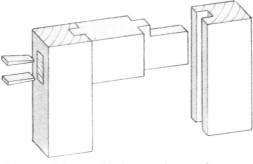

Grooved haunched mortise and tenon

Stub mortise and tenon

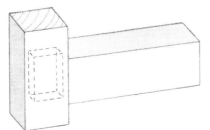

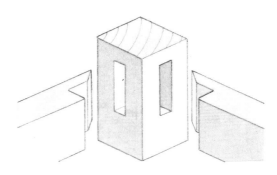

Secret haunched and mitred mortise and tenon

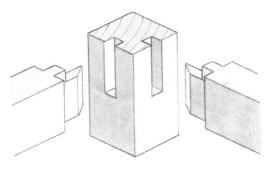

Corner mortise and tenon

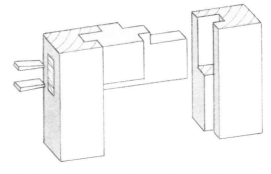

Rebated haunched mortise and tenon

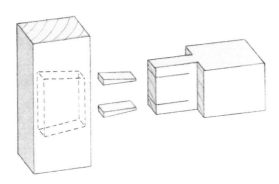

Fox-wedged mortise and tenon

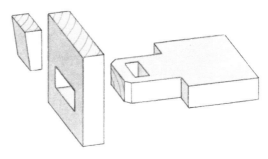

Simple tusk tenon

Butt joints and mitres

Butt joint

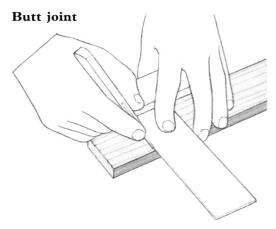

This is the simplest form of joint, used for convenience rather than strength, since end grain does not take glue well. The first step is to mark both ends perfectly square, preferably using a square and marking knife.

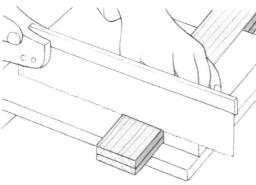

2 Cut both ends to be butt-jointed perfectly square with a tenon saw.

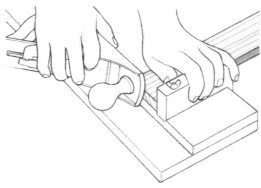

3 Plane to the scribed line.

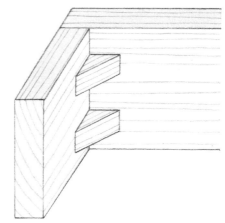

4 Nail and glue. If possible, reinforce with glued blocks. Butt joints can also be screwed or dowelled to add strength.

Mitred angle butt joint

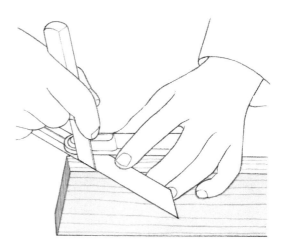

A plain mitred joint is not particularly strong and, like the butt joint, is used mainly for joining ends in framing, veneering, light construction and small boxes and chests. Mark out accurately with a mitre square and cut with a tenon saw. Strengthen by skew nailing as illustrated.

Rebated mitred butt joint

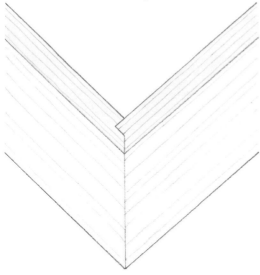

Reinforced mitre

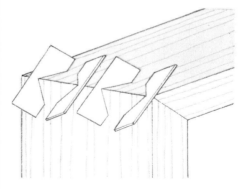

This is a strong joint, ideal for picture-framing, clock frames, box construction and the like: nails and screws are totally avoided. Make saw slots in a plain mitred joint and insert keys, or splines, which are made from veneer or thin ply.

Stronger than a plain mitre, this joint is useful in, for example, plinths, when it is not seen close-to but has to support a heavy weight.

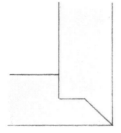

Adding a dowel to the rebated (rabbetted) mitred butt joint gives worthwhile extra strength.

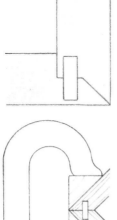

Another method of strengthening a plain mitre is to insert a hardwood tongue. Cut the groove with a router or plough plane. To give the tongue, or spline, appropriate strength, make it short- or cross-grained.

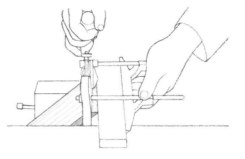

Cramp oddly angled joints by gluing triangular blocks either side to provide parallel surfaces for the cramp. Paper put between block and wood makes subsequent removal much less messy.

A board end is usually not wide enough to provide a firm base for a router or plough plane; add extra width with a second, mitred board end.

Rebate (rabbet) or lap joints

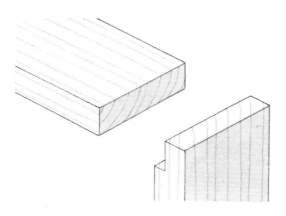

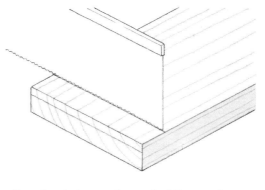

3 Saw the timber to the marked lines, using a sharp tenon saw.

The rebate, or rabbet, joint is so called for the obvious reason that the rebated, or recessed, piece receives the end of the other piece, providing not only a larger gluing area than a simple butt joint but resistance to inward pressure. It can be nailed in two directions.

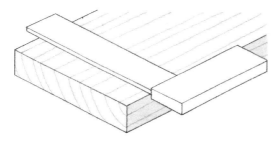

1 To mark up a rebate, or rabbet, joint, first draw the face line perfectly square. Its distance from the end of the board is determined by the thickness of the other piece.

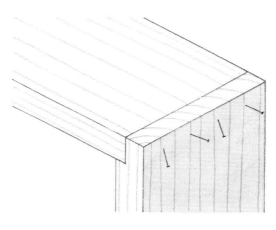

4 Glue and pin (or nail) the joint, in both directions if desired.

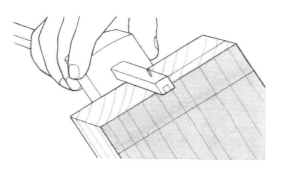

2 Gauge the end of the board to one-third of its thickness with a marking gauge.

Points to watch
• When cutting these simple joints with a tenon saw, steady the work in a bench hook (see pp 44–5); it really does help make the operation accurate.
• Start a tenon saw cut with the blade at about 30°; as the cut progresses, bring the handle down to the horizontal.
• It is easy to arrange rebate joints so they are concealed in a carcase construction, *left*.

Bare-faced tongued and grooved angle joint

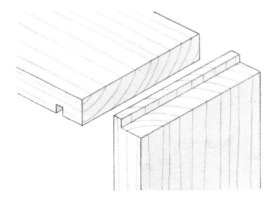

This joint is relatively strong, but the short, end-grained lap may break under heavy strain.

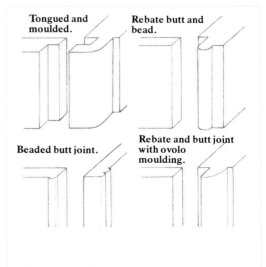

Tongued and moulded.

Rebate butt and bead.

Beaded butt joint.

Rebate and butt joint with ovolo moulding.

Decorative joints
All these joints are basically rebated, or rabbetted, but their finishes make them especially suitable for high-quality joinery and cabinet-making.

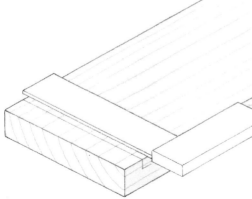

1 On face of grooved piece, working from end of timber, square off two lines with marking knife, at distances equal to three-quarters and whole thickness. Continue lines to both edges and gauge to depth—one-quarter thickness.

2 On face of rebated piece, square a line to tongue depth. Continue to edges to three-quarters thickness, then to end grain; use cutting gauge.

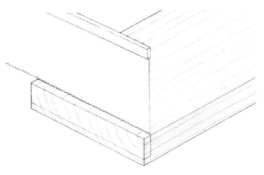

3 Cut grooved piece to depth with tenon saw, working inside waste to ensure tight fit for tongue. Clean out with chisel. Cut away waste on rebated (rabbetted) piece with tenon saw and clean up with shoulder plane.

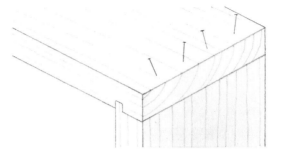

4 Glue and pin (or nail) finished joint.

Halving joints

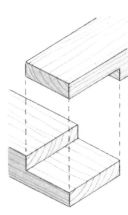

Corner half lap.

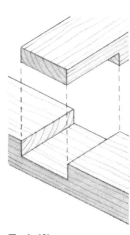

Tee half lap.

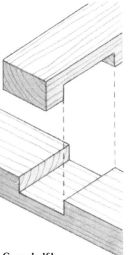

Cross half lap.

A halved joint always consists of half the thickness cut away from one component, and half the thickness cut away from the other.

Use the halved joints illustrated here in flat frame construction, leg and rail construction and for lengthening posts when building sheds. The corner half lap joint is stronger than the tee half lap.

All these joints are easily and quickly made, and they are sometimes just as suitable as more complex ones.

Ensure that the two saw kerfs for the sinking width are not too far apart. It is better to have the joint too tight than too loose—the former defect can be remedied. For extra strength, glue and screw.

'Halved and lap joint' is a term often used loosely. The halved joint is always lapped, whereas the lapped joint is not always halved.

Making a halved joint

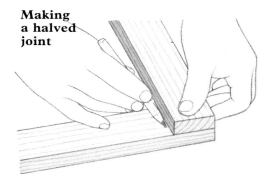

1 Mark lines square, equal to the width of the halving on the face sides and square ends.

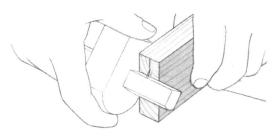

2 With a try square, continue these lines on to the edges. From the face side, gauge lines half the wood thickness up to the end and across the end grain.

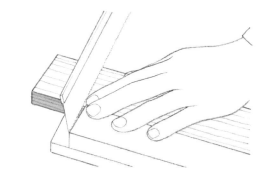

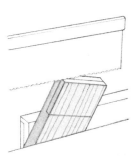

3 Make the four cuts with a tenon saw, supporting the work in a vice or bench hook. Keep inside the waste to ensure a tight fit. Clean up the halving with a paring chisel. Check for flatness with a rule or a try square, then glue and pin.

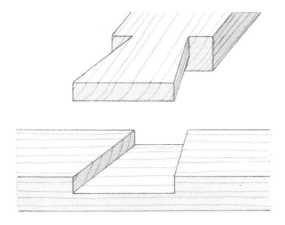

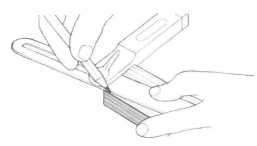

Tee dovetail half lap joints: the version above resists pulling and pushing stresses.

Straight bevelled half lap joint

Angle double-bevelled half lap joint

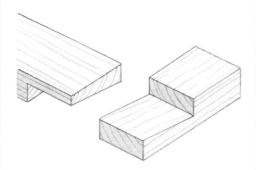

Angle bevelled half lap joint

1 First cut the pin—the piece to be inserted. Score lines all around for width and depth with a marking knife and guage, as for a tee half lap joint. Saw accurately and clean up with a chisel; then mark two one-in-six slopes on the pin for the dovetail. Saw out the waste. Clean up with a chisel.

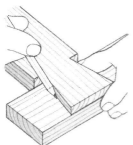

2 Hold the pin over the socket piece. Mark sinking lines, edges and depth. Saw to the depth line.

3 Clean out the waste with a chisel. Check for flatness and fit. Glue and screw.

These heavy-duty joints will all resist pulling stresses in one direction, and the angle double-bevelled half lap will resist them in two directions. Straight bevelled half laps are used for lengthening wall plates, joists and rafters. The other two joints are used for heavy structural work such as timber-framing in houses. Mark and set out all bevelled half lap joints as for straight half laps, except for the depth, which should be marked out with a template made from a tapered piece of wood.

Housing joints

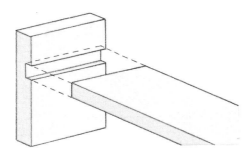

Through housing: for shed and hut framework, partitions and shelf-end supports.

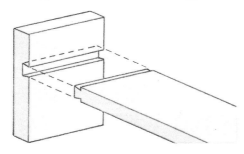

Through dovetail housing: resists an endways pull. Can be stopped if required.

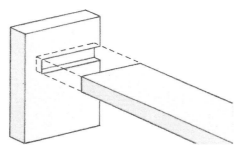

Stopped housing: for shelf-end supports in bookcases and cabinets and staircase strings.

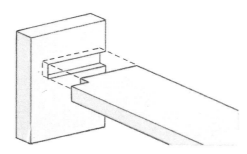

Stopped housing with shoulder: for same uses as stopped housing, but the housing is neatly concealed.

Making a through housing

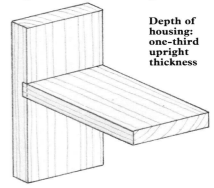

Depth of housing: one-third upright thickness

The general principles for making a through housing joint should be applied to all housing joints. Remember that shelves should be sufficiently short to prevent their bowing and the joints working loose.

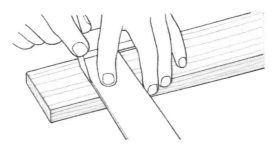

1 To mark up a housing joint, first square parallel lines across the upright, using a try square and a marking knife. The housing must be the same thickness as the shelf to ensure a tight fit. Continue these lines on to both edges.

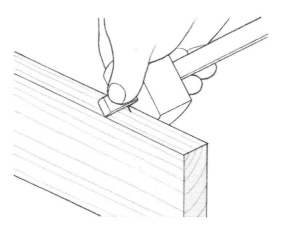

2 Set the marking gauge to one-third the thickness of the upright piece. From the face side, gauge the housing depth on both edges of the upright, between the squared lines.

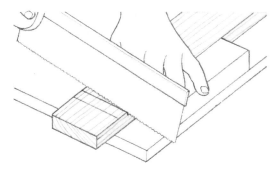

3 With a tenon saw, make two saw cuts to the housing-depth line, making sure that the saw kerfs are within the waste wood. For a wide housing, make saw cuts in the waste to facilitate chiselling out the waste.

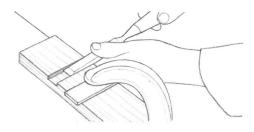

4 Chisel from one edge to the centre of the housing, removing a little waste at a time. Turn the wood around and chisel toward the centre from the other edge. Continue working toward the centre from alternate edges until all the waste has been removed.

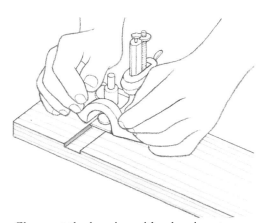

5 Clean out the housing with a hand router or 'old woman's tooth' as far as the gauged lines. Check the housing for flatness with a straightedge or try square. Glue the inside of the housing, insert the shelf; pin or screw.

Using a router on a housing joint

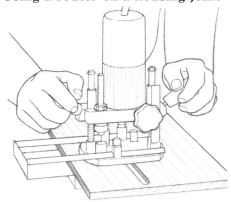

Use the plunging router for cutting housings across and with the grain. Pre-set the depth stop so the router cuts the housing in multiple stages. Securely fix some waste wood to the work to prevent breaking out. Clamp a grooving-board template to the work and bench to guide the router along the housing.

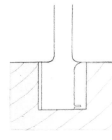

Use a straight router bit for cutting straight-sided housings. Cut solid wood with a high-speed steel bit, and abrasive manufactured boards with a carbide-tipped bit.

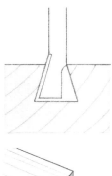

Use a dovetail router bit with a table attachment for dovetail housings.

Remove the rounded end produced by the router cutter in a stopped housing by paring the end square with a chisel.

Mortise and tenon joints

The mortise and tenon is the strongest means of joining the end of one piece of wood to the edge of another. The **tenon** is the piece of shaped wood that projects from the end of the **rail**. It fits into a specially made hole, or **mortise**, in the edge of the **stock**, or **stile**.

The joint varies in complexity from the relatively simple stub tenon, or closed mortise and tenon, to the relatively complex compound mortise and tenon (used for mortise lock rails on doors) and the tusk tenon, with its hole for a peg wedge.

In their numerous variations, mortise and tenons are among the most extensively used joints in woodworking. In quality joinery, they are excellent for making window frames, doors and door frames, staircases and roof structures. In cabinet-making, they are ideal for all types of construction, from flat frame and carcase work to legs and rails.

The mortise and tenon is extremely strong, and, when made correctly and accurately, seldom requires reinforcing with nails, screws or any other type of metal fastening. However, it can be made even stronger by the use of haunches, draw boring or wedges (either in the tenon or the mortise). These resist any tendency for the joint to twist, as indeed to the shoulders on the tenon. To ensure a really strong joint, the tenon must fit 'hand-tight' into the mortise.

As with most other types of joint, the proportions between the two pieces are of greatest importance. The basic rules are that the tenon thickness is one-third of the rail thickness, and that the tenon width is no more than four times the tenon thickness. If wider than this, excessive shrinkage could occur, leaving the tenon slack. With a stub tenon, where the tenon is not cut right through the stile, the mortise depth is about two-thirds of the stile width.

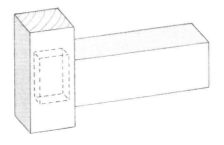

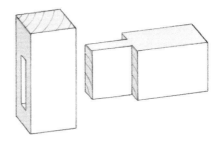

Stub mortise and tenon: the tenon is cut only partly into the stile, thus preventing unsightly end grain. Can be reinforced with dowels or wedges. Use for intermediate rails in flat frame construction, and for legs and rails.

Through mortise and tenon: one of the strongest angle and tee joints, it is often reinforced with wedges. Use where strength and rigidity are needed. The mortise is cut right through the stile.

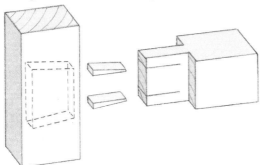

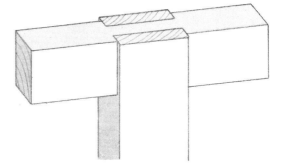

Fox-wedged mortise and tenon: the tenon is expanded inside the mortise by hardwood wedges driven into its end, and it is slightly shorter than the mortise depth. The mortise bottom is tapered slightly for the wedges.

Bridle joint: this can withstand pressure from above and from the sides. Use in cabinet-making on leg and rail construction. It can be reinforced by draw boring, using a dowel with an offset dowl hole.

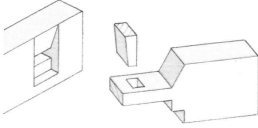

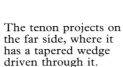

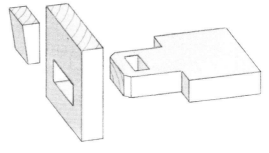

Tusk tenon: a strong but complex joint, which is used on building sites for the framing of floor joists.

The tenon projects on the far side, where it has a tapered wedge driven through it.

This simpler form of the tusk tenon is often used in refectory tables. It is generally

not glued so that it can readily be dismantled.

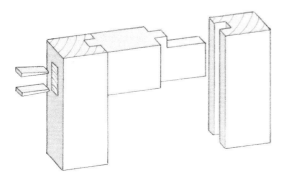

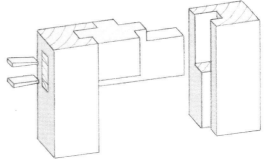

Grooved haunched mortise and tenon: the tenon width is reduced by the depth of the groove. Use on panelled doors and

carcase ends that need panelling. The panels are assembled dry to prevent movement and should not fit too tightly.

Rebated (rabbeted) haunched mortise and tenon (or long and short shoulder tenon) tenon shoulders are of

unequal length. Use on frames that need glazing. Hold the glass in the rebate with beading or putty.

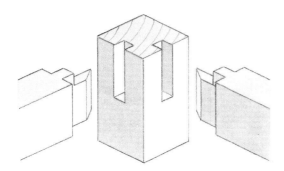

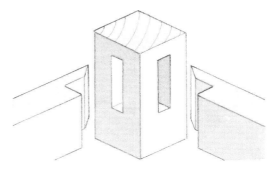

Haunched and mitred mortise and tenon: the end of the tenon is mitred to achieve maximum depth. The mitred

tenons should not touch each other. Use for leg and rail construction where a leg joins a side or a front rail.

Secret haunched mitred mortise and tenon: the haunch is concealed in the leg. Use, for example, on a

stool or a chair in which the top ends of the legs or posts are exposed.

Simple mortise and tenons

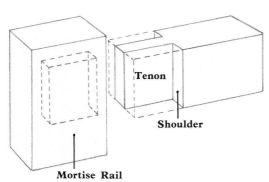

Mortise   **Rail**

                Tenon

              Shoulder

1 The simple stub mortise and tenon is used for joining two fairly narrow pieces of wood at right angles.

As a general rule, the tenon should be one-third the thickness of the wood.

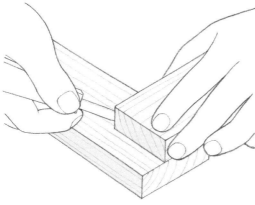

2 Make the stub tenon so that it penetrates only two-thirds into the stile. First mark out the mortise length on the face of the stile with a try square, then continue the lines on to the edge of the stile.

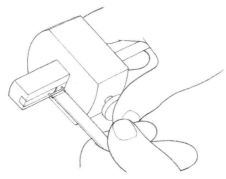

3 Set the mortise gauge spurs to the mortise chisel width.

(This should be one-third the thickness of the rail.)

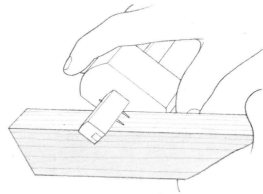

4 With the spurs of the gauge, make two holes on the stile face edge so that the spurs will be prevented from overshooting at the end of the mortise lines. Then, from the

face side, working away from the body, gauge parallel lines for the mortise width. (For a through tenon, mark the opposite edge also, plus the wedge positions.)

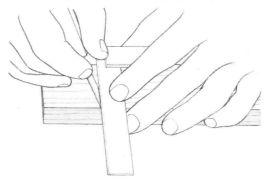

5 From the squared end of the rail, mark the tenon length. With a try square and

6 From the face side of the tenon, gauge lines from the

marking knife, square shoulder lines across both faces and both edges of the rail.

shoulder up to the end, across the end grain and down to the other shoulder line.

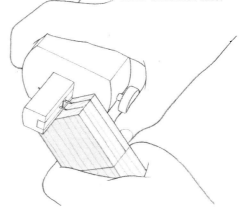

118

Chopping out a mortise

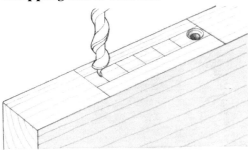

Cutting a tenon

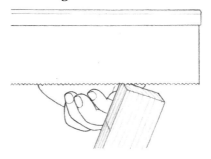

1 Placing a piece of waste wood between a G-cramp and the stile, secure the stile to the bench. Bore, rather than chisel, out the bulk of the waste—it saves time.

Then place the chisel vertically just inside the near mortise line. Make a series of cuts about $\frac{1}{8}$ in/3 mm apart. Stop $\frac{1}{8}$ in/3 mm from the far mortise line.

1 Incline the rail away from the body and secure in a vice. With the tenon saw, make saw cuts, as shown, on both sides of the

tenon down to the shoulder line, taking care to keep within the waste lines. Reverse the stile and repeat the process.

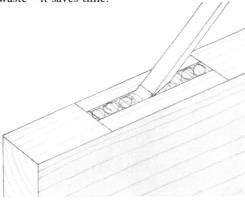

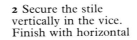

2 Lever out any waste. Return the chisel to the near mortise line and repeat the sequence, cutting only as deep

as the chisel will penetrate without sticking. Check the mortise for depth.

2 Secure the stile vertically in the vice. Finish with horizontal

saw cuts down to the shoulder line.

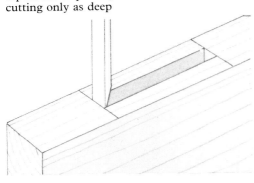

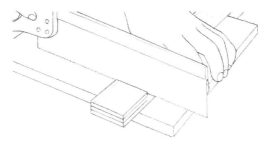

3 When the correct depth has been achieved, square up the ends with the

chisel held upright. Check again for depth.

3 Remove the stile from the vice and place in a bench hook. Make a saw cut across the stile, keeping inside the waste, until

the waste falls away. Complete the other side in the same way. Check for fit. Use a shoulder plane to clean up the tenon.

Specialized mortise and tenons

Wedged mortise and tenon
Method one

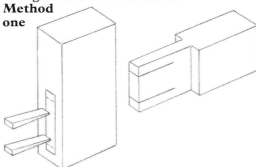

Cut the mortise, tenon and wedges; $\frac{1}{4}$ in/6 mm from each edge saw wedge-shaped slots two-thirds into the tenon. From $\frac{1}{8}$ in/3 mm outside each mortise edge, chisel inward toward the mortise bottom. Glue and clamp; drive wedges home when glue sets; plane wedges flush.

Method two

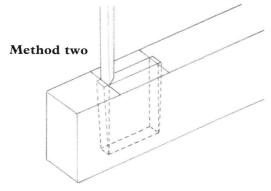

1 Cut the mortise and tenon. Taper the mortise inward as above. Cut wedges to fit. Glue the tenon into the mortise.

2 Glue the wedges and drive them into the tapered slots. Keep the tenon straight by tapping the wedges evenly each side. Glue and cramp. Plane the wedges flush.

Draw bore mortise and tenon

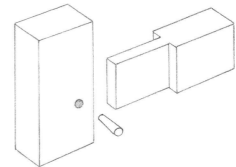

Use this joint wherever a mortise and tenon is likely to be pulled apart and clamping is not possible. The position of the central hole is most important. If too far off-centre, the tenon or dowel may be split.

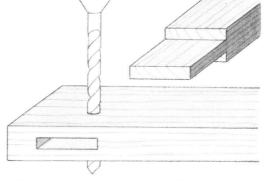

1 Cut the mortise and tenon.
2 Bore a hole through the mortise. Put the joint together dry. Mark the mortise-hole position on the tenon, then dismantle the joint again.

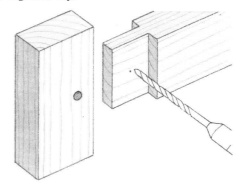

3 Mark the tenon slightly off-centre from its mortise-hole mark, toward the shoulder. Bore a hole at this new mark. Glue and assemble the joint. Drive in the dowel to draw the joint together.

Blind mortise and tenon

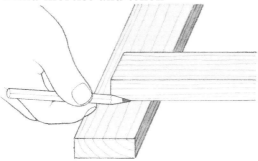

1 Locate the mortise position on the stile edge. Across this edge, square lines the tenon width less $\frac{3}{16}$in/ 5 mm on each side. Set mortise gauge to one-third the stile thickness or to the chisel width. Gauge from the face side. Chop out the mortise to two-thirds the depth of the stile.

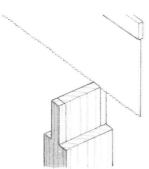

2 Set out the tenon from the squared end of the rail in the usual way. Make the four saw cuts. Then clean up the tenon with a shoulder plane.

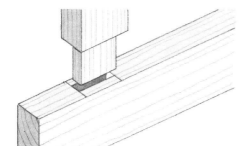

3 Secure the rail vertically in the vice. Reduce the tenon width equally on both sides until the tenon fits the mortise. Assemble, glue, wedge or dowel if so desired.

Bridle joint

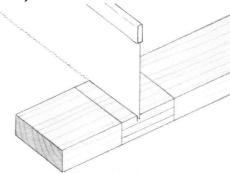

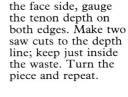

1 Mark the tenon width and continue the lines on to the edges to the depth line. Set the mortise gauge to divide the material into three equal sections. From the face side, gauge the tenon depth on both edges. Make two saw cuts to the depth line; keep just inside the waste. Turn the piece and repeat.

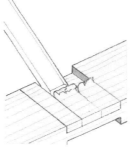

2 Clean out waste with a chisel. Check for flatness with gauge.

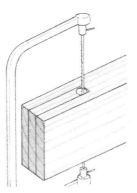

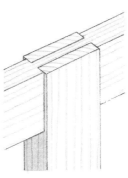

3 Mark the mortise depth on the mortise piece. Square lines across the edges. With the gauge already set as in **1**, gauge lines from the face side all around. Remove waste with a coping saw and a chisel.

Haunched mortise and tenons

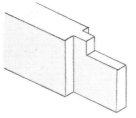

Square haunch   **Secret haunch**

Making a haunched mortise and tenon

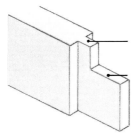

Length of haunch equal to its thickness

Width of haunch equal to one-third of total rail width

1 When marking out the mortise, leave a piece of waste, or horn, on the stile to stop the wood splitting when

chiselled near its end. Gauge the mortise lines the full width of the tenon and on the end grain for the haunch recess.

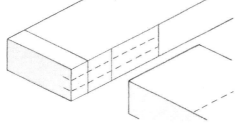

2 Chop out all the mortise except the haunched part. For a through tenon, chop out the mortise from

both sides and taper it to receive wedges. Then mark the depth of the haunch recess on the horn end.

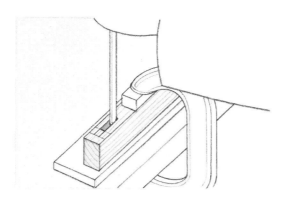

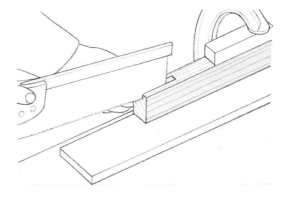

3 Put the stile into the vice. With the tenon saw, cut down to the

gauged line for the haunch recess, cutting just inside the waste.

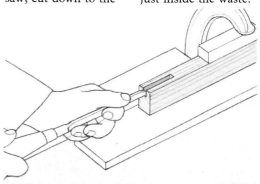

4 Placing a piece of waste wood between the G-cramp and the stile, secure the stile to the bench. With

the chisel, chop out the waste between the saw cuts for the haunch recess.

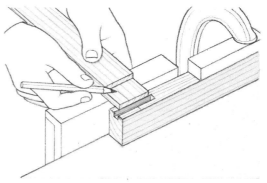

5 Mark out the tenon and cut to its full width, that is, including where the haunch will be cut. Then place the tenon against the mortise

and mark the position for the haunch against the recess. Then mark the length and width of the haunch.

Wedges

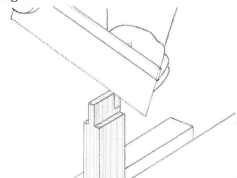

6 Place the rail in the vice. Cut the haunch carefully with a tenon saw, then cut two wedges from waste wood.

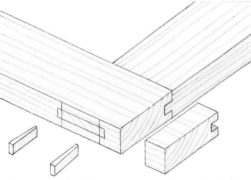

7 Assemble the joint dry and check the fit; then glue and assemble. Drive in the wedges, alternately and evenly, so that the tenon keeps straight in the mortise. When the glue has dried, cut off the horn and any wedges protruding.

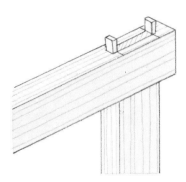

In joinery, most tenons are glued and wedged. Wedges should be of hardwood, and care should be taken to shape them so that they taper gradually to the end of the tenon. When driven home, they should fit perfectly along their whole length.

Making panels and frames

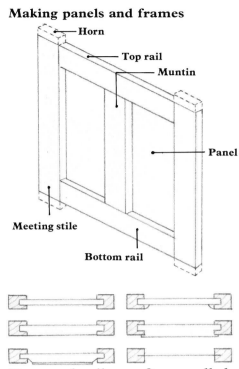

Horn — Top rail — Muntin — Panel — Meeting stile — Bottom rail

Doors and walls are often panelled. A panel may be flat, bevelled, or bevelled and fielded, and it is generally grooved or rebated (rabbeted) into the surrounding stiles and rails. Because such large cross-grain pieces are prone to buckle and crack, panels should be rift-sawn or quarter sawn; they are also assembled dry and must not fit the frame tightly. Mouldings and beadings are fixed to the frame, not the panel.

Mark up together

Cramp

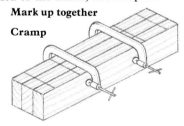

Repetitive work, on frames for example, can be done quickly and accurately by clamping rails or stiles together and marking them out at the same time. Templates made from brass, ply, thin wood or hardboard are also invaluable, for instance when dovetailing. When boring holes at set places, use a dowelling jig.

Dovetail joints

The dovetail joint is a modification of the mortise and tenon joint that achieves great strength without the need for a long tenon. In this type of joint, a tenon, or pin, of inverted wedge shape fits into a complementary socket, or mortise, so that the joint is locked in all directions except one. The fan-shaped projections between the pin-sockets are known as tails. In high-quality work, the pins are usually much narrower than the tails, but for simpler jobs, or in machine-made joints, the pins and tails are of equal width. An advantage of dovetailing is that it can join woods of different thickness. Normally the pins are formed in the thicker piece, the tails in the thinner piece. Dovetail joints are ideal for making boxes and joining corners of furniture where the wood is thin, as in drawers.

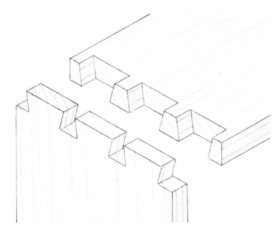

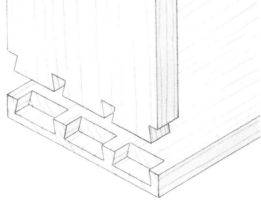

Ordinary box, or through, dovetail is the simplest dovetail joint and is fairly easy to make. It is used for boxes and the backs of drawers. The two pieces should be of the same thickness.

The lapped dovetail is valuable for joining drawer sides to the drawer front, since end grain shows only at the sides. The front is usually thicker, and the length of the pins is equal to the thickness of the sides.

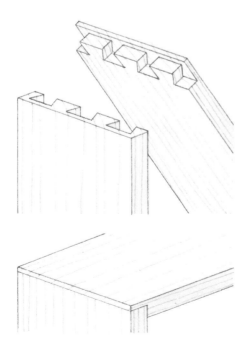

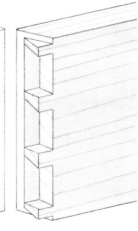

The double lap gives a 'secret joint', *left*. The pins can be in either piece but for drawers are best made in the front.

The mitred dovetail is another 'secret joint', *above*. It gives the best effect but is very difficult to make.

Making a box dovetail joint

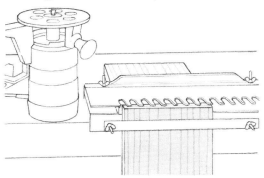

Box or lapped dovetails can be cut with a router, using a special bit, jig and template. The pieces of wood are clamped in the jig, one vertical, one horizontal, and are offset by half the pitch, using the stop screws.

The router must be fitted with a guide bush that runs within the fingers of the template. The dovetail bit itself should be set in the router at the correct depth, using a gauge provided by the manufacturer.

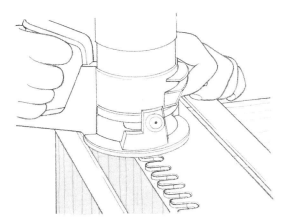

The router is guided manually along the template as it cuts the pin-sockets and tail-sockets out at the same time. It is advisable to practise on waste wood and to adjust the bit depth to give accurate fit.

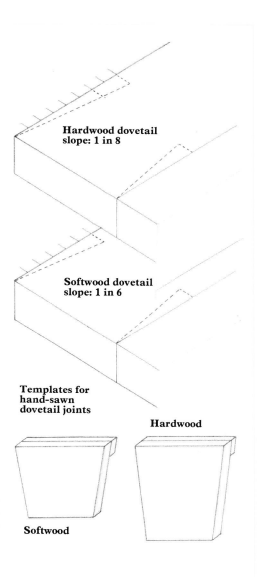

Hardwood dovetail slope: 1 in 8

Softwood dovetail slope: 1 in 6

Templates for hand-sawn dovetail joints

Hardwood

Softwood

Dovetail joint angles

Much of the strength of the dovetail joint depends on the angle of slope of the pins. If the slope is too steep, there is very little holding power and consequently a weak joint. If the slope is too acute, there is a danger of the pin splitting when the joint is put together. The correct slope is 1 in 6 for softwoods and 1 in 8 for hardwoods: softwoods compress more easily, so they require a steeper slope. Templates are available for marking off shapes as required.

Cutting dovetails

Making a box dovetail joint

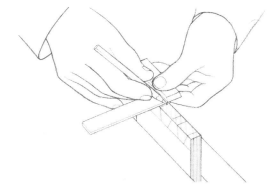

1 The pieces of wood to be dovetailed must be planed smooth and the ends shot

perfectly square. Set the cutting gauge to exactly the thickness of the wood.

4 Use a try square to square lines across the end of the wood. Then use an

adjustable bevel or, preferably, a dovetail template to mark out the sloping lines.

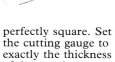

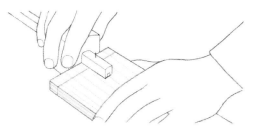

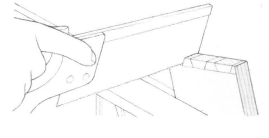

2 Using the cutting gauge, lightly mark both faces and both edges of each piece of

wood. These 'shoulder lines' mark the full depth of the pins, tails and sockets.

5 Secure the tail-piece vertically in the vice, and with the dovetail saw make kerfs down

the sloping lines to the shoulder line, keeping to the waste side of the line.

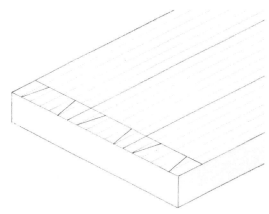

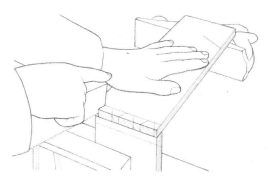

3 Decide on the number of pins and their width, relative to the tails. On the tail-piece, measure out the divisions and mark them in pencil. The following method gives three tails, twice the width of the pins, in a stock 108 mm

wide. Divide into 18 segments, allowing one segment at the end for the half-pin recess, then four segments for a tail, two for a pin and so on. All the segments should add up to 108 mm.

6 Clamp the pin-piece upright in the vice, with the face toward you. Turn a plane on its side and set the pin-piece to exactly the same height above the workbench. Now use the plane to support the tail-piece, which should be

placed horizontally, face-up on the pin-piece, in the correct position for the joint. Holding it firmly in place, run the saw down through the kerfs in the tail-piece to make marks on the pin-piece below.

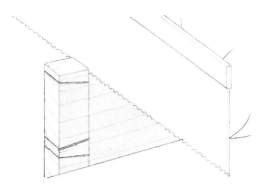

7 Use a try square to pencil in the vertical cuts on the pin-piece. These should go from the marked saw lines down to the shoulder line. Make saw kerfs inside the waste.

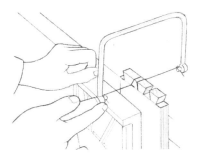

8 Secure the tail-piece in the vice, remove most of the waste with a coping saw and finish off with a narrow, sharp, bevel-edged chisel. The half-pin recesses should be cut out with a saw. Repeat for the pin-piece, using the largest possible chisel.

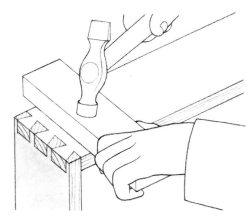

9 Test the joints for fit, tapping the pieces of wood home with a hammer. Keeping inside the waste during cutting should have resulted in a tight fit. Adjust the fit if necessary, glue and then clamp.

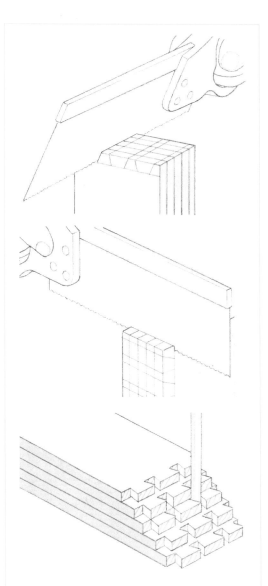

Experienced cabinet-maker's method

When making several identical box dovetail joints, the tail-pieces can be cut simultaneously. They are clamped together, upright, in a vice, and the tail divisions and sloping lines are pencilled in. Saw kerfs are made first down one side of each tail, then down the other. The pin-pieces are prepared in the normal way, pairing them with individual tail-pieces. The tail-pieces are clamped together again for sawing out the half-pin recesses. They are then staggered and clamped for chiselling out the waste. This is repeated for the pin-pieces.

Edge joints

These joints are for joining boards by their edges. As such, they are not intended to bear heavy, structural loads, but they are strong. The simplest and most useful of them, the rubbed joint, is ideal for constructing table tops and it does not require the use of expensive clamps. The loose-tongued joint is tough enough for joining boards in wide stair treads; it is also suitable for joining chipboard, which is not strong enough to be tongued. The tongued-and-grooved joint is another secure version; as are the dowelled edge joint and the slot-screwed edge joint. In terms of strength there is little difference between these last four: choice will be determined by convenience. However, those with the ability and the equipment to sink accurately positioned dowels will probably opt for the dowelled edge joint.

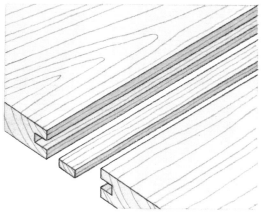

Loose tongued and grooved joint (splined joint): sink a groove of equal width and depth in both boards, slightly deeper than tongue depth. Glue, assemble and clamp.

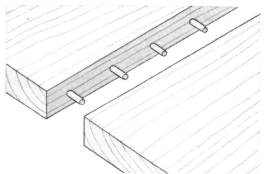

Dowelled edge joint: mark dowel positions on boards. Bore holes slightly deeper than dowels. Glue and insert dowels in one board. Put glue into holes in other board; locate, then clamp.

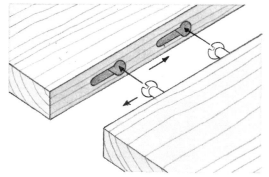

Slot-screwed edge joint: Insert all but $\frac{3}{8}$ in/10 mm of each screw on one edge. Bore screw-head holes. Make shank slots. Glue edges. Position heads and tap home.

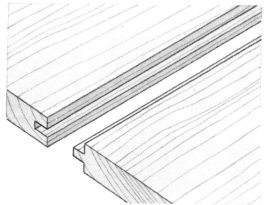

Tongued and grooved joint: Mark third of board thickness on edges with gauge. Sink groove half thickness of board with plough plane. Form tongue with fillister plane. Glue and clamp.

Colour and grain must be considered when selecting boards to be edge-jointed. If possible, use quarter-sawn timber; it keeps its shape better. If through-and-through sawn boards are used, arrange them with the hearts opposite; this will help to prevent movement. Boards about $\frac{3}{4}$–$1\frac{1}{2}$ in/19–38 mm thick are usually best for these joints. Ensure the edges are free from dead knots and other defects. Choose boards whose colour and grain match. The grain of the boards should run in the same direction, otherwise cleaning up the faces will entail planing against the grain in one direction.

Making a rubbed joint

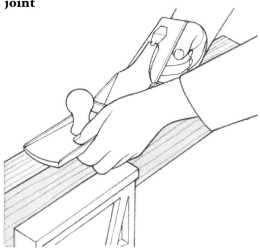

1 Put two boards in the vice. Plane them with a try plane, using the finger tips pressed against the board face as guides. Make the final shaving the full board length.

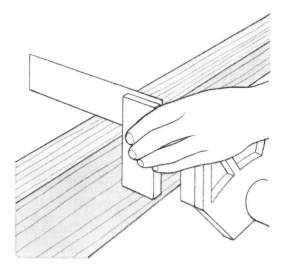

2 Check frequently for accuracy, using a try square and a straight edge.

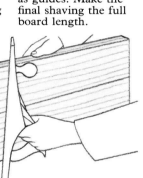

3 Alignment should also be checked. Place the boards edge-to-edge. They should be perfectly straight and flat, with no daylight showing through.

4 Choose quality Scotch (animal) glue. Make up a fresh batch and keep it as hot as possible. The glue should run off the brush like paint. Glue the two edges liberally.

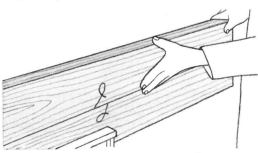

5 Rub the two edges together, working the glue into the pores of the wood. When movement becomes stiff, the glue is beginning to set. Keep removing the surplus glue.

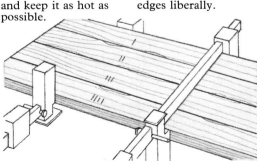

6 Bring the boards into final alignment. Clamp if three or more boards are joined at the same time. Do not touch until set which usually takes 24 hours.

Dowelling

Dowels, simple solid timber rods cut perfectly circular in cross-section, are increasingly popular among professional and amateur woodworkers for joining wood without the labour of constructing more complex joints. Holes must be bored in to the surfaces to be joined so that the dowels fit them tightly, and the join is completed by gluing. Dowels are available in a range of sizes to suit most applications, and, for strength, they are usually made from hardwood.

Employing them effectively requires some care. The first consideration should be the proportions of the dowel to the wood to be joined. The dowel diameter should be about a third of the thickness of the timber into which the dowel will fit. The length of the dowel should be one and a half times the thickness of the wood, or 6 mm/$\frac{1}{4}$ in less than the combined depths of both holes drilled.

Then comes the major problem: accurately aligning the dowel holes on each piece to be joined. Various types of jig can be bought to assist the operation, but there are also home-made alternatives, which will cover most situations.

Obviously, the dowel holes must be bored clean and true. Make them a little deeper than actually necessary, to ensure full penetration and to create a reservoir for excess glue. The edges of the dowel holes should be slightly bevelled to allow easy insertion; a groove in the side of a dowel helps surplus air and glue escape as the joint is pulled together.

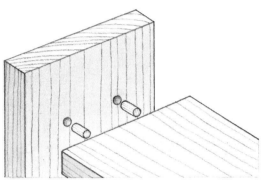

Dowels used for middle rails, table and stool construction

Use of dowels in top and bottom rails, table and stool construction

Groove in dowel to help excess glue and air to escape

Edge slightly bevelled to allow easy insertion

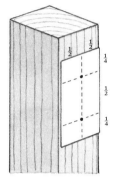

A card template is adequate for marking dowel positions on door frames, for example, where no more than two or three dowels are needed. Cut a square of stiff card the same size as the timber cross-section. Mark the centre line and a line at the quarter and three-quarter points. For frames over 3 in/ 75 mm wide, use three dowels, one dead centre. Prick through the card at the intersections with a sharp pencil and use the holes as guides for marking up both surfaces.

Manufacturers use dowels more and more in furniture construction. They provide what is, essentially, a reinforced butt joint, which is much cheaper to mass-produce than conventional joints such as the mortise and tenon.

Sizes and spacing for dowels

Carcasing (cabinet bodies)	set the dowels 4 in/ 10 cm apart; use no fewer than three.
Diameter of dowel required for various thicknesses of manufactured board	$\frac{1}{2}$ in/12 mm board, 6 mm dowel; $\frac{5}{8}$ in/15 mm board, 8 mm dowel; $\frac{3}{4}$ in/18 mm and thicker, 10 mm dowel.
In doors and door frames	Set dowels 1–2 in/ 2.5–5 cm apart; use no fewer than two.
Diameter of dowel required for framing materials	Framing material $\frac{3}{4}$–1 in/18–22 mm thick use 10 mm dowels; 1$\frac{1}{4}$ in/35 mm or more, 12 mm dowels.

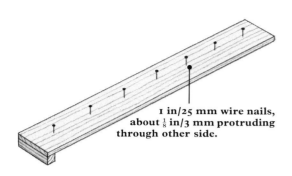

1 in/25 mm wire nails, about ⅛ in/3 mm protruding through other side.

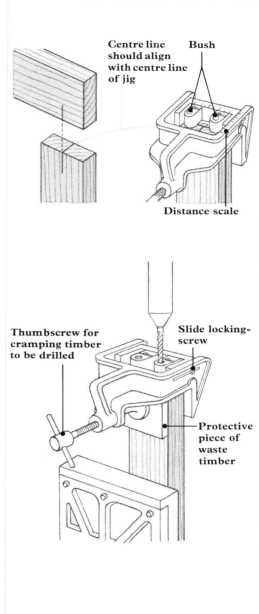

Centre line should align with centre line of jig

Bush

Distance scale

Thumbscrew for cramping timber to be drilled

Slide locking-screw

Protective piece of waste timber

Simple to make in the workshop, this jig permits plywood or chipboard (flakeboard) cabinet carcases (cases) to be marked up accurately.

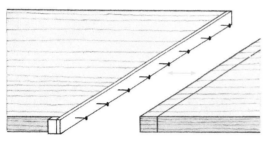

To use the jig, 1, place nail points against board end to be dowelled. Lightly tap the jig frame so that the nail points sink in enough to leave visible marks.

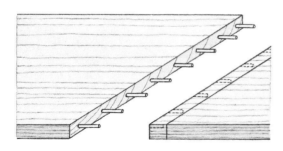

2 Drill the marked points to create the dowel holes. Repeat with the other board end. A 'lip and spur' drill is especially efficient at boring into end grain without wandering. Insert the dowels; bevelling the ends helps them slide in smoothly.

Dowelling jigs
With a cast-iron frame and accurately machined parts, the dowelling jig permits fast, accurate drilling of dowel holes. Bushes with various internal diameters are supplied so that different drill bits can be inserted for boring holes of different diameters. The position of the bushes is adjustable, and the timber need only be marked with a centre line. The timber to be drilled is cramped in with a thumbscrew—an off-cut of waste wood gives protection.

Working with manufactured board

Manufactured boards are cheaper to buy than solid wood; they are comparatively simple to work with, because they do not distort after construction; and they are available in large sheets. They are, as a result, especially suitable for wide, flat components such as panels, shelves and doors.

The surfaces of these boards are pre-finished by the manufacturer, so they should not be planed. The edges, however, can be planed, and this should be done from the end inwards, to prevent edges chipping.

As the edges of manufactured boards are unattractive and easy to damage, they should be lipped with strips of square or rectangular wood, preferably hardwood. Some chipboard (flakeboard), multiply and many of the laminated boards are porous, and these should be well sealed before a surface finish is applied. When wall-papering on hardboard, size the surface with a suitable hardboard primer.

Multiply can be fixed with nails, pins, screws or glue. Prime all screw and nail heads with an oil-based paint; they will rust and show through an emulsion paint. Choose nail and screw sizes to ensure a firm grip in the piece underneath.

Do not insert screws or nails into the edges of ply or chipboard, or, indeed, into the end grain of any of the laminated boards unless the edges carry lipping or there is a solid wood dowel to provide firm lodging. Equally, screws or nails should be never be driven between the cores in laminated boards.

Hardboard pins and round-headed screws give the best hold in hardboard, although most woodworking adhesives are suitable for untempered hardboard. If gluing the smooth face, roughen up the surface to assist sticking. When working with hardboard, avoid damaging the smooth face; no amount of aftercare can restore the original surface.

Hardboard and three-ply are the easiest boards to bend, and hardboard is extra-flexible when bent with the rough-textured face on the outside. Do not bend three-ply or multiply after the edges have been jointed.

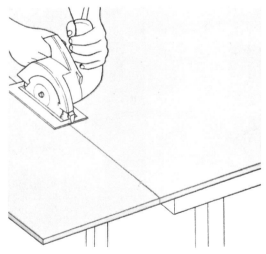

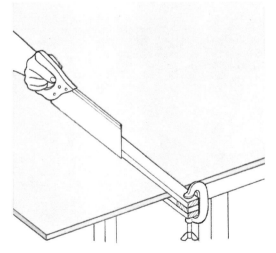

A power saw is the quickest and most effective means of cutting manufactured boards. For laminated boards, plywood and abrasive boards, use a tungsten-carbide-tipped blade. As a power saw cuts on the upward stroke, score the upper surface of the board on the cutting line to prevent break-out. Place a large board between two saw horses and support it by firmly clamping two timber battens near the cutting line. Always support the off-cut to prevent the board snapping near the end of the saw cut. Take care not to damage the corners during cutting.

Use a tenon saw or a fine-toothed panel saw on manufactured board if a power saw is not available. Keep a separate saw for cutting only manufactured boards because the resin they contain quickly blunts saw teeth. Chipboard (flakeboard) can be particularly resinous. To prevent break-out when sawing laminated boards, score both sides of the cutting line or stick some masking tape over it. Always cut into the laminate on the down stroke, never on the up stroke; keep the saw teeth well clear of the surface on the upward stroke and chipping should be eliminated.

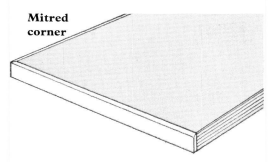

Lipping manufactured boards

Mitred corner

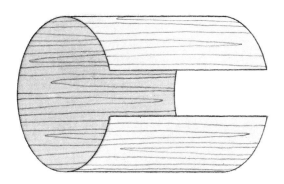

Plywood can be bent to a curve or even a circle because it is highly resilient. The thinner the ply, the further it will bend. To make a very tight curve, position the ply with the grain running across the curve. To retain the curve, slightly dampen the outer plies on the bend. Place the bent wood in formers and leave to dry.

Chipboard should have lipping fixed to it by grooving the board and tonguing the lipping. Glue the joint and clamp. When dry, plane the lipping flush with the board's surface.

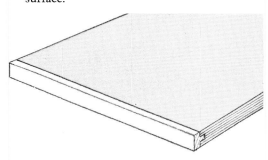

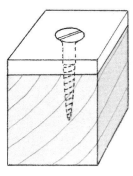 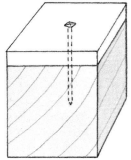

Fix lipping to ply or laminated board preferably with a tongue-and-groove joint (tongue on board), or by gluing and clamping. Position the lipping a little proud of the board's surfaces. Plane flush when the glue has dried. Avoid pinning if possible.

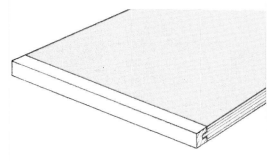

When screwing through plywood, make a pilot hole in the face and countersink. Do not overtighten, especially on soft ply.

Secure joints with nails while gluing. Leave their heads projecting so they can easily be extracted when the glue has dried.

When screwing through hardboard, prime the screw head to prevent it rusting. Do not over-screw.

When pinning hardboard, use copper hardboard pins with diamond-shaped heads.

Lippings are strips of wood applied to the edges of manufactured boards for protection. They also conceal end grain and any other blemishes. Lippings should be little thicker than the board to which they are applied, and they are mitred or butt-jointed at the corners.

Joining manufactured board

Knockdown (KD) fittings solve many of the problems of joining manufactured boards, which, because of either their fibrous or laminated construction, are clearly unsuitable for joining by traditional methods. The fittings, made of wood or plastic, are particularly suitable for veneered chipboard (flakeboard), plywood and blockboard (laminated board made with substantial rectangular sections of timber).

The fittings are all relatively easy to use and genuinely simplify the making of furniture. This in turn provides greater scope for the woodworker to tackle complex projects, previously impractical because of insufficient joinery skill. Finally, KD fittings have the advantage of allowing quick assembly and dismantling of finished work.

A wide range of fittings is available essentially in three categories: those which are threaded; those which interlock; and those which operate with a cam-action.

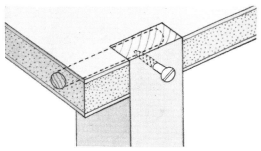

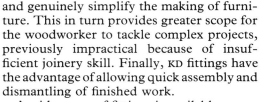

Reinforce the edges of chipboard (flakeboard) to be attached to solid wood by inserting a wooden dowel at right angles. Use a round-headed screw if possible.

Plastic bush: for joining two pieces of chipboard (flakeboard) at a corner. Insert a plastic bush into one edge, then insert the screw.

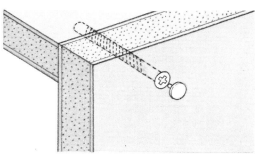

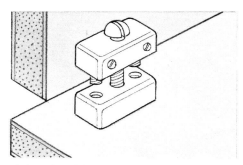

Confirmat one-piece connector: used for frame construction, securing frames to panels, or panels to panels, this is a strong joint.

Bloc joint: for rigid, right-angled butt joints; ideal for carcase construction. Screw a plastic block to each panel. Align the dowels and screw the panels together.

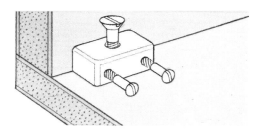

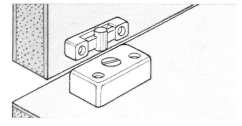

Modesty bloc: for right-angled butt joints on light construction work, shelf supports, plinths and pelmet fittings.

Cam bloc: for rapid construction and dismantling of right-angled joints in units. The two pieces are locked together by giving the cam a half turn clockwise.

Joining plywood

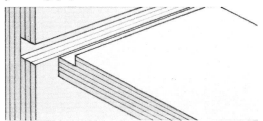

All housing joints, mortise and tenons, and dovetails can be used to join pieces of plywood. Never screw into the edge of plywood, otherwise the plies will split.

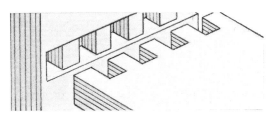

Tee comb or box joint: for joints that need to be strong; use solid wood wedges for even greater strength. Ensure each tenon is at least $\frac{1}{2}$ in/12 mm in width.

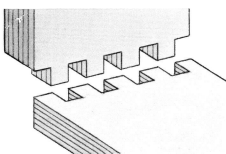

Comb joint: for boxes and drawers. Both pieces of ply should be the same width and thickness. Cut more tenons than recesses in one piece, and more recesses than tenons in the other piece.

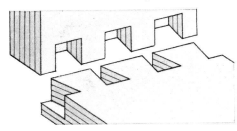

Lapped dovetail joint: use drawers, using either a stopped joint or a through one. The ply edges are sometimes difficult to finish.

Joining blockboard

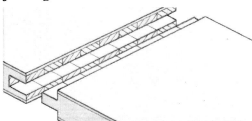

Tongue-and-groove joint: use where two pieces of laminated board of the type illustrated are to be joined end-to-end. Cut this joint only across the core strips.

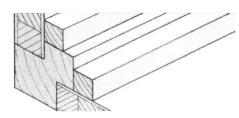

Solid wood corner joint: use where two pieces of blockboard butt on to solid wood at a corner. Make the join using glue, screws or glue blocks.

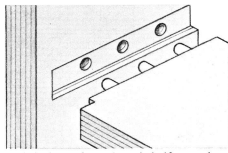

Stopped dado and dowel joint: for shelves. Insert the dowels into the ends of the laminated board shelf, ensuring that the solid core strips run the length of the shelf.

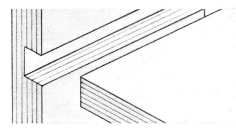

Housing joint: for shelves. To obtain maximum strength, the solid core strips should run lengthwise along the shelf.

Frame assembly

After days, even weeks, spent carefully designing and constructing a piece of furniture, it is surprising how often work is spoiled by lack of care during the assembly and final gluing-up stages.

Each joint should be tried separately to ensure that it will go home true, and then sub-assemblies, such as the stile and two rails shown below, should be checked carefully before any gluing is done.

Clear the bench of all tools and, before gluing, and cover it with newspapers to catch the drips. Open cramps to the required length and see that they are free of dried glue from previous work.

Even a lightly closed cramp can cause an indentation in the wood surface which may be difficult to remove, so cushion blocks are essential. Cut these carefully to the correct length to ensure that pressure will be put on the joint, and make sure the sides are in contact with the work and all faces of the cramp are parallel, or twisting may result in the finished piece.

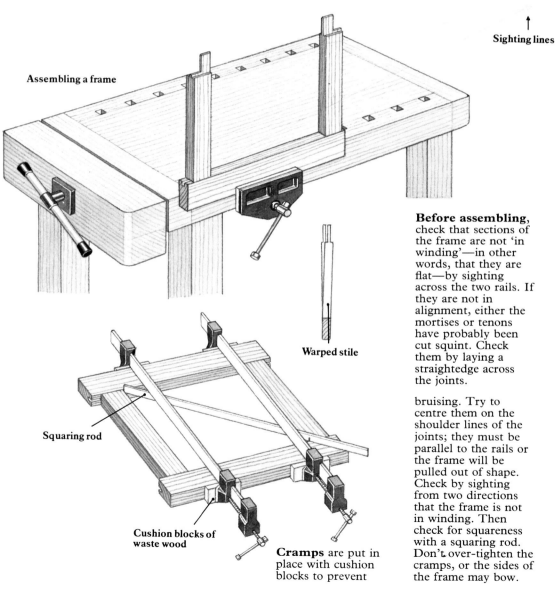

Sighting lines

Assembling a frame

Warped stile

Squaring rod

Cushion blocks of waste wood

Cramps are put in place with cushion blocks to prevent

Before assembling, check that sections of the frame are not 'in winding'—in other words, that they are flat—by sighting across the two rails. If they are not in alignment, either the mortises or tenons have probably been cut squint. Check them by laying a straightedge across the joints.

bruising. Try to centre them on the shoulder lines of the joints; they must be parallel to the rails or the frame will be pulled out of shape. Check by sighting from two directions that the frame is not in winding. Then check for squareness with a squaring rod. Don't over-tighten the cramps, or the sides of the frame may bow.

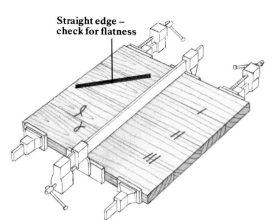

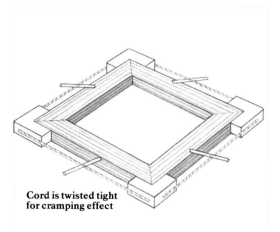

Cord is twisted tight
for cramping effect

Cramping solid boards requires special precautions. Ensure that the grain of each piece runs in the same direction, that the heart side is reversed in each piece, and that the grain pattern is matched to give a satisfactory appearance. Mark the joints and plane the edges straight and

square. Try each of the joints in turn: there must be no gaps. Glue the joints and apply the cramps, checking the surface is flat. Lifting and bowing can be checked by placing at least one cramp over the top of the work. Clean off surplus glue.

Tourniquet cramp
A tourniquet cramp is easily improvised and is extremely useful for assembling picture frames or small boxes with mitred corners. Make the cushion blocks by drilling a hole in the centres of the blocks and cutting square sections to hold the corners, plus notches for the cord.

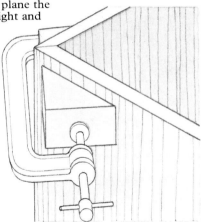

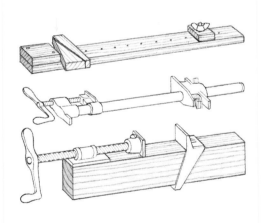

Cramping up odd shapes, for example corners which do not meet at a right angle, may appear difficult, but the simple solution is temporarily to glue appropriately shaped blocks to the piece, thus creating

parallel edges so that a cramp can pull the joint together. Subsequent removal of the blocks is simplified if, before gluing, paper is placed between the block and the work.

Home-made cramps
Cramps are expensive, so the woodworker would do well to make up a set of his or her own. A length of timber with a stop, either fastened or adjustable with a peg at one end, can easily exert enough pressure for gluing, in conjunction with folding wedges, hammered in against a suitably placed stop at the other end. Also available are cramp ends, which can be joined by a hardwood bar or by metal tubing.

Adhesives and glues

The terms glue and adhesive are generally interchangeable, but glue is perhaps more apt for the natural products, such as Scotch, or animal glue, and adhesive for the modern synthetic products.

It is often hard to make a choice between the enormous variety of glues and adhesives available to the woodworker. Some are expressly made for sticking wood, others for sticking miscellaneous materials too. To make a rational choice, the woodworker has first to be clear about two questions: what exactly has to be stuck? And where will the end result ultimately be used? Indeed one might also ask whether glue is really necessary at all. Pieces of wood can, after all, be held together satisfactorily using nails or screws, and if, at some stage, a piece may need taking apart for repair, it may well be best not to use glue.

Using the correct adhesive for a job does, however, have distinct advantages. In certain circumstances, a well-glued joint can be 100 per cent efficient compared with an efficiency as low as 15 per cent for a poorly nailed joint. Cutting complex joints is time-consuming, and may well be beyond a woodworker's capabilities or equipment; glue is the simple alternative in such instances, as it is when thin and fragile woods make it impossible to cut a complex joint, or where inaccessibility makes use of nails or screws impossible.

Timber which is damp—with a moisture content of more than about 20 per cent—will not glue satisfactorily. So if wood has been stored outside, it should be brought indoors a day or two before gluing is attempted.

Wood which is dirty, dusty or greasy will not glue. Ideally, joints should be glued on the same day they are cut, and with some oily woods, such as teak, the joint must be glued within a few hours, otherwise the natural oils will come to the surface and prevent the glue adhering. If necessary, an oily wood can be de-greased using a solvent such as cellulose thinners. Provided surfaces have recently been cut, sawn or planed there is no need to sand or 'tooth' any surface before gluing. Do ensure, however, that blunt cutters have not burnished or even slightly burnt the surface. Try to avoid gluing end-grain joints; the glue tends to be quickly absorbed by the open pores. If it is essential to glue end grain, give the open joint a coat of diluted glue to seal the surface, and glue as normal when dry.

NAME	
Natural	**Thermoplastic**
Animal, or Scotch	Polyvinylacetate (PVA)

USES	
For traditional cabinet-making and hand veneering. Good initial 'tack' as glue cools, but wets surfaces.	General purpose for all interior woodwork, useful shelf life. 'Creeps' under load.

SETTING TIME	
1–24 hrs	20 mins–1 hr

STRENGTH	
Good	Good

WATER RESISTANCE	
Poor	Poor

GAP FILLING	
Good	Poor

HEAT RESISTANCE	
Poor	Poor

CLEANING AGENT	
Warm water	Water

BRAND NAMES	
Certofix, Croid Aero, Croid No. 1	Borden Wood, Bostik 8— woodworking, Dunlop woodworker, Clam 7, Evo-stick Woodworker, Gloy Titabond

ot melt	**Thermosetting** Epoxy	Urea Formaldehyde	Resorcinol Formaldehyde	**Elastomeric** Synthetic rubber
ed in an ctrically heated e gun. Bonds s etc. to wood. ues at high aperature— ɔ° C.	Two-part adhesive. Useful for wood/metal/ glass bonds. No shrinkage. Skin irritant. Expensive.	Water-resistance makes it useful for damp situations and gap-filling properties for good strong jointing. Limited shelf life.	Excellent for boat-building, and furniture and woodwork to be used out of doors. Stains wood. Limited shelf life.	Useful for sticking down plastic laminates and veneers to wood. Flexible joints. Most types have highly inflammable fumes.
out 1 min	5 mins–24 hrs depending on type and temperature.	3 mins–24 hrs depending on type and temperature.	3 mins–24 hrs depending on type and temperature.	5–11 mins.
ry good	Excellent	Excellent	Excellent	Fair
od	Excellent	Very good	Excellent	Fair
od	Good	Good	Good	Poor
or	Excellent	Very good	Very good	Poor
rasive	Before set: white spirit, warm soapy water	Before set: warm soapy water	Before set: warm soapy water	White spirit
ɔ-stick Hot Melt, id Hot Melt, stik Hot Melt	Araldite, Araldite Rapid, Borden Superfast, Super Epoxy, Bostik 7, Deucon '5 minute'	Aerolite 306, Cascamite, Casco- resin one shot	Aeroduo: Resorcinal RX5	Bostik 3, Dunlop Thixofix, Evo-stick 'Impact', Unibond, Unistick

Specially shaped work

From Windsor chairs to bow-fronted chests of drawers, bent, curved or other specially shaped woodwork is commonplace. Creating it presents a special set of problems.

The problems are essentially that if solid timber is cut to a curved shape it is inevitably weakened in the process; and that while thin sections of most woods will bend easily, they spring back to their original form once released. The most satisfactory way to produce specially shaped woodwork is by steam bending or by building up a series of smaller, thinner pieces of wood, gluing them together and clamping them in a mold or former.

Steaming is perfectly feasible in a home-made, metal steaming chest fitted with an ordinary domestic electric kettle element, which provides enough heat to steam pieces of timber up to 3 ft/1 m long. Such a chest is relatively simple to construct (see diagram in box *opposite*).

Laminated bends have approximately twice the strength of bends cut from solid timber. The thinner the laminates used for a given thickness, the stronger the final structure: but consider the extra effort in gluing and cutting that will be involved. Choose straight-grained, flat timber for this purpose, otherwise twisting may occur. Beech usually makes an ideal laminate.

Bends or curves

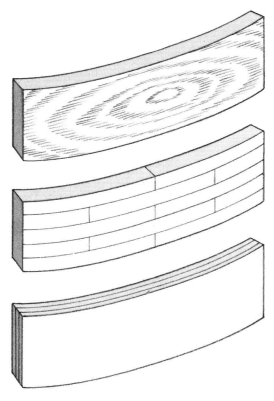

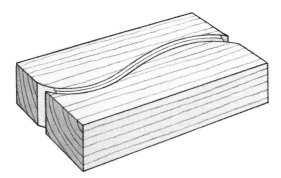

Bends should only be cut out of solid timber if the curve is to be shallow. In any circumstances this is a wasteful operation. If the curve is at all steep, the grain will be short, and, hence weak at the ends. The short-grain problem can be overcome by the brick construction method—overlapping rows of small timber pieces, smoothed, then veneered back and front. The best method, however, is to construct a laminated bend.

Gluing veneers into saw kerfs is a satisfactory alternative to laminating if just the ends of a thick timber section need bending. Saw the kerfs where the curve is required. Fill the kerfs with glued strips of veneer exactly the same thickness as each kerf. Hold the curved shape in a former until the glue sets.

Make a former out of strong, solid timber or other materials, such as chipboard, glued up into a block. Cut a matching shape in the male and female parts, making them 1 in/2.5 cm larger all around than the required finished piece. Coat the former with wax.

Laminated bends

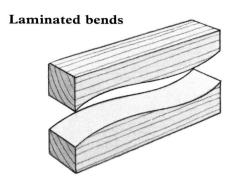

1 Cut laminates at least $\frac{1}{2}$ in/13 mm larger all around than the finished piece required and as thin as necessary to accomodate the curve; $\frac{1}{32}$–$\frac{1}{8}$ in/0.8–3 mm is a useful norm. Place a rubber sheet on each side of the former to even out any faults.

Approximate radius of curvature at which the breakage rate is unlikely to exceed 5 per cent during bending of straight-grained, air-dried timber 1 in/2.5 cm thick.				
Species	Approximate radius			
	Unsupported		Supported by strap	
	in	mm	in	mm
Beech	13	330	$1\frac{1}{2}$	38
Ash	12	305	3	76
Birch	17	432	3	76
Elm	$9\frac{1}{2}$	241	$\frac{1}{2}$	10
Oak	13	330	2	50
Honduras mahogany	28	711	12	305
African mahogany	36	910	33	840
Burma teak	28	711	18	460
European spruce	32	810	30	762

2 Using a synthetic resin glue, apply an even layer to each laminate with a glue spreader. Assemble the 'sandwich'; grain direction of successive laminates need not be at right angles. Continue until the desired thickness has been achieved. It is not necessary to use an odd number of laminates, as with plywood.

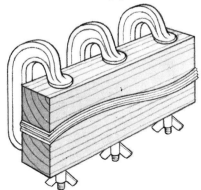

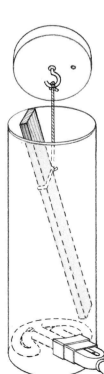

Steam solid wood for one hour for each 1 in/2.5 cm thickness of the wood. Bend the steamed wood to the shape required, using a former, or curve it around strong pegs or blocks fixed to a baseboard. If a tight bend is required, support the outside surface of the bending material with a mild, or spring-steel, strap-clamped to the ends of the work. Also use these cramps to fasten extension handles to the ends of the work for better leverage on a tight bend. Leave the work to cool and dry. Remove the cramps.

3 Apply the cramps, securing the middle ones first. Wipe away any excess glue. When the glue has set, trim off any irregularities at the edges.

The desire to add a finish to woodwork, either to decorate or to protect it, is as old as the craft itself. Shellac was used as a finish in India at least 3,000 years ago, and it may have been predated by the use of laquer in China. Certainly the Egyptian pharaohs used a range of paints and lacquers, both on wood and in mummification.

Varnish was made and used by the Romans, and continued as one of the most important finishes available to woodworkers throughout the Middle Ages, fulfilling what is arguably its highest potential in the hands of the Italian musical instrument makers of the seventeenth century. Varnish is simply a resin in solution—a fact of which new generations of woodworkers are sometimes unaware. It accounts for many finishes in current use; many others should more accurately be termed clear finishes.

In the middle of the nineteenth century came the first truly radical development in finishing for thousands of years. Until then, all finishing materials had been essentially natural—animal or vegetable by-products. Now, artificial substances such as nitrocellulose appeared; and in the first decade of the twentieth century, a Belgian chemist, Leo Baekeland, developed Bakelite, the first of the plastics, an event directly foreshadowing the appearance of the plastic laminates. Synthetic resins, including the first of the acrylics, followed in the 1920s and 1930s: again, forerunners of many modern finishes.

Many woodworkers feel—wrongly—that there is an unbridgeable gulf between the traditional finishes, with pedigrees stretching back through the millennia, and the modern synthetic finishes. Without doubt, French polish, arguably the ultimate traditional finish, is in a class of its own for visual effect; equally true, it is inferior for many purposes to modern finishes—where durability is the aim.

Veneering is an important aspect of finishing that is also covered in this section, and it would, likewise, be wrong to underestimate the role of modern materials in this highly traditional craft. Solid timber, once the standard groundwork, or base, for laying veneers, is no longer the automatic choice. Instead, woodworkers are advised to make use of the much more stable manufactured boards to achieve fine finished work at a realistic cost and to conserve that increasingly precious resource—solid wood.

FINISHING

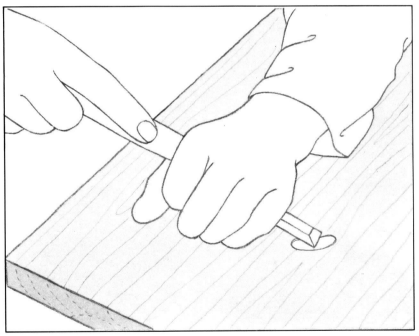

Veneers

Veneering—covering wood with a thin laminate or layer of fine, decorative wood—is one of mankind's most ancient crafts. Examples of veneer work from Ancient Egypt date back 4000 years. Competently cutting, joining and laying veneers requires both technical skill and artistic flair.

There are several reasons for veneering. Attractive timbers with wild or distorted grain are often too unstable or weak to be used in solid form. The cost of making furniture from solid pieces of the more attractive timbers, such as rosewood or ebony, is prohibitive. The demand for solid wood furniture would deplete or even exhaust the world's supply of decorative hardwoods. And above all, it makes sense in these times of strong, stable, manufactured boards to combine such useful qualities with the attractive appearance given by veneering.

Relatively few of the 50,000 or so species of tree on the planet are used for veneers, but veneers still vary enormously in appearance because different methods of growing and cutting produce widely different results from the same species. In the past, all veneers were cut by a large circular saw. Today veneers from all but the hardest woods, such as ebony and laburnum oysters, are produced by the knife cutting method.

The first stage in making veneer is to soften the logs by immersion in tanks of hot water or by steaming. Various methods of cutting are then possible. Veneers for constructional purposes (ie making plywood) are produced by the rotary (or rotary lathe) method: a whole, de-barked log is rotated against the blade, which cuts away the veneer in a long continuous belt.

Most veneers for decorative purposes are cut by flat-slicing. Typically, the log is sawn in two, laid on the resulting flat base and flat-sliced across the crown by a mechanical blade to give veneers with attractive heartwood patterns. But many different effects are possible, depending on the angle of the cut, the initial shape of the log and the part of the tree from which it comes.

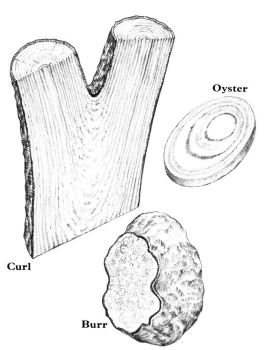

Sought-after figures (patterns) of veneer: the curl is obtained by slicing where grain divides; the oyster by cutting radially through the slim trunks of trees like laburnum or olive; the burr, from the bulbous growth found on the trunk and branches of some species.

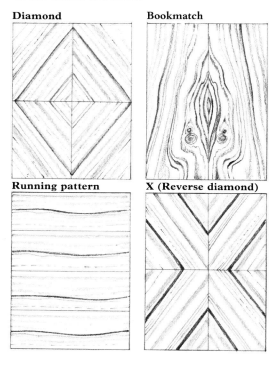

Veneer matching is necessary when covering a wide area or when the veneer sheets are narrow. The principal types of match shown above rely on the fact that consecutive slices of veneer taken from the same flitch (log) have similar patterning.

Arrows show direction of grain

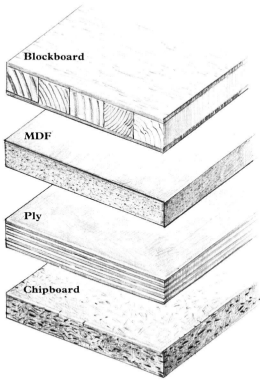

Blockboard

MDF

Ply

Chipboard

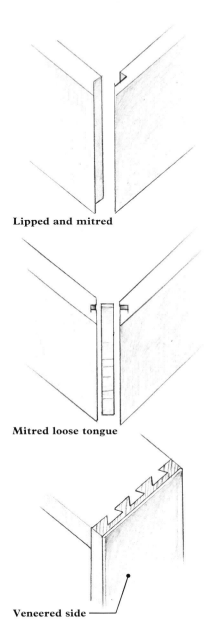

Lipped and mitred

Mitred loose tongue

Veneered side

The groundwork—the timber on which veneer is laid—radically affects the finish.
Groundwork must have little or no tendency to warp, and it must be clean; if necessary, scour with abrasive paper or drag saw teeth over it in opposing directions. Splits must be filled, knots removed and filled. Veneer ply on both sides to prevent warping, laminating across the grain as with batten board. Veneer solid timber only if the growth rings are at 90° to the surface.

MDF or flakeboard

Ply

Lipping is necessary with most manufactured boards: their edges are unattractive and they are difficult to veneer properly because of the coarse end grain. So fix a 'lip' of matching wood to the edge, with a tongue and groove joint. Lipping is not necessary on MDF or flakeboard; just stain it to match the veneer.

Veneering over complex joints, such as dovetails, should be avoided unless the joint is out of sight on the underside of the work. Natural shrinkage in joints causes unevenness that 'telegraphs'—shows—through the veneer, sometimes even causing cracking. The solution is to make 45° mitred joints, either plain or with a loose tongue for extra strength.

145

Veneering with Scotch/animal glue

Veneering by the Scotch glue method

Properly made Scotch glue is strong, and it has a fine consistency; ultra-close bonding without lumpiness, is possible.

The ground—the material on which the veneer is laid.	**1** Use solid or manufactured board (but not chipboard or flakeboard, which distort).	**2** Repair defects, lipping if necessary. **3** Clean if dirty.	**4** Warm to room temperature if board has been stored cold.
The veneer	**1** Select. **2** Mark upper (smoother) surface.	**3** Cut to size plus $\frac{1}{4}$ in/6 mm all round.	**4** If buckled, damp both sides and leave under a weight.
The glue	**1** Only clean, fresh, best-quality Scotch glue with no lumps.	**2** Heat to creamy consistency: with brush held 3 in/8 cm	above pot, glue should flow without breaking into drops.
Equipment all assembled in advance	**1** Veneering hammer. **2** Iron. **3** Hot water in pot.	**4** Craft knife. **5** Cutting board. **6** Metal straight edge.	**7** Gummed-paper tape. **8** Newspaper. **9** Lint-free rag.

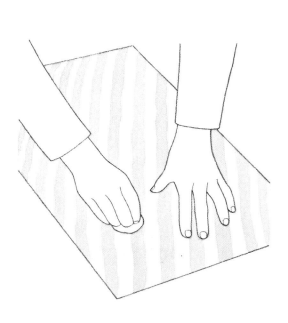

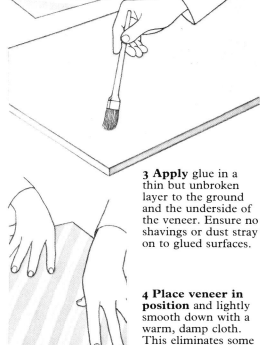

3 Apply glue in a thin but unbroken layer to the ground and the underside of the veneer. Ensure no shavings or dust stray on to glued surfaces.

4 Place veneer in position and lightly smooth down with a warm, damp cloth. This eliminates some of the air bubbles, and the moisture helps prevent the veneer curling up.

1 Cover bench with clean newspaper and fix ground down securely. Total cleanliness is vital.

2 Damp the upper surface of the veneer with a wet rag. Lay veneer face-down beside the ground.

Angle and dimensions of handle are not critical

10 in/25 cm

3½ in/9 cm

6 in/15 cm

5 Iron over a section of the veneer, with a damp cloth under the iron to prevent scorching. The iron should be hot enough quickly to evaporate a spot of water on the sole, but not so hot as to cause 'spitting'. Keep the sole clean by rubbing it occasionally with fine abrasive paper.

To make a veneer hammer

This tool, which is easy to make, is essential for veneering. The wood should be strong, since fair pressure is exerted on it. Rosewood, teak or iroko are ideal (they resist water), but any hardwood will do. The blade should be brass or aluminium to prevent corrosion.

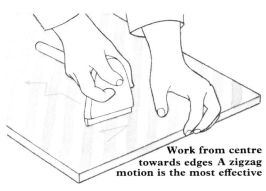

Work from centre towards edges A zigzag motion is the most effective

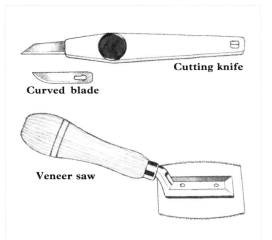

Cutting knife

Curved blade

Veneer saw

6 Work out the excess glue with the veneer hammer. Work with the grain as much as possible—this cuts down stretching. Wipe surplus from hammer blade and edges of work. Repeat the process, first softening the glue as in **5**, until whole area is covered. When the glue sets, feel the surface with the fingertips for irregularities and go over them again with the iron and hammer.

Cutting veneers

The thickest ('saw-cut') veneers are cut with a veneer saw or, alternatively, a dovetail. The saw is held straight along a length of timber clamped in place. Most veneers can be cut with a craft knife. A rounded blade allows a rocking, slicing motion, so helping to prevent splitting when cutting across the grain. A sharp-pointed blade allows a firm, even pressure.

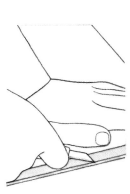

7 Trim edges.

147

Veneering/caul method

Making a joint/hammer veneering

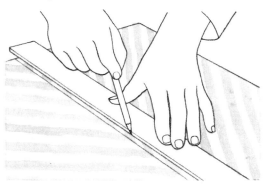

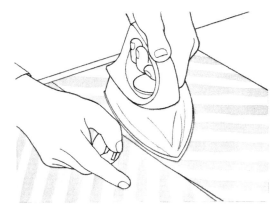

1 Overlap the two sheets of veneer and lay a steel rule or straightedge along what is to be the line of the joint. Press the rule down tightly and cut through both thicknesses of veneer with a craft knife. If the cut is long, cramp both ends.

2 Heat the waste strip of veneer with the iron and then simply peel it away.

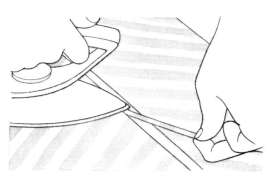

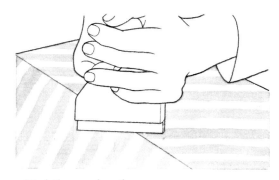

3 Heat the joint area again and carefully lift the overlapping piece in order to extract the remaining piece of veneer from underneath.

4 Lightly re-glue the edges of the veneer along the joint line.

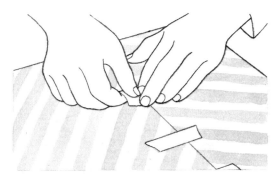

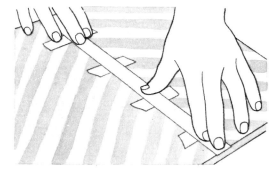

5 Wipe away any surplus glue and . . .

6 Tape across and along the joint to prevent a gap opening up—as the glue sets, the veneer will shrink slightly.

Caul veneering

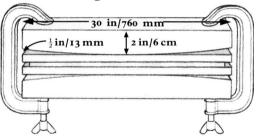

This method of veneering, which amounts to constructing a simple press, comes into its own with complex patterns. Components can be pre-positioned as a complete pattern and secured with tape. The cauls are simply flat sheet material: blockboard $\frac{3}{4}$ in/ 18 mm thick is ideal.

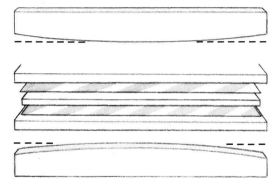

Procedure: **1**, Cut two cauls, each slightly larger than the panel to be veneered. **2**, Make cross-bearers, each with one edge slightly curved, so that when tightened, pressure is applied from the centre outward. **3**, Apply the Scotch glue (animal glue) to groundwork.

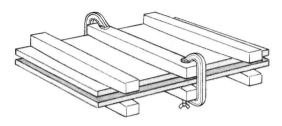

Procedure (contd.); **4**, Heat the cauls and assemble the 'sandwich', *centre*. The paper absorbs excess glue: Use veneer pins to hold the veneers in place. **5**, Tighten the G-clamps, squeezing surplus glue toward the edges.

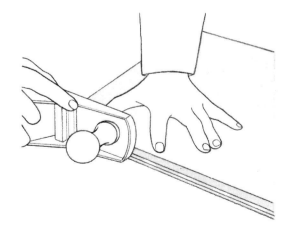

Planing the edges of veneer
The edges of some veneers tend to break away when cut with a knife, so planing becomes necessary in order to obtain a close-fitting joint. If just one or two edges need planing, hand-hold the veneer between two boards slightly larger than the veneer; then 'shoot' the edges straight with a finely-set plane. If several edges need trimming, cramp the sheets between two lengths of timber.

Alternative veneering adhesives
Cauls enable adhesives other than Scotch glue (animal glue)—for example, resin adhesives—to be used to attach veneer to groundwork, so eliminating the cumbersome business of heating up the cauls.

One of the best alternatives is glue-film, a thin layer of glue backed with paper. It is placed glue-side down on the groundwork and smoothed over with a domestic iron set at 'rayon', or cool. The backing paper is then peeled off, the veneer placed in position and worked over slowly with the iron until adhesion is complete and secure.

When resin, or cold, glues are used, first roughen the groundwork with a wood rasp, clean off any dust and pour on the glue. Spread the glue evenly, using a spatula, and lay down the veneer so that it extends $\frac{1}{4}$ in/ 6 mm over all edges of the groundwork. Smooth it down by hand, then press the glue from the centre to the edges with a roller. Clamp in the usual manner.

149

Parquetry

One of the most attractive and fascinating ways of decorating furniture is to make up patterns of veneer shapes, taking advantage of contrasting colours or grain direction. The term marquetry is often loosely applied to this whole field, but, in fact, should be used only for the making of pictorial or floral designs, in which curved shapes have to be cut freehand. The correct term for patterns made up of straight-line, geometrical shapes, such as squares or diamonds, is parquetry.

Such shapes can be used either practically (for instance as chess or checker boards), or decoratively. If the latter, the pattern may be overall, or confined to decorative banding around edges.

To achieve a satisfactory result, great care must clearly be taken to cut and join the veneers accurately and cleanly. It is important, therefore, to choose veneers which are flat and straight-grained, with nicely contrasting colours, such as sycamore (light) and walnut (dark).

Be sure to mark the face side of the veneer: this enables the veneer pieces to be kept right side up and right way round during cutting—not always easy because some veneers change colour in different lights. For the same reason, the veneer pieces should be laid in the order in which they were cut: any inherent pattern will then run naturally through the design.

Another almost essential precaution is to cut extra pieces when preparing a batch of veneer. The fragile material is easily damaged during cutting or assembly, and having spares readily available saves untold frustration.

Finally, to assist assembly, construct a simple jig, or cutting board, with a soft plywood base slightly larger than the final area of veneer required. Using panel pins, fasten a strip of wood, with one perfectly straight edge, along one edge of the base to act as a stop.

Leave plenty of time for assembling parquetry, and double-check that all necessary equipment is at hand before you start work.

Building up a parquetry pattern: squares

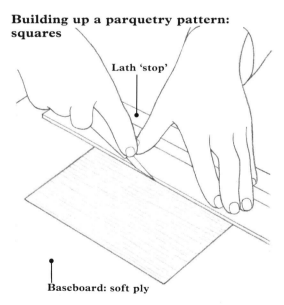

Lath 'stop'

Baseboard: soft ply

1 Preliminaries: besides the jig (*see main text*), a steel strip is required, its width exactly that of the squares to be cut. A steel rule or straightedge is ideal. Cut a straight edge on the veneer as a starting point, and with both this edge and the rule pressed firmly against the stop, cut off a strip. Repeat, building up a stock of strips with contrasting colours.

2 Tape alternately coloured veneer strips together, tightly butt-jointing them. Gummed brown-paper tape is better for this purpose than self-adhesive tape: when wetted, the paper expands and, after sticking down, it contracts as it dries, which has the effect of pulling the edges of the veneer together.

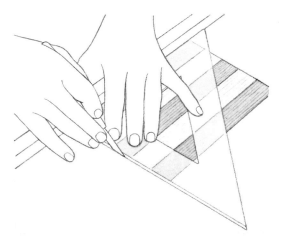

3 Use a set square to cut away the squares themselves.

First press veneer and set square hard against the stop and trim a perfectly straight, square edge as a starting point. If a diamond pattern is required, cut at 60° rather than 90°, employing the longest edge of the set square.

Fixing marquetry inlays

Marquetry inlays of various patterns, including flowers and shells, can be bought from specialized suppliers. To incorporate them in a veneer or timber surface, first temporarily position the shape on the surface with double-sided tape. Mark guide lines across the shape with a pencil. With a craft knife, cut through the veneer using the shape as a template. Remove the veneer and glue the shape into the empty space.

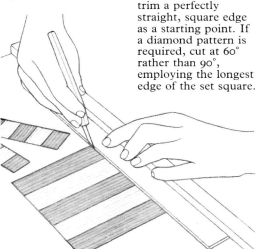

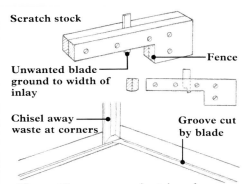

4 Turn the taped strips through 90° and, with the trimmed ends now against the

stop, cut through the strips, forming a series of light and dark squares.

After cutting across grain, trim edges of groove with a cutting gauge

5 For a cube pattern, reverse alternate strips end-to-end and tape together. Ensure that all corners are exactly aligned and the tape is on just one side of the veneer. Trim away surplus squares; check the pattern is square; add border if wanted. Lay on groundwork, using the caul method.

Simple inlay

Lines and banding can be inlaid into a veneer or solid wood surface with relative ease. First mark up the surface. Then grind a piece of cutting steel (an unwanted knife blade is suitable) to the exact width of the inlay. Fix the blade into a scratch stock so that, when the stock's fence is pushed against the edge of the surface to be inlaid, it will cut a groove the same width as the inlay and slightly shallower. Press inlay into place using the cross-pein of a hammer.

Preparing for finishes

Clear finishes can neither disguise nor conceal blemishes on wood, and paint only sometimes hides them. So when preparing work for the final finish, there is only one standard worth achieving: all surfaces totally blemish-free.

If the piece of work has been constructed in the home workshop, tool marks ought, at the cabinet-making stage, to have been removed by planing and the use of cabinet scrapers. By contrast, a ready-made piece of 'whitewood', or raw-wood, furniture will probably require extra attention, for example, pencil marks cleaned off, and rough joints sanded or planed. Flat surfaces too may need careful smoothing with fine abrasive paper.

Assuming major defects have already been dealt with, the first step in preparing work for finishing is to go over it thoroughly with abrasive paper several times. In the process, it is essential to remove all spots of excess glue that may have spread from joints or have been wiped over surfaces by mistake. Any glue left behind seals the grain and stands out conspicuously after staining or lacquering, so it must be removed completely.

The usual choice of abrasive paper for general work is 180 or 240 glasspaper or garnet paper. Wrap it around a cork block if the surfaces to be worked on are flat and wide enough. Otherwise cut the abrasive sheet into four, fold each quarter again and hold with the fingers and thumb of one hand.

The greatest care must be taken to rub *with* the grain. Scratches across the grain may not be obvious at this stage, but when covered by stain or transparent finishes they form bold, black lines. Where horizontal and vertical pieces of timber join, use a scrap of wood as a mask in order to avoid scratching the adjacent timber.

Next, examine the surfaces for dents or bruises. Sweat these out with a hot iron and damp rag (*see box*).

Finally, damp the article down by wiping it all over with a clean rag soaked in clean water. This raises the grain, and the resulting whiskers of wood fibre can be denibbed by rubbing with a piece of flour paper or a previously used piece of 5/0s glasspaper or garnet paper (*see box*).

If the grain is not raised and removed in this way, it is likely to rise when the finish is applied, giving it a rough and rather, unattractive appearance.

Rubbing down tips

Crack out abrasive paper before folding by drawing it across a sharp edge. This makes the glue bonding the abrasive medium to the paper crack in a random pattern; if it breaks cleanly along a single fold, the sheet tends to split across.

Keep the paper flat; use a cork block whenever possible.

Keep the paper clean; slapping it against the bench knocks the dirt out.

Work *with* the grain, never across it.

Glass paper soon loses its 'bite'; garnet paper is more expensive but lasts considerably longer.

Keep abrasive papers dry; damp softens the glue, and this can spoil work. For the same reason, ensure the surface is dry before rubbing down.

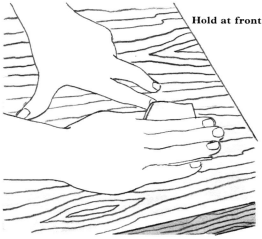

Hold at front

Heel of hand flat on surface to be rubbed down

1 Rubbing down, or flatting, with abrasive paper is always the first stage of preparing work for the finish, assuming major defects such as dents and chips are already repaired. At the rubbing-down stage, it is especially important to remove excess glue. It may not show up much on raw wood, but it seals the grain and after application of clear finish stands out conspicuously.

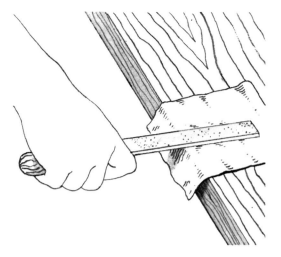

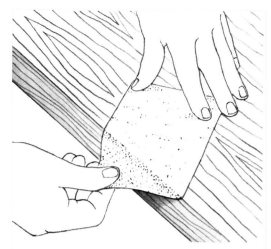

2 Sweating out bruises (dents) requires a domestic iron (a hot file is a useful substitute) and a clean, damp rag. Thoroughly wet the bruise and surrounding area. Allow to soak for several minutes. Cover the bruise with the damp cloth and apply the hot iron, the cloth prevents scorching. Repeat until the bruise is lifted. Allow the wood to dry and then clean it up thoroughly with abrasive paper.

Using abrasive paper
If a piece of work is small or lacks flat surfaces, it is impractical to use abrasive paper wrapped around a cork block. Instead, tear the sheet in four equal pieces. Fold one of the quarters again and hold it with the thumb and little finger, using the middle three fingers to exert the downward rubbing pressure. Do not let the paper buckle up, this causes scratches.

Grading abrasive paper
Several systems exist for grading abrasives, to the confusion of the woodworker. Read across the chart to find equivalents, or a lack of them, in other systems.

Glasspaper	Garnet, aluminium oxide and flint papers	Silicon carbide	Emery paper
	$10/os$	400	
	$9/os$	320	
	$8/os$	280	
	$7/os$	240	
	$6/os$	220	
00 (flour)	$5/os$	180	0
0	$4/os$	150	FF
1	$3/os$	120	F
$1\frac{1}{2}$	$2/os$	100	1
F2	0	80	$1\frac{1}{2}$
M2	$\frac{1}{2}$	60	2
			$2\frac{1}{2}$
S2	1	50	3
$2\frac{1}{2}$	$1\frac{1}{2}$	40	4
3	2	36	
	$2\frac{1}{2}$	30	
	3	24	
	$3\frac{1}{2}$	20	

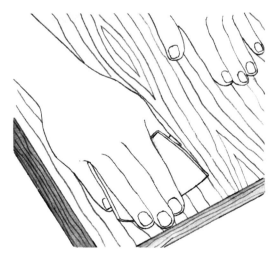

3 Denibbing: the fibres which constitute wood grain run roughly parallel, rather like bundles of fine wires. If wood is cut, even in the same direction as the grain, some fibres are inevitably severed. If dampened, they swell, and the severed ends rise up above the surrounding area. Rub surfaces gently with flour paper to denib these whiskers.

Grain filling

Staining simply means dyeing wood. It is usually done to create colour, so that the piece of work matches another or some existing interior design scheme, or to enhance the appearance of otherwise featureless, uninteresting wood. Woodworkers' stains are not protective, nor do they provide a finish in the same way as, say, lacquer. They simply colour wood without obliterating its inherent features.

The range of stains available to the woodworker falls into four main types. Water stains are dyes dissolved in water. Oil stains are dyes dissolved in petroleum-based solvents. Spirit stains are dyes dissolved in alcohol, usually methylated spirits. The fourth type, waterborne chemical stains, are different from the others because they are not dyes but chemicals, which react with other chemicals in wood, so producing colour. Stains can be mixed only with others in the same group, and each group can be diluted by the addition of the base solvent.

Inexperienced woodworkers should start off by using only water stains, which are relatively cheap, stable and tolerant of a certain amount of misuse. They may be purchased as dry powders to be made up as required, and colours can be adjusted by mixing. Some powders may be slow to dissolve, so mix them in well and allow the stain to stand for an hour or so before using it.

All types of stain are applied in a similar manner, and by far the most important part of the technique is wiping off the surplus stain after the initial application of a generous amount. Slow or half-hearted wiping-off is the most usual cause of unevenly coloured work or inconsistent colouring from piece to piece. The surplus dye must be attacked immediately with a piece of absorbent, lint-free cloth, rubbing firmly in the direction of the grain, never across it.

If using oil stain, the wiping-off stage is even more important because surplus oil left to dry on the surface can prevent subsequent finishes from adhering properly.

Allowing stain to dry thoroughly before sealing is another important point. It can be disconcerting to find that the stain colour changes as it dries, but the original hue is always restored by the later application of a transparent finish. Avoid rubbing down with abrasive paper before sealing, the dye penetration may be deep.

1 **Apply the stain liberally** with a brush, a sponge or a piece of clean, lint-free cloth. If the area is sufficiently small, cover it completely in one application; otherwise work in sections, covering them completely.

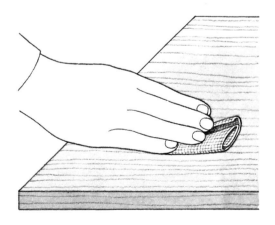

2 **'Wetting out'** is the term used to describe correct application of stain: surplus stain is bound to be left, and this must be wiped away promptly, using a clean, lint-free cloth. Rub hard, working with the grain rather than across it, and make sure that every trace of excess stain is removed.

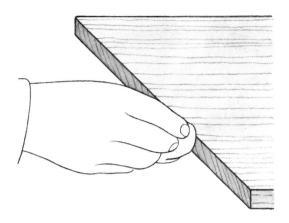

3 If much end grain is in evidence, damp it with water before applying the stain. This cuts down absorption and improves colour.

Staining tips

Test the colour of the stain on an off-cut before attempting the job itself.

Liberal application is essential. Put on too little stain and patching results.

Wetting out the whole area is essential. Some oils and resins in wood resist wetting, causing uneven coverage. If this occurs, try adding some washing soda (sodium carbonate) to the stain.

Mix sufficient stain for the whole job before applying it.

Rub hard when wiping off the excess stain and make certain all excess is removed from all parts of the work.

Allow to dry for at least two hours in a well-ventilated room before applying the sealant.

Do not rub down with abrasive paper until the stain is sealed or loss of colour could result.

4 Allow the stain to dry completely—at least two hours in a well-ventilated room— before applying the sealer. Use of a warm-air blower speeds up drying. Failure to dry properly may cause problems with the finish. Drying may change the colour of the stain slightly, but a clear finish will restore the original hue.

Natural colour

Some chemicals enhance or enrich the natural colour of wood and, therefore, have the status of 'authentic' dyes. Ammonia, for example, adds warm tones to oak; it can be applied either as a dilute liquid or by fuming in an enclosed space with ammonia vapour. Potassium bichromate adds a deep brown to mahogany. Copper, or ferrous, sulphate generally give cold colours.

There are, in addition, the true natural stains. Mahogany crystals dissolved in water produce a warm brown colour, similar to red mahogany. Vandyke crystals dissolved in water produce a neutral brown; negrisene produces a deep blue-back.

Dark marks can be removed from wood, or it can be lightened all over, by the use of bleaches. Sodium hypochlorite and oxalic acid are commonly used for removing dark marks, since they will not appreciably lighten surrounding areas. Oxalic acid is poisonous and should be carefully handled, neutralized with acetic acid and then washed off with water. The two-part super bleach consists of an alkaline solution, followed by concentrated hydrogen peroxide, and its effect is greatly to lighten most woods, bleaching others, such as beech and pine, almost white.

Filling the grain

Even after thorough preparation—rubbing down with abrasive paper and sweating out bruises—small imperfections can still come to light on a piece of work: a flake of veneer may work adrift; a sliver of wood may break off. Stoppers or fillers are the answer to such problems, and since they are available in a wide range of colours, a matching repair can be made.

Assuming all surfaces are completely free of such blemishes, work is ready for grain-filling. This is an overall operation, not a local repair, and is carried out on the wood before any form of finish is applied. The working ingredient of filler is a fine powder, such as china clay or silica, and its function is literally to fill, or 'choke', the grain, so creating a completely smooth surface that will absorb relatively little of the finishing agent. If sufficient care is taken with application of the finishing agent, such a surface is capable of giving the ultra-high-gloss 'glass' finish required of certain types of work, particularly, of course, fine cabinet-making.

Filler is also used to determine colour, for it is available in various shades such as light oak, walnut or mahogany. Different shades can be combined with different woods to create a very wide range of effects. But 'natural' fillers, containing no pigment, are a useful option for the inexperienced because, with the addition of suitable pigments, they can be coloured to match any timber.

Filler is bought in cans as a ready-mixed paste and, because the solvent tends to separate out from the solids, must always be thoroughly stirred before use. Apart from its filling properties, the substance is designed to wipe off cleanly when partially dry, to adhere well and to accept most finishes without reacting.

Filler is applied in liberal amounts, with the object of covering the entire surface; the excess then has to be wiped away, and judging the right moment to do this is the secret of success. Wait too long, and the surface will not wipe clean unless the filler is softened with a suitable solvent; wipe too soon, and the still-soft filler can be removed completely, making the whole process a waste of time.

Before the filler dries completely, clean out any corners with a quirk stick made specially for the job: split off a piece of hardwood of the right size and shape it to fit with a chisel.

Grain filling

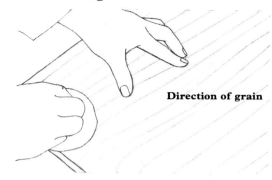

1 Apply the filler with a coarse rag. To rub it in effectively, work across the grain; a circular motion is good. Liberally cover the whole surface, up to the edges and into corners. Unfilled areas cause problems later.

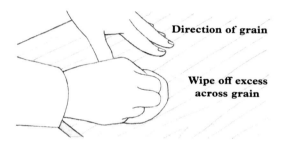

2 Allow the filler to dry partially before wiping away the excess. When filler starts drying, it looks dull rather than shiny. Preliminary tests will reveal how long to wait before the excess can be removed by a simple, clean wipe across the grain.

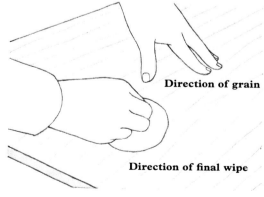

3 A final wipe *along* the grain, but only after the excess has been removed by turning the rag over and rubbing hard, 'straightens up' the filler and completes its application.

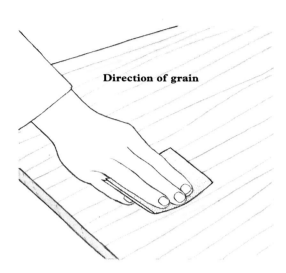

Direction of grain

Filling tips

Filler will only fill grain—don't expect it to cover other blemishes.

Experiment on off-cuts before trying to fill a finished piece of work.

Cover the bench with clean paper or cloth before filling; cleanliness is essential and there must be no scatching. Keep cloths used for filling in a clean place.

Don't cover too large an area when applying the filler: excess must be wiped away before it dries completely.

Sacking (hessian) is the best material for applying filler; keep some just for this purpose.

4 When the filler is completely dry, lightly abrade the surface to remove any imperfections. Use flour paper or a sheet of old abrasive paper, and work with the grain.

Filling holes with stoppers

There is a choice of several forms of stopping. Professionals favour the shellac stick for many repairs, for, once applied, it is almost invisible. Cellulose jam (partially congealed lacquer) is another clear stopping agent; press it into the hole with a spatula and lightly rub with abrasive paper when dry. Waxes are best applied in inconspicuous places. Branded stoppers need careful matching with the surface colour. To apply

hard shellac stopper, first prick the surface of the area to be filled with a pin; this assists adhesion. Then heat a soldering iron (but a file tip will do) and, holding the shellac stick over the hole, melt a few drops into the hole. When the shellac is solid, cut away the excess with a sharp chisel. Rubbing with wax before chiselling often prevents the shellac shattering and ensures its clean removal.

French polish

As a finish, French polish is in a class of its own. It is largely natural: the basic ingredients are shellac, a resin exuded by the lac insect, and methylated spirit or denatured alcohol, which acts as the solvent. It is not easy to apply successfully. It damages easily, and is not particularly heat- or water-resistant. But in the hands of an expert, it can produce a finish of breathtaking depth and beauty, the classic finish in fact, of many antiques and much fine furniture. Its lack of durability is to some extent compensated for by the fact that it is reversible: with the correct solvent, it can be removed and restored—in contrast to the modern, non-reversible finishes, such as the polyurethane varnishes, household paints or melamines. These are all much more heat- and water-resistant, but difficult to repair if damaged.

French polishing is really a craft in its own right and needs to be learned and practised under the eye of an expert. The basic requirements, however, are relatively simple. First, make up a 'rubber'—a cloth and wadding pad with which to apply the liquid polish. The wadding should be non-medicated cotton wool or pound wadding (refined cotton), the cloth clean linen or cotton. (Medicated cotton compresses when wet, becoming slimy.) The wadding must be folded inside the cloth in the prescribed manner, and the completed rubber must be the right size for the job in hand: fist-sized for a dining-room table, pigeon's-egg-sized for a picture frame.

Much of the knack of French polishing lies in knowing how much pressure to apply to the rubber and when to recharge it with polish. Beginners tend to use the rubber too wet: the rubber is correctly charged if, when squeezed, it deposits a slight excess of polish on the surface of the wood. Care must also be taken not to leave 'whips' of excess polish on the surface when the direction of the polishing strokes changes. As the rubber dries, extra pressure needs to be applied.

Another important rule is to look after the corners; failure to work polish into awkward peripheral areas shows up all too clearly. The whole process, in fact, requires care and patience. Several thin coats of polish are needed to produce the best appearance, but if a further application is made before the previous coat dries, the polish turns thick and sticky, becoming extremely difficult to manage.

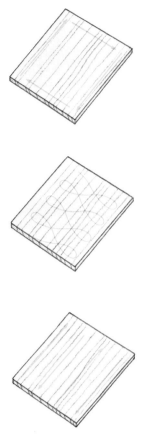

French polishing
1 Having charged the rubber, sweep it in parallel, overlapping lines along the grain. The rubber must be slid on and off the wood without stopping. Pay attention to corners and edges. This first step seals the surface.
2 Now 'body up' the initial thin skin. Recharge the rubber and work it over the entire surface several times so that each part is passed over from different directions. Use a combination of figure-of-eight and loop patterns; work with a continuous movement, without stopping, right into corners and up to edges. Work the polish well into the grain. Apply extra pressure as the rubber dries. By the end of this stage, a full coat has been built up and burnished.
3 Finally, add some methylated spirit or denatured alcohol to the rubber and work it along the grain.

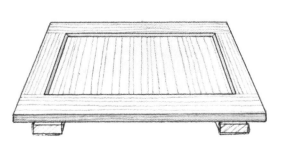

Holding work steady is essential when French polishing. Flat panels, such as doors, should be secured with rebated (rabbeted) pieces of timber screwed to the bench. Larger pieces that do not have legs should be supported with padded pieces of timber to avoid scratching.

1 Fold a rectangular piece of wadding once across the centre line.

2 Fold one corner across diagonally at an angle of about 60°.

3 Fold the other corner across diagonally to create an arrowhead-shape.

4 Tuck in the loose ends, so creating an egg-shape.

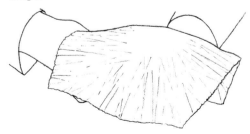

5 Drape linen or cotton cloth over the wadding.

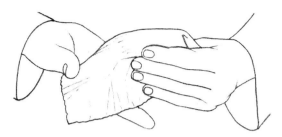

6 Smooth out the cloth and pleat the sides to take up excess fabric.

7 Pinch the point and, holding the cloth tightly . . .

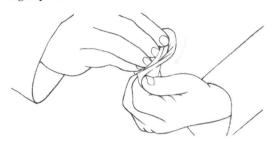

8 Fold the cloth back along the side of the rubber.

9 The remaining, excess cloth is twisted to give the rubber a taut, smooth face.

Folding and charging a 'rubber'

It is essential to create a taut, smooth surface for the 'rubber', and to make it pointed for working into tight corners. When recharging, undo the cloth and apply fresh polish directly to the wad. Practised French polishers will lubricate the surface of the rubber from time to time with a spot of raw linseed oil; beginners are advised not to—knowing when to do this and how much oil to use can only be learned by practise.

Non-reversible finishes

Non-reversible finishes are so called because, by contrast with French polish or nitrocellulose, they are intended to be permanent. They are not, as a rule, easily removed for restoring because they harden in two stages. First, the solvent evaporates, leaving the surface hard enough to handle. Then it continues to 'cure' by chemical reaction until the full potential is realized, a process which may take up to ten days, although casual examination usually reveals little difference after two days at an average temperature of 68 °F/20 °C.

These finishes—comprising all the modern clear finishes such as polyurethane 'varnish', household paint and two-pack materials—are often petro-chemical based and purpose-made by the research chemist, with desirable qualities such as durability and heat-resistance. Industrially, they are applied by spray guns or other mechanical devices to achieve a high-quality finish without further treatment. This, of course, does not preclude their use in the small workshop, but it pays to be aware that brushing on finishes is, by contrast with spraying, a difficult method of coating a surface. Too much brushing induces aeration, and if the solvent is fast-drying, this would produce appalling results. Do not, therefore, brush hard; let the finish flow on to the surface.

Then there is the problem of brush strokes showing, even after the finish has dried, and of drips and runs. Always use the minimum possible number of even, gentle brush strokes and avoid dragging the brush over the edges, thus squeezing excess liquid out of the bristles. Brush from the centre of a surface outward, toward the edges.

The most important surface on a piece of work should be coated last, so ensuring that there is the least chance of dust or dirt settling on the still-wet surface. The best environment for applying finishes is, of course, as dust-free as possible. Since initial drying is by evaporation, some circulation of air, preferably warm air, is desirable. Strong draughts on the other hand raise dust, which damages the finish.

Generally two applications are sufficient for these types of finish. After the last one is applied, the work should be allowed not just to dry but to harden for the length of time recommended by the manufacturer. It is then ready for the finishing touches.

Successful application of non-reversible finishes requires the minimum of brushing. Try to make the liquid flow on to the surface. Work in a dust-free area.

1 For a really high-quality finish on a non-reversible lacquer, allow it to harden and then remove all the brush marks by rubbing with wet and dry paper (used wet). If the marks are prominent, use 320 wet and dry, followed by 400. When the surface looks dull all over, it is ready for one or other of stages **2** or **3**.

2 For a high-gloss surface finish, apply a motorcar bodywork polish (not wax) and burnish it to a brilliant gloss—hard work but worth it.

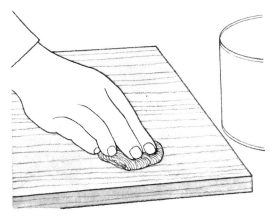

3 For a satin finish, apply some wax to the surface with 000 or a finer grade steel wool. Remove any excess with clean steel wool, then gently buff, using a soft cloth.

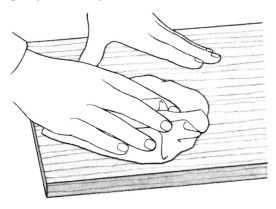

4 Hand-buffing with a soft cloth is a means of removing smears and generally cleaning up finishes. The buffing action should not be too rigorous.

Tips on non-reversible finishes

Follow the maker's instructions fully.

Wear overalls to prevent fibres falling off sweaters or other clothing.

Ensure the ground is properly pre-pared for finishing. (See pages 152–3.)

Work in a dust-free area with adequate ventilation.

Clean the brush as soon as application is complete.

When using wet and dry paper use plenty of water to keep the paper cutting.

Work carefully on edges and corners so as not to remove the finish.

'Flat' the finish when using wet and dry paper, don't groove it.

Don't use excessive amounts of wax, the feel of a finish will be spoilt.

Melamine lacquers and urea/formaldehyde retain their clarity well.

Purchase thinners from the same manufacturer that produced the finishing lacquer.

Restoring and cleaning

Much old or antique furniture can be improved significantly in appearance by cleaning. As a first step, use good-quality toilet soap, warm water and a nail brush or hand brush for working into recesses.

If this is ineffective, mix white spirit (paint thinners) with 10 per cent raw linseed oil and apply, waiting a few minutes for softening to take place. If any marks are truly stubborn, rub lightly with 000 steel wool. Then wipe the surface clean, removing every trace of oil, and give it one light application of French polish.

Only very rarely should old furniture be stripped: this destroys the patina and hence much of the value. If in doubt, consult an expert as to what to do.

Most modern furniture is finished with lacquer that does not require waxing; wiping with a damp cloth is enough. Many disfiguring marks on recently made furniture turn out to be contained within the layers of wax polish that have been progressively built up. Try removing them with white spirit (paint thinners) and, if needed, 000 steel wool. The marks made by the steel wool will be hidden by a single layer of wax.

Hinges

The most familiar, indeed the classic, pattern for a hinge is two leaves, joined by a steel pin through a centre piece composed of 'units' and called the knuckle: the standard butt hinge. The knuckle usually has an odd number of units, and the leaf with the larger number of units is customarily fitted to the carcase, or frame, while the other leaf is fitted to the moving part.

Hinges are available in brass, steel and nylon; steel ones have different finishes such as electro brass and bright zinc plate. Most are supplied in pairs.

There are actually two types of standard butt hinge. The narrow suit hinge, which has leaves $\frac{5}{8}$–$\frac{7}{8}$ in/15–22 mm wide, is used for wardrobes, larger doors or flaps.

If a door is panelled, position the hinges level with the inner rail edges. With a flush-faced door, position one hinge its own length from the door top, the other just over a hinge length from the bottom.

Fix hinges with a deep housing in the door and a shallow one in the carcase. This presents a clean, unbroken line and prevents possible binding along the stile.

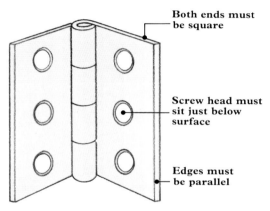

Both ends must be square

Screw head must sit just below surface

Edges must be parallel

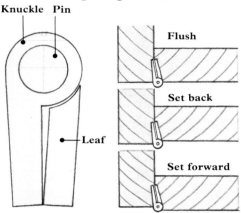

Knuckle Pin

Leaf

Flush

Set back

Set forward

The standard butt hinge Used for doors, windows and furniture. Most smaller sizes are of solid-drawn brass; larger sizes of steel or nylon. Before fitting, check that the ends and sides are parallel and square. If necessary, file true with a smooth file. Fix with screw heads that sit just below the hinge surface.

To set back a door, gauge marker lines to just short of distance from pin centre to leaf edge, **A**, and to knuckle depth, **B**.

Position a hinge set either back or forward of the main carcase. Because of the risk of a door frame warping, flush-fitting doors are not recommended.

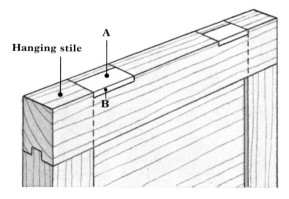

Hanging stile

A

B

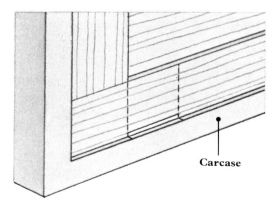

Carcase

To mark out a stile, 1, mark out the recess, using the hinge itself as a template. Then gauge **A** along the door edge, and **B** along the front of the door.

2 Mark the hinge positions on the carcase after marking the door. Lay the carcase on its side and wedge the door in position, allowing for clearance top and bottom. Transfer the door hinge position to the carcase inside.

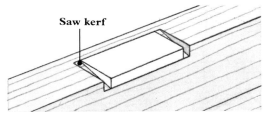

3 To remove waste wood from the hanging stile, make an initial, slanting saw cut on the waste side at each end.

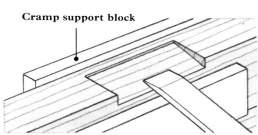

4 Clamp a supporting block against the work. Chop across the grain with a chisel and pare down to the gauge lines. Slope the recess from full knuckle depth in front to single-leaf thickness at the back.

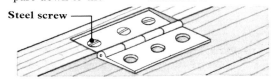

5 Press the hinge leaf into place once the recess base is completely flat. Secure the leaf initially with a single steel screw in the centre hole.

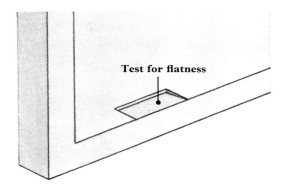

6 Remove carcase waste with a chisel. Screw hinge to the door, using one steel screw in the centre hole of each leaf. Check for alignment. Insert suitable screws in all holes.

Variations on the butt hinge

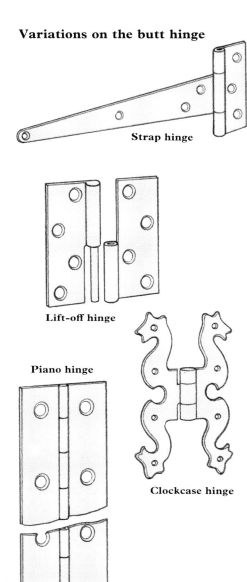

One useful variation of the butt hinge is the lift-off hinge: use where a door needs to be removed easily. Use strap hinges on narrow sections. Use a piano hinge where support is needed along the whole length of a joint. The clockcase hinge often has a ball tip and one plate wider than the other to allow for a projecting moulding. In the flush hinge, the flaps fold into each other; it does not need to be recessed.

Special hinges

Undoubtedly the most difficult part of fitting a hinge is obtaining the final fine adjustment between the door and the carcase so that the door moves easily and there is a small but equal clearance gap all around the cabinet. To achieve this with traditional, standard butt hinges is laborious; moreover there is every likelihood that the hinges will need adjusting if they wear or the wood moves.

Special hinges have, therefore, been developed. These more up-to-date designs reduce the labour involved in the initial fitting of the hinge to the workpiece and greatly simplify the adjustment of the door.

In most traditional cabinet work, the doors fit within the framework of the cabinet; in modern designs, however, doors often 'lay-on' or overlay the framework, and in most modern hinges there are screw adjustment points, allowing easy final alignment of the door with the carcase without removing the hinge. By contrast, traditional hinges can be adjusted only by removing the screws and packing holes or leaves.

It would be wrong, however, to assume that special hinges are foolproof; whatever the hinge, accurate work at all stages is essential for success.

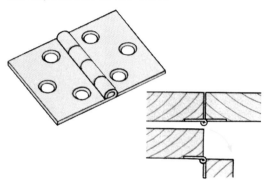

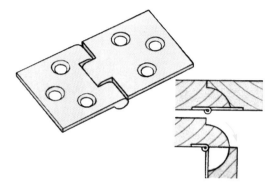

The back flap hinge is used where there is considerable stress on the hinge screws, for example, on box lids, bureau falls and table leaves. The common pattern is square-shaped when closed.

The extra-wide leaves spread the screw fixing over a large area. Fix two screws near the knuckle and one near the end. Available from 1–2 in/ 25–50 mm.

The rule joint hinge, or table hinge, is similar to a back flap hinge except that one leaf is extra-wide. It is made especially for a table that has matched rule joint

moulding along the table edge and flap. Fit the long leaf to the flap, leaving a gap for the shape of the moulding. Recess the leaves and knuckles.

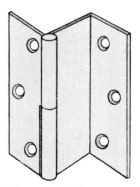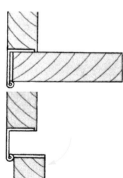

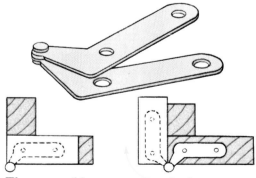

The cranked cabinet hinge enables a door to open through 180°; a typical use is on cabinets with sliding shelves. Screw the narrow leaf to the

front edge of the carcase and the broad leaf to the door. Various styles and sizes are available in both brass and chromium plate.

The centre hinge, or pivot hinge, is made straight or cranked. Use where ordinary butt hinges do not fit, for example in shaped cabinets, or where butt hinges would

intrude, for example on finely veneered work. Recess the plates in the top and bottom edges of the door and cabinet.

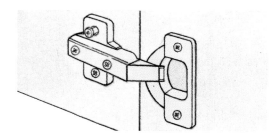

Fitting locks

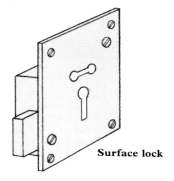

Surface lock

The concealed hinge is for modern cabinetwork. Various types and sizes are available. Fit the hinge to the door and the baseplate to the carcase. Adjust the arm position if necessary. This hinge is simple to align with the door and carcase.

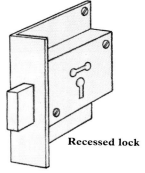

Recessed lock

Etruscan pattern keyhole

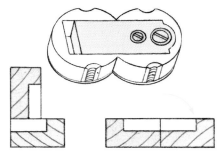

The flush-fitting flap hinge has no protruding parts. Use for 'lay-on' flaps on writing slopes or cocktail cabinets, where it is important to have a perfectly smooth surface. Fit the hinge by drilling holes $1\frac{3}{8}$ in/35 mm in both carcase and flap. Use screw adjustment to ensure that the base of the cabinet and the flap are flush.

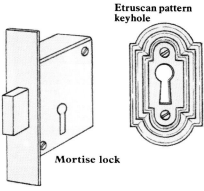

Mortise lock

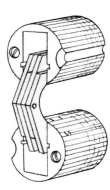 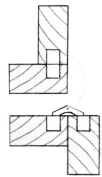

The cylinder hinge, or invisible hinge, distributes a load efficiently. Its two fully recessed cylinders are completely hidden when the door or flap is closed. Drill a hole in each piece. Use the screw adjustment to make a tight fit. Available from $\frac{3}{8}-\frac{5}{8}$ in/ 10–15 mm diameter.

A surface, or straight, cupboard lock is screwed directly to the door and the keyhole made to match. With a recessed, or cut, lock, mark out the body recess. Drill the hole for the key barrel. Then mark and cut out the complete keyhole. Cut away the recess for the lock body. Then mark out for the plate on the face and edge. Saw and chisel away the waste. Screw the lock in position. Recess the mortise lock in the door edge. Remove the waste by boring and chiselling.

Creating a piece of woodwork to one's own design is generally accepted as the most satisfying, indeed the ultimate, possibility of the craft. As might be expected, it requires a high degree of planning.

Before conceiving any specific ideas on design, go right back to basics. Work out the overall dimensions of the piece with reference to where it is to be kept, what other furniture or woodwork it is to match and how it is to be used. Only when this has been done should one progress to the rough sketch stage, making a series of drawings to approximately the same scale that cover different aspects of the work. Try to get the dimensions roughly correct.

The essence of fine woodwork and, in particular, fine furniture design, is careful consideration of the basic, mundane factors. The materials, type of construction and finish should be governed by the style of the article, its function and where it is to serve. It is scarcely less important at this stage to take into account the tools themselves and one's own woodworking capabilities.

Take time over the rough-sketch stage, and do not select a sketch for further development until it contains all the desired elements.

The next step is producing scale drawings to assess actual dimensions and proportions.

Again, do not shirk going through several drafts: slight alterations in component size can dramatically affect appearance. Choose a scale that permits front, side and plan views of the job, together with all major details. Most people use an Imperial scale of 1:4 or a metric scale of 1:5.

Drawings do not always give the correct overall impression, especially of proportions, but models can. Use balsa wood or stiff card and work to the same size as the scale drawing.

After the model stage, make full-size drawings, especially of the joints, to finalize intricate details. Many professionals set out full-size drawings on a piece of plywood (known as a 'rod'); these are useful for marking out and checking.

From these drawings, it should now be possible to write a cutting list with component sizes and to itemize the tools required.

Probably the most elusive factor in design is pleasing proportion. Time and again, wooden artefacts and furniture, from wardrobes to cigarette boxes, are perfect in every respect except this. A sound way of avoiding such dissatisfaction is to be guided by classic proportions, one of the best-known formulas for which is the Golden Section, discovered by the Greeks in the 5th century BC.

PROJECTS

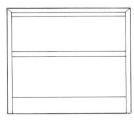 

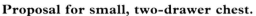

Proposal for small, two-drawer chest.

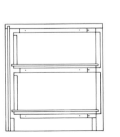

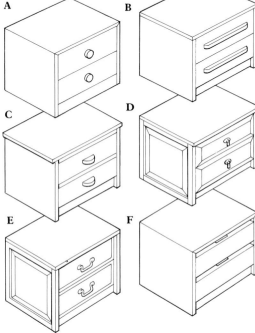

A Solid wood; dovetailed corners; too flat and uninteresting.
B Lipped and veneered ply top and ends; bar handles; drawer runners and kickers difficult to fit; handles too dominant.
C Sides dovetail-housed into top; 'D' handles; extended top and overall proportions unpleasing.
D Framed and panelled ends; drawer fronts bevelled; drop handles; too complex, fussy.

E Moulding round drawers; drawers set in; again, too complex.

F Dovetailed corners; finger grips in drawer fronts; clean lines.

Ergonomics

Ergonomics is the study of the relationship between a human being and his environment; in the USA, it is also known as biotechnology. Its object is to facilitate the design of ideal environments by allowing for the space—the height, depth, width—required for an activity. Applied specifically to furniture design, ergonomics helps prevent excessive reaching, bending or stretching, or the adoption of uncomfortable postures. It also assists in determining the size, layout and shape of a work area or surface.

No matter what type of table a woodworker wishes to make, height should usually be the primary consideration. If the table is to be used for machining, typing or dining, the height of the top surface from the floor should be between 27 and 29 in/ 68.5 and 73.5 cm. For use while standing, such as in the kitchen for preparing food, this height should be between 34 and 36 in/86.5 and 91.5 cm.

It is important that the height of a table intended to be sat at relates to the height of the stool or chair that will be used. The distance between the seat surface and the top surface of the table should be between 10 and 12 in/25.5 and 30.5 cm. The smaller distance feels more comfortable, although it cannot always be achieved because of the clearance necessary for the thighs under the top rails of the table frame.

Space under a table, is, as might be expected, well worth taking into account. A sitter needs to be able to stretch out or cross the legs in comfort, and this gives rise to the generally accepted minimum width of a dining table of 30 in/76 cm. Occasional tables may, of course, vary in height, though the lower limit is usually 12 in/30.5 cm and the upper limit 24 in/61 cm.

The most important function of a chair is that it supports the sitter in comfort and allows him or her to adopt a posture that does not create muscular stress or restrict the blood flow to the lower limbs.

To enable the feet of the sitter to rest comfortably on the floor, the height of the chair seat at the front should be 16 to 18 in/41 to 46 cm. To accommodate the curvature of the spine and to maintain the pelvic girdle at a natural angle, the seat should have a slight slope of 3 to 5°. Seat length (or depth) should be 14 to 16 in/35.5 to 46 cm, and a comfortable width is generally recognized as 18 in/ 46 cm across the front.

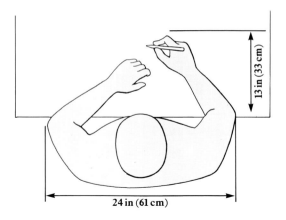

13 in (33 cm)

24 in (61 cm)

When determining the size of a dining-table top, *above*, allow a minimum of 24 in/ 61 cm per person for sitting clearance and 13 in/33 cm from the edge of the table. The positioning of shelves or storage units at appropriate heights – particularly those lower than a work surface – also requires care to avoid excessive bending and stretching. The heights, *below* and *below right*, vary according to whether access is required from sitting or standing positions.

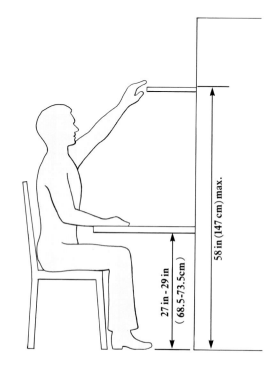

58 in (147 cm) max.

27 in - 29 in (68.5-73.5cm)

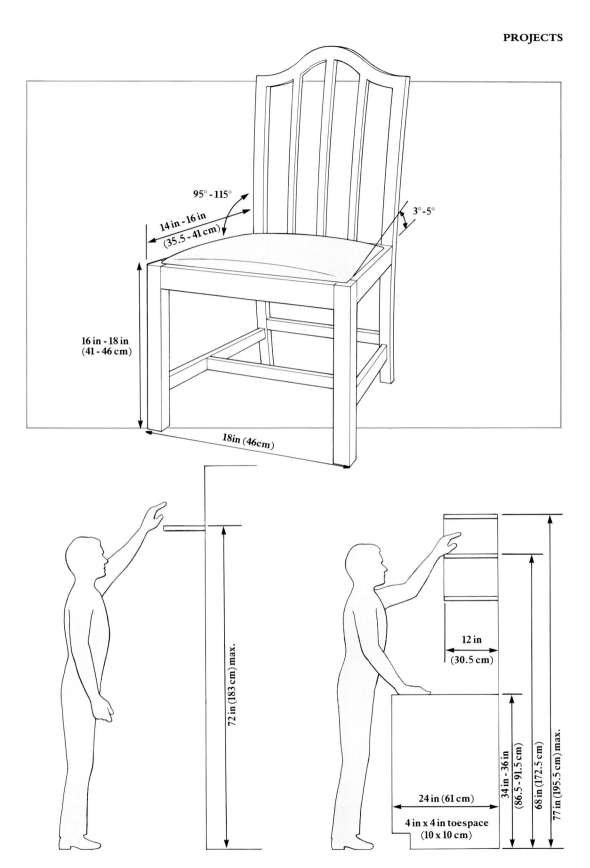

95° - 115°

14 in - 16 in
(35.5 - 41 cm)

3° - 5°

16 in - 18 in
(41 - 46 cm)

18in (46cm)

72 in (183 cm) max.

12 in
(30.5 cm)

34 in - 36 in
(86.5 - 91.5 cm)

24 in (61 cm)

4 in x 4 in toespace
(10 x 10 cm)

68 in (172.5 cm)

77 in (195.5 cm) max.

Welsh dresser

This type of traditional 'farmhouse' furniture was generally made of oak or elm, with fruitwood added for decoration.

Construction of the lower portion of the dresser may take one of two forms, depending upon whether it is to be a dovetailed carcase on a separate plinth (as illustrated) or a carcase with sides to the floor and an oversailing top. The tongued-and-grooved back is screwed to the back rails.

Drawer rails are stub-tenoned into the ends and hung from the top and the back rails. Drawer runners are tongued into grooves, worked along the front and back drawer rails, and are housed into the ends of the carcase.

The upper portion is a simple shelved unit that relies on the top rail and the back for lateral stability. It is located on the lower carcase with dowels. The whole structure is extended so that it may be screwed to the back edge of the top of the lower carcase.

The cornice may be either a separate unit located with dowels or applied. If the latter, a frieze rail is first attached and glue-blocked; moulding is mitred at the corners and glued and pinned in place. The cornice moulding may be a single piece of wood or a composite.

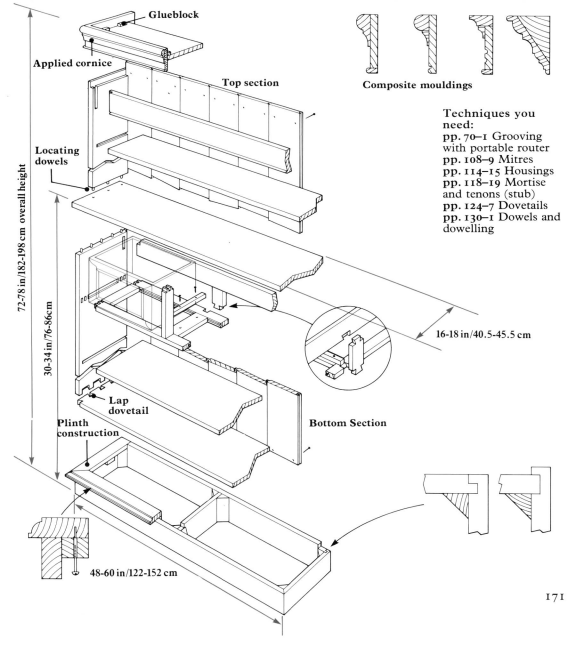

Glueblock

Applied cornice

Top section

Composite mouldings

Locating dowels

Techniques you need:
pp. 70–1 Grooving with portable router
pp. 108–9 Mitres
pp. 114–15 Housings
pp. 118–19 Mortise and tenons (stub)
pp. 124–7 Dovetails
pp. 130–1 Dowels and dowelling

72-78 in/182-198 cm overall height

30-34 in/76-86cm

16-18 in/40.5-45.5 cm

Lap dovetail

Bottom Section

Plinth construction

48-60 in/122-152 cm

Kitchen units

Cabinet top

Rail glued to
cabinet top and
back panel

Rail screwed to
wall

Cabinet back
panel

Modern kitchen units are usually made from MFC (melamine-faced chipboard, or flake-board), but there is no reason why they should not be made from solid wood and plywood or other manufactured board, as long as all surfaces are adequately sealed with a suitable surface finish. For durability and ease of cleaning, work tops are best covered with a plastic laminate; marble, tiled or ceramic tops are alternative choices.

The five-drawer chest in the illustration is constructed in a fairly traditional way, with drawer rails and runners secured to end panels. A back is not required because the carcase is attached to lengths of timber screwed to a wall.

As long as the carcase is rigid, drawer rails may be dispensed with and side-hung drawers used. Drawer sides are grooved (this can be quickly achieved, using a portable electric router) and wooden, metal or plastic runners secured to the carcase sides.

Techniques you need:
pp. 114–15 Grooving with portable router
pp. 116–17, 122–3 Mortise and tenons (stub and haunched)
pp. 124–7 Dovetails
pp. 130–1 Dowelling, tonguing
pp. 132–7 Plywood, blockboard, chipboard, including lipping
pp. 132–3 Cutting manufactured boards
pp. 134–5 KD/QA fastenings

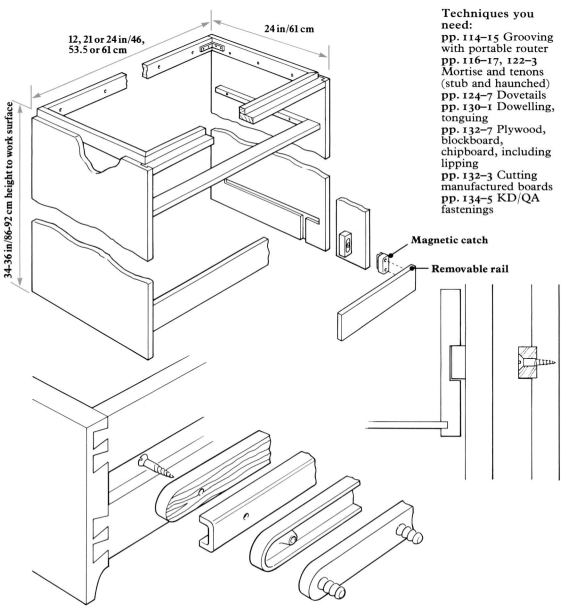

12, 21 or 24 in/46, 53.5 or 61 cm

24 in/61 cm

34-36 in/86-92 cm height to work surface

Magnetic catch

Removable rail

Dresser and display cabinet

The top section of the dresser relies for rigidity on the back rails and a snugly fitting, applied cornice.

The lower section is considerably more complex. It has framed and panelled ends and must incorporate drawer runners, kickers and guides. The top is secured by screwing through the top drawer rail and kickers and by using wooden buttons at the back.

The display cabinet's simple carcase presents few construction problems. The moulding for the hood can be produced in sections, using a template and a portable router or a scratch stock. The glass door has a rebated (rabbeted) frame with the moulded upstand mitred at the corners. Ribs are stub tenoned into the frame and have a grooved moulding glued to the front edge. Where ribs intersect, a cross halved joint is used with canvas glued on for reinforcement.

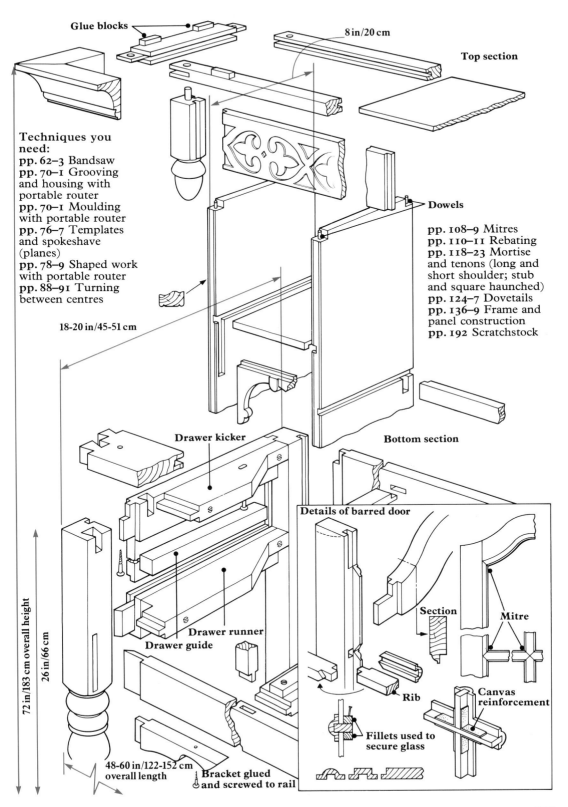

Glue blocks

8 in/20 cm

Top section

Techniques you
need:
pp. 62–3 Bandsaw
pp. 70–1 Grooving
and housing with
portable router
pp. 70–1 Moulding
with portable router
pp. 76–7 Templates
and spokeshave
(planes)
pp. 78–9 Shaped work
with portable router
pp. 88–91 Turning
between centres

18-20 in/45-51 cm

Dowels

pp. 108–9 Mitres
pp. 110–11 Rebating
pp. 118–23 Mortise
and tenons (long and
short shoulder; stub
and square haunched)
pp. 124–7 Dovetails
pp. 136–9 Frame and
panel construction
pp. 192 Scratchstock

Drawer kicker

Bottom section

Details of barred door

72 in/183 cm overall height

26 in/66 cm

Drawer runner

Drawer guide

Section

Mitre

Rib

Canvas
reinforcement

Fillets used to
secure glass

48-60 in/122-152 cm
overall length

Bracket glued
and screwed to rail

175

Games table

Panels of veneered chipboard (flakeboard) give this piece its attractive appearance. The corner posts and plinths are solid wood.

The panels may be jointed to the corner posts using loose tongues or tongues worked on the ends of the panels using a portable electric router. Loose tongues or dowels can be used to secure the top.

The plinths are made from solid wood rebated (rabbeted) along one edge and mitred

at the corners. The drawer opens from both sides of the table, so two drawer fronts are required; each is a composite, with a piece glued to the lower edge to match the corner posts exactly. The top can be veneered for a different game each side.

The chipboard top must be lipped before it is veneered, and the lipping must be of sufficient width to accommodate the necessary grooves, recesses and screws for hinges.

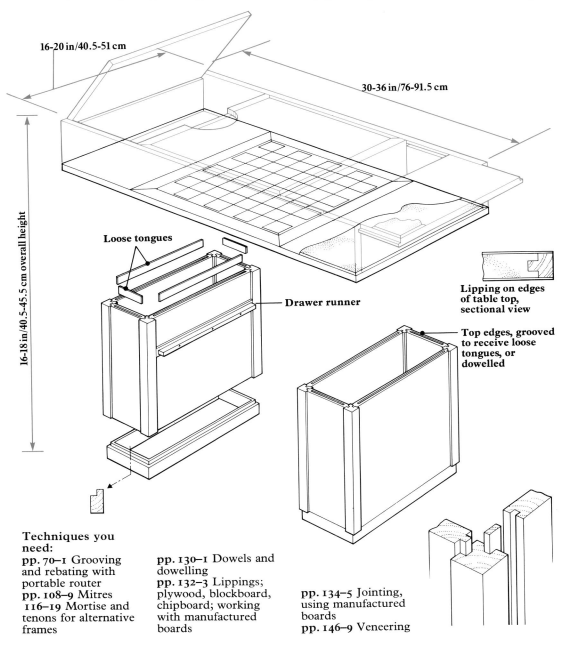

16-20 in/40.5-51 cm

30-36 in/76-91.5 cm

16-18 in/40.5-45.5 cm overall height

Loose tongues

Drawer runner

Lipping on edges of table top, sectional view

Top edges, grooved to receive loose tongues, or dowelled

Techniques you need:
pp. 70–1 Grooving and rebating with portable router
pp. 108–9 Mitres
116–19 Mortise and tenons for alternative frames

pp. 130–1 Dowels and dowelling
pp. 132–3 Lippings; plywood, blockboard, chipboard; working with manufactured boards

pp. 134–5 Jointing, using manufactured boards
pp. 146–9 Veneering

Drop-leaf dining table

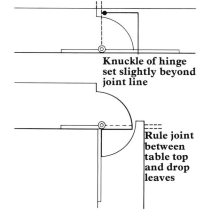

Knuckle of hinge set slightly beyond joint line

Rule joint between table top and drop leaves

Here the basic carcase construction is that used for a Pembroke table, with the brackets knuckle-jointed to separate pieces, which are glued and screwed to the main rails.

Two cross-rails are slot-dovetailed from below into the side rails and are reinforced with glue blocks. Between these, blocks are glued and screwed to secure the top to the tenoned wedged pedestal.

The feet of the pedestal support are taper slot-dovetailed into the column and may be reinforced with a shaped metal plate.

A rule-joint is used along the hinged edges of the drop leaves—this gives support along the entire length of the leaf when it is open.

A rule-joint hinge is let into the underside of the top as shown. The entire knuckle and the leaves must be cut in, and the pin of the knuckle set slightly forward of the joint line to allow clearance when the leaf is dropped.

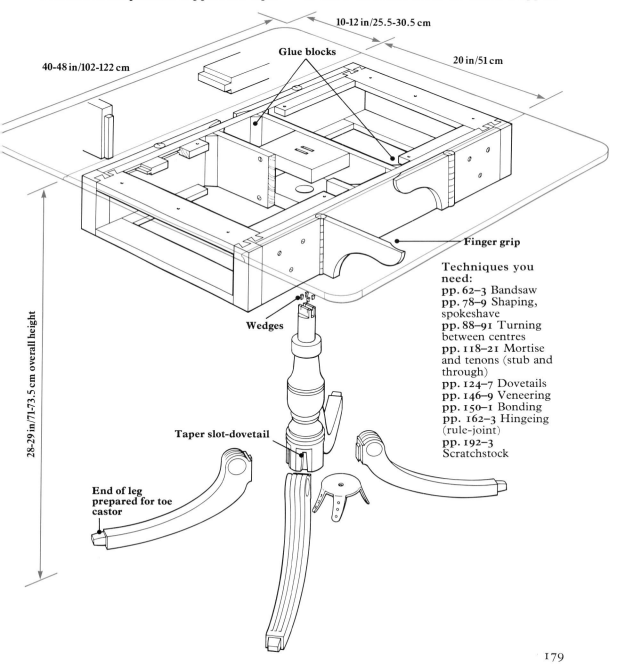

10-12 in/25.5-30.5 cm

Glue blocks

40-48 in/102-122 cm

20 in/51 cm

Finger grip

28-29 in/71-73.5 cm overall height

Wedges

Techniques you need:
pp. 62–3 Bandsaw
pp. 78–9 Shaping, spokeshave
pp. 88–91 Turning between centres
pp. 118–21 Mortise and tenons (stub and through)
pp. 124–7 Dovetails
pp. 146–9 Veneering
pp. 150–1 Bonding
pp. 162–3 Hingeing (rule-joint)
pp. 192–3 Scratchstock

Taper slot-dovetail

End of leg prepared for toe castor

Dining table and chairs

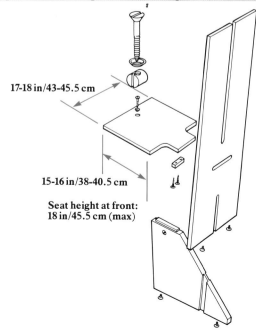

17-18 in/43-45.5 cm

15-16 in/38-40.5 cm

Seat height at front:
18 in/45.5 cm (max)

This dining table and chair set has been made in KD, or knock-down, form. The components are slotted together and, where necessary, are bolted or screwed for additional strength. For speed and accuracy, it is recommended that the slots are cut with a portable electric router.

Plywood or MDF (medium density fibreboard) may be used. The latter, which was the chosen material for the furniture illustrated, machines well, is stable, has equal strength in all directions, does not require its edges lipped and accepts most surface fin-

ishes without elaborate surface preparation.

When sheet and board materials are used in furniture, different construction techniques (see pages 134–5) to the traditional ones are required because of the difficulty of cutting dovetails and mortises. If traditional joints are used on man-made materials, there is usually a significant loss of strength.

Before applying a finish, especially to the table surface, ensure that all blemishes and irregularities are removed, otherwise they will be highlighted and spoil the overall effect. A spray finish is ideal.

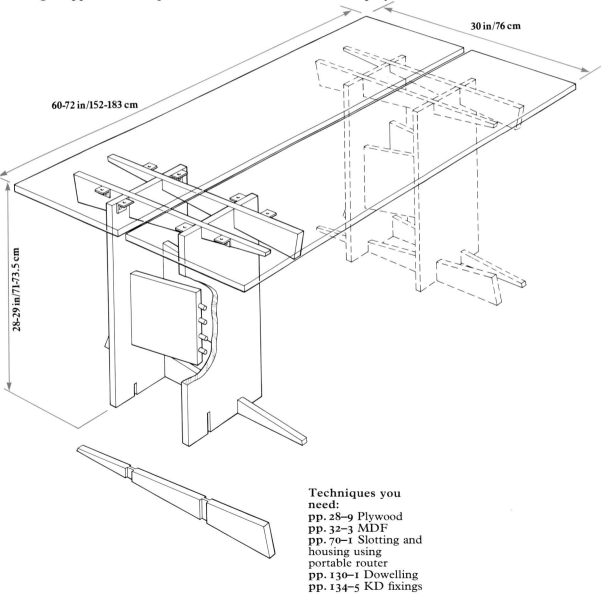

30 in/76 cm

60-72 in/152-183 cm

28-29 in/71-73.5 cm

Techniques you need:
pp. 28–9 Plywood
pp. 32–3 MDF
pp. 70–1 Slotting and housing using portable router
pp. 130–1 Dowelling
pp. 134–5 KD fixings

Butler's table

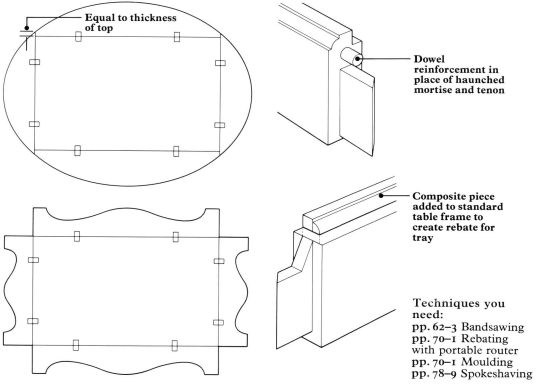

Equal to thickness of top

Dowel reinforcement in place of haunched mortise and tenon

Composite piece added to standard table frame to create rebate for tray

Techniques you need:
pp. 62–3 Bandsawing
pp. 70–1 Rebating with portable router
pp. 70–1 Moulding
pp. 78–9 Spokeshaving

There are numerous variations on the theme of the butler's table, including folding frames gateleg tables and an assortment of tray shapes. The essential feature of the design is that the area of the top can be increased by dropping the hinged sides and ends. Two of the more popular tray types have been illustrated here.

Construction of the tray is fairly straight-forward. Its base may be well seasoned, stable hardwood or lipped and veneered plywood or chipboard (flakeboard). Ensure that lippings are wide enough to accept the screws of the hinges, which must be special limited-movement hinges in order to hold the dropped sides level with the tray base.

The table frame is rebated (rabbeted) to receive the tray base, which should fit the frame closely. The tray sides rest on the top edges of the rails.

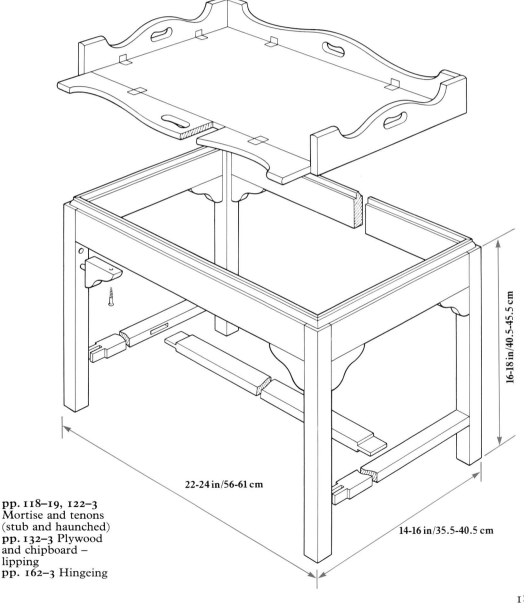

16-18 in/40.5-45.5 cm

22-24 in/56-61 cm

14-16 in/35.5-40.5 cm

pp. 118–19, 122–3
Mortise and tenons (stub and haunched)
pp. 132–3 Plywood and chipboard – lipping
pp. 162–3 Hingeing

Desk

'Larnello' tongue

Plywood loose tongue

Insert dowel close to inner edge of mitre—this permits the dowel to be longer

The main frame of this desk is rebated (rabbeted) on both faces to receive thin plywood or chipboard (flakeboard) panels. It is also mitred at the corners. Intermediate rails give additional stiffness and act as spacers for the front and back rails as well as tracking rails for the honeycomb core, which is stapled in place. Where joints are to be cut or items screwed on, blocks of wood are

incorporated. Adhesive is applied to one surface of each of the panels and the composite assembly is pressed or weighted.

Circular recesses for the translucent acrylic tubing are cut in the shelves. The lower end of the acrylic tube passes through the desk top and is held in position by a plastic end plate screwed to the top's underside after the light tube has been introduced.

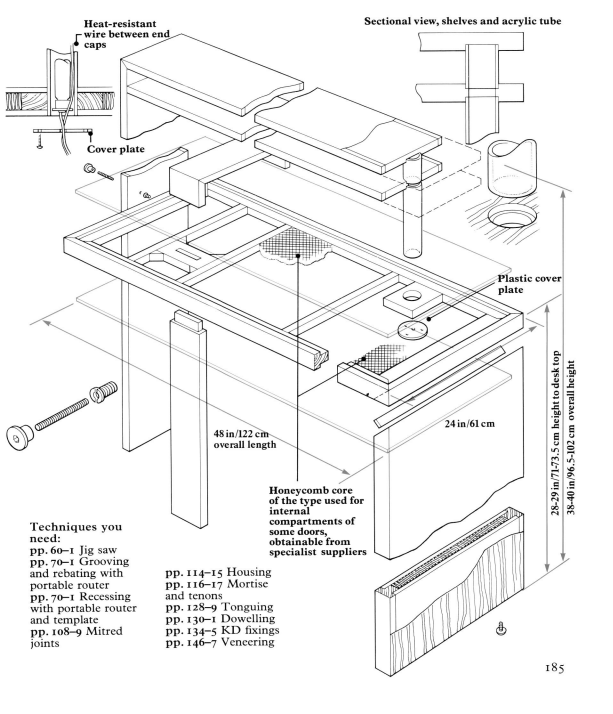

Heat-resistant wire between end caps

Cover plate

Sectional view, shelves and acrylic tube

Plastic cover plate

48 in/122 cm overall length

24 in/61 cm

Honeycomb core of the type used for internal compartments of some doors, obtainable from specialist suppliers

28–29 in/71–73.5 cm height to desk top

38–40 in/96.5–102 cm overall height

Techniques you need:
pp. 60–1 Jig saw
pp. 70–1 Grooving and rebating with portable router
pp. 70–1 Recessing with portable router and template
pp. 108–9 Mitred joints

pp. 114–15 Housing
pp. 116–17 Mortise and tenons
pp. 128–9 Tonguing
pp. 130–1 Dowelling
pp. 134–5 KD fixings
pp. 146–7 Veneering

Serpentine chest

This type of chest of drawers, with its elegantly curved front, is relatively commonplace in the Old World; in North America, its less complex cousin, the bow-fronted chest, is much more familiar.

Traditional constructions are used throughout—lap dovetail joints for the top rails and base, stub mortise and tenon joints for the drawer rails, and drawer runners housed into the carcase sides and tongued into the drawer rails.

The chest may be made as shown in the photograph, with legs glued, screwed and glue-blocked, or it may have bracket feet.

The drawer fronts can be cut from solid wood, but this is wasteful. It is better to make laminated drawer fronts or to use 'brick' construction, achieving the final stage with a compass plane before applying the veneer.

The drawer stops may be pieces of ply-wood pinned to the drawer rails, or short-grained solid wood stub-tenoned into the rails. The front edge of each stop is pared away until the drawer closes satisfactorily.

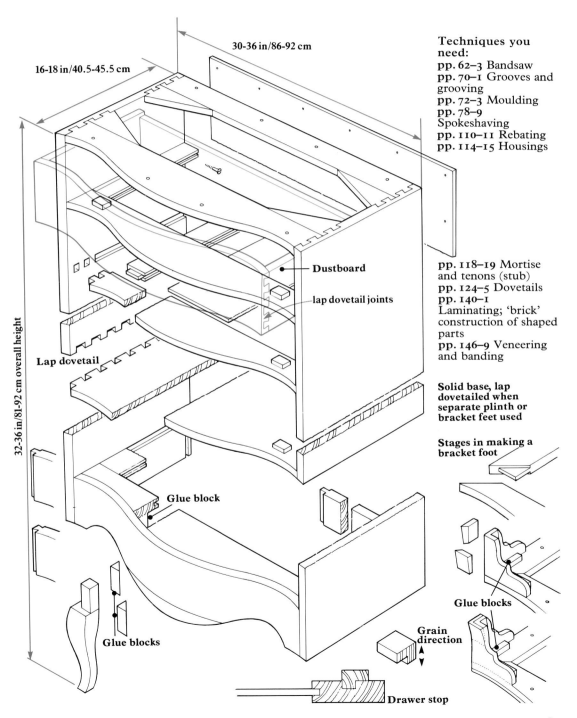

30-36 in/86-92 cm

16-18 in/40.5-45.5 cm

32-36 in/81-92 cm overall height

Techniques you need:
pp. 62–3 Bandsaw
pp. 70–1 Grooves and grooving
pp. 72–3 Moulding
pp. 78–9 Spokeshaving
pp. 110–11 Rebating
pp. 114–15 Housings

pp. 118–19 Mortise and tenons (stub)
pp. 124–5 Dovetails
pp. 140–1 Laminating; 'brick' construction of shaped parts
pp. 146–9 Veneering and banding

Solid base, lap dovetailed when separate plinth or bracket feet used

Stages in making a bracket foot

Dustboard

lap dovetail joints

Lap dovetail

Glue block

Glue blocks

Glue blocks

Grain direction

Drawer stop

Bed

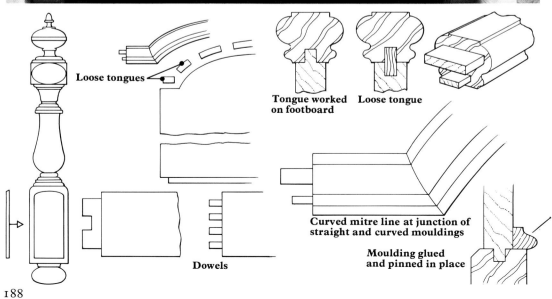

Loose tongues

Tongue worked on footboard

Loose tongue

Curved mitre line at junction of straight and curved mouldings

Dowels

Moulding glued and pinned in place

Before embarking on this project, it is advisable to make a full-size drawing of the turned corner posts to ensure correct proportions. The drawing will also be invaluable for checking progress during turning.

Mortise and tenon or dowel joints are used for the main components, and the panels are secured with tongues worked along their edges or with loose tongues.

The mitre line at the junction of the straight and curved sections of the moulding on the footboard must be drawn full-size to establish the curvature, and a template made to check the accuracy as work progresses. This mitre should be reinforced with dowels.

The padded headboard should be put together as a separate component. Plastic flexible foam glued to plywood, covered in the chosen fabric and buttoned, can be applied to the headboard panel.

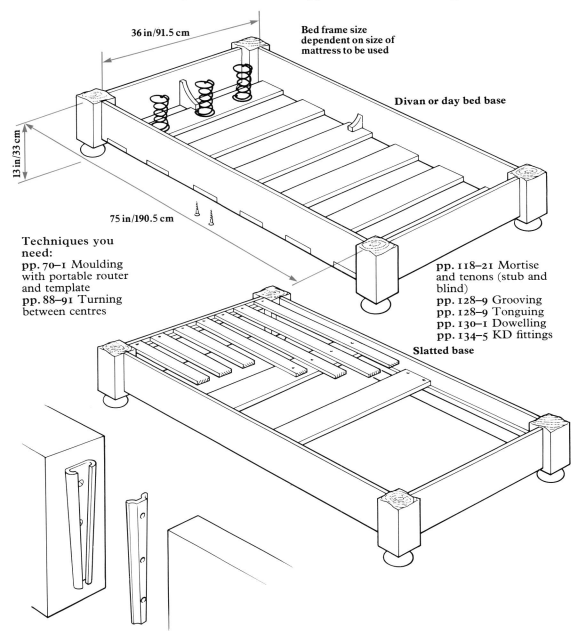

36 in/91.5 cm

Bed frame size
dependent on size of
mattress to be used

Divan or day bed base

13 in/33 cm

75 in/190.5 cm

Techniques you
need:
pp. 70–1 Moulding
with portable router
and template
pp. 88–91 Turning
between centres

pp. 118–21 Mortise
and tenons (stub and
blind)
pp. 128–9 Grooving
pp. 128–9 Tonguing
pp. 130–1 Dowelling
pp. 134–5 KD fittings

Slatted base

Writing table

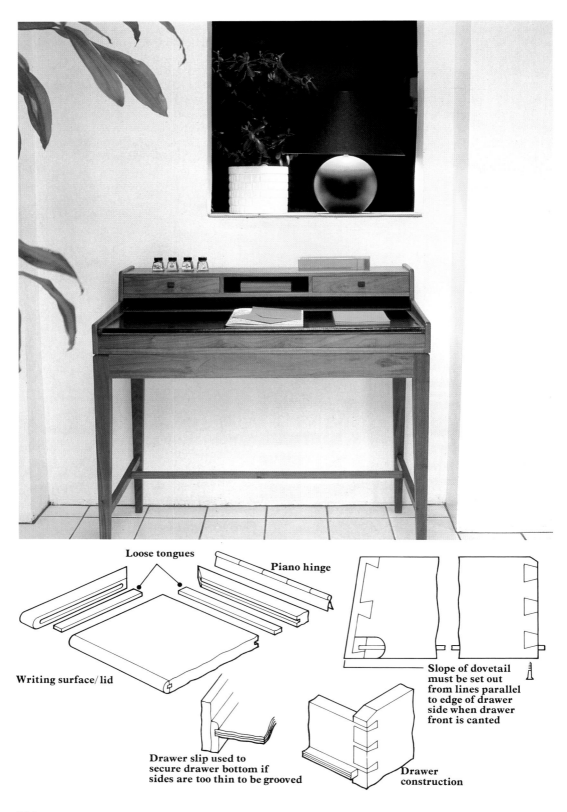

Loose tongues

Piano hinge

Writing surface/lid

Slope of dovetail must be set out from lines parallel to edge of drawer side when drawer front is canted

Drawer slip used to secure drawer bottom if sides are too thin to be grooved

Drawer construction

This useful piece of furniture consists simply of a shallow carcase attached by means of wooden buttons to a table frame.

The shaped end of the carcase should be made from carefully selected, dry material so that it remains flat. Note the grain direction for the end, which allows lap dovetails to be used. Shelves may be housed into the ends, dowelled or loose-tongued; or use stub mortise and tenons. The writing surface/lid is a composite assembly, consisting of lipped chipboard covered with a suitable material (leather is ideal) and hinged along the back edge to the bottom shelf of the carcase.

The table frame is mortised and tenoned throughout. Ensure that the long stretcher rail is set sufficiently far back to allow clearance for shins and feet. The carcase could be partitioned or trays fitted for desktop paraphernalia.

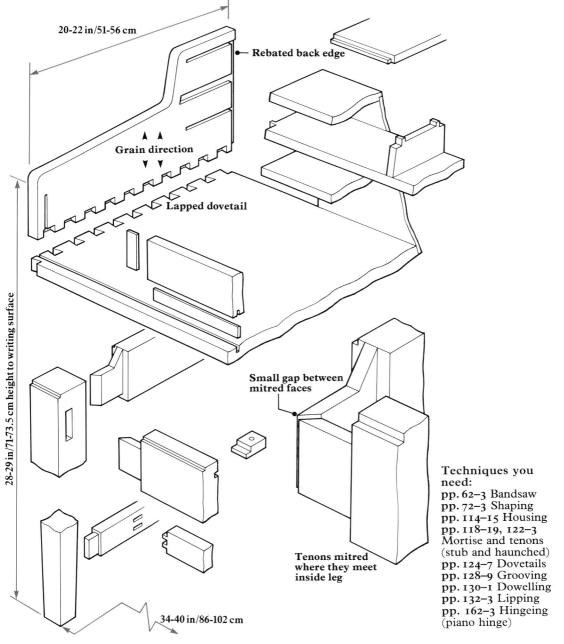

20-22 in/51-56 cm

● Rebated back edge

Grain direction

Lapped dovetail

28-29 in/71-73.5 cm height to writing surface

Small gap between mitred faces

Tenons mitred where they meet inside leg

34-40 in/86-102 cm

Techniques you need:
pp. 62–3 Bandsaw
pp. 72–3 Shaping
pp. 114–15 Housing
pp. 118–19, 122–3 Mortise and tenons (stub and haunched)
pp. 124–7 Dovetails
pp. 128–9 Grooving
pp. 130–1 Dowelling
pp. 132–3 Lipping
pp. 162–3 Hingeing (piano hinge)

Side table

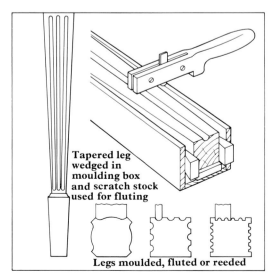

Tapered leg wedged in moulding box and scratch stock used for fluting

Legs moulded, fluted or reeded

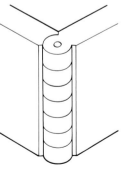
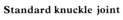

Standard knuckle joint

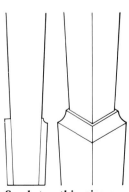

Spade toe: thin pieces of timber glued in place, then shaped

The table top is hinged in two halves, so a table with a circular top is available when required. Card-table hinges should be used to hinge the two sections together. The back rail of the main frame is lap-dovetailed into the D-shaped rail, which may be laminated or of brick construction.

A central rail provides additional rigidity and is slot-dovetailed and glue-blocked in place. Front legs are bridle-jointed to the D rail as shown. Knuckle joints allow the rear leg frames to be hinged and should be cut to allow limited movement of the rail so the legs are equally spaced when the frames are open.

The rear legs also need to be cut to fit

snugly around the back edge of the main frame, as illustrated.

The legs may be moulded by using power tools, but the traditional method gives good results, although it is slower. This requires a purpose-made moulding box and a scratch stock. The leg is wedged in position in the box; this then acts as a fence for the stock, which is fitted with a suitably shaped blade to produce the scratch moulding.

The spade toe is stronger if it forms part of, and is shaped from the original leg material; an easier method is to taper the leg and add pieces of the same wood with similar colour and grain features shaped as required.

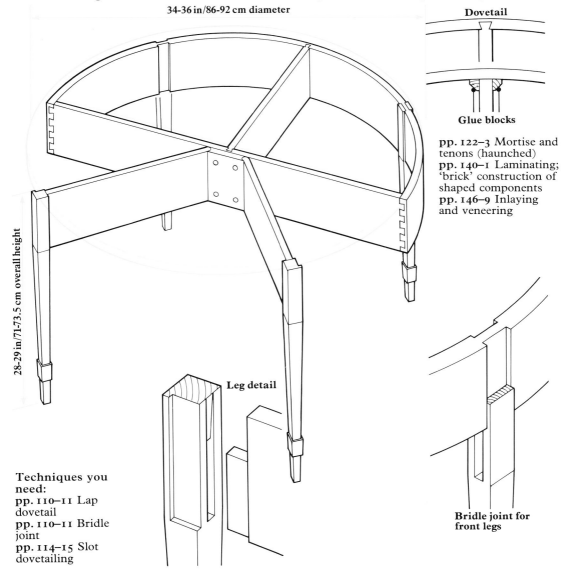

34-36 in/86-92 cm diameter

28-29 in/71-73.5 cm overall height

Dovetail

Glue blocks

pp. 122–3 Mortise and tenons (haunched)
pp. 140–1 Laminating; 'brick' construction of shaped components
pp. 146–9 Inlaying and veneering

Leg detail

Bridle joint for front legs

Techniques you need:
pp. 110–11 Lap dovetail
pp. 110–11 Bridle joint
pp. 114–15 Slot dovetailing

193

Softwoods

The tree	Wood colour and quality	Technical profile	Applications
Cedar *Cedrus* **spp.** The true cedars are the Atlantic or Atlas cedar from Morocco, the Cedar of Lebanon and the deodar of northern India; not to be confused with 'commercial' cedars grown elsewhere. True cedars grow large: to 200 ft/60 m.	All three species have similar wood. The strongly scented heartwood is light brown, generally distinct from the paler sapwood. The growth rings are usually well defined.	The main qualities of cedar are durability, sometimes measured in centuries, and resistance to fungi and termites. The wood works easily, with little dulling of cutting edges, takes nails well and gives a fine finish with paint or lacquer.	In Britain, park-grown cedar is used for garden furniture, fencing and trellis because of its durability. Cedar of Lebanon is a superb decorative timber, typically used for interior panelling. The other two species are used commercially.
Cypress *Cupressus* **spp.** The true cypress belongs to the warm temperate parts of the globe, typically the Mediterranean. Naturally grown, its commercial significance is slight, but as a plantation tree it is widespread in East Africa, South Africa and Australia.	Grain tends to be straight, texture fine and even. The yellowish to pinkish-brown heartwood is usually easy to tell from the paler sapwood. Newly seasoned cypress smells like cedar.	The wood works readily with little dulling of cutting edges. The knots can, however, be troublesome, and though straight-grained timber finishes cleanly, tearing is common with disturbed grain. Durable and moderately strong, it takes nails well, as also paint and lacquer.	Outside construction work is the principal fate of cypress—a reflection of the wood's strength and durability even if it is in contact with the ground. Significant quantities end up as boxes and crates. Selected timber is suitable for joinery.
Douglas Fir *Pseudotsuga menziesii* Known by several names, including Colombian or Oregon pine, this is one of the great trees of western North America. It commonly reaches 200 ft/90 m and the bole, or trunk, is exceptionally straight, often free of branches up to 70 ft/21 m.	Typically the heartwood is light reddish-brown, with paler sapwood, but there are regional variations. The growth-ring pattern is marked, the grain usually straight. For a softwood, it is medium-weight, slightly heavier than European redwood. American timber can be resinous.	Douglas fir combines strength with ease of working. It takes nails and screws well and is moderately durable. Resistance to decay is average.	This is one of the few conifers that yields considerable lengths of clear timber with generous width. Thus it is North America's most important construction wood, used typically for roof beams, poles, piles and the framework of bridges. It also gives pulp for paper.
Fir *Abies* **spp.** Only the *Abies* species are true firs; confusingly, the word occurs in the names of other trees such as Douglas fir. True firs grow to about 130 ft/40 m, occurring widely in North America, central and eastern Asia and central and southern Europe.	The many fir species have generally similar wood, pale creamy-white to pale brown in colour. They are generally lightweight, sraight grained, odourless and non-resinous.	In the case of fir, lightness goes with brittleness. The wood is easy to work, but its softness means tools need to be kept sharp to ensure a smooth finish. Fir is prone to attack by fungi and is not easy to preserve.	Though plentiful, fir is not nearly as important in the world timber trade as, for example, spruce. However, it features in construction work, joinery and packaging, and fuels much of eastern Canada's vast paper-pulp output.

The tree	Wood colour and quality	Technical profile	Applications
Hemlock *Tsuga* spp. There are two hemlocks, the eastern and the western, both trees of North America. The first is widespread in the east and reaches 75 ft/23 m. Equally widespread, the western hemlock reaches 200 ft/60 m.	Western hemlock gives the superior timber: pale brown in colour, straight-grained and with an even texture. The growth rings are well marked, but not so much as those of eastern hemlock, which resemble the rings of Douglas fir.	Both types dry rather slowly but are then moderately stable. Hemlock is the lightest softwood in common commercial use, but it is stronger than spruce. Both hemlock species work readily; but beware of chipping out at the tool exit and splitting.	Western hemlock is a major commercial timber, exported worldwide from North America. It serves for structural work in houses, for boxes, crates, plywood and pulp. Eastern hemlock is used for inferior work such as fencing.
Larch or Tamarack *Larix* spp. Larch is widespread over northern Asia and North America, where is is known as eastern larch or tamarack. It also occurs patchily in Europe. Unlike most softwoods, it is deciduous.	This may seem rather coarse because there is such a contrast between the alternate bands of hard summerwood and soft springwood. The heartwood is yellowish-brown. Larch can be exceptionally knotty.	Larch is one of the toughest, densest commercial softwoods; it is challenged in this respect only by pitch pine. Most larch species work readily, though with some tendency to split when nailed.	Mine shaft props, stakes, poles and piles are the traditional uses for this strong material. The heartwood is used when durability is especially important, for example in boat planking and exterior work which will come in contact with the ground.
Parana Pine *Araucaria angustifolia* This tree grows mainly in the Brazilian state of Parana, but also in Paraguay and northern Argentina. It is medium to large in size, reaching about 130 ft/40 m. The trunk is straight and branchless for almost its whole length.	Brown at the heart, sometimes with bright red streaks, it is otherwise pale. It is mostly straight grained and the texture is unusually even, with no growth rings at all.	To prevent distortion, drying has to be carried out with care. Ease of working is parana pine's great virtue, giving a clean finish with most operations. It stains, polishes and takes paint well.	Because it is almost knot-free and because of the fine, even texture, parana pine is highly popular with the home woodworker. Exported worldwide from Brazil, it is also used for staircases, cabinet framing, drawer sides, mouldings, shop fittings and vehicles.
Pitch Pine *Pinus* spp. There are numerous pitch pines, and they go by a multitude of names, but two are of outstanding importance: the American pitch pine and the Caribbean. Most of the pitch pines grow to about 130 ft/40 m.	This is the heaviest of the commercial softwoods, some 40 per cent heavier than European redwood. The timber is yellow- to red-brown with marked growth rings and is often very resinous.	It is heavy, hard, stiff, resistant to shock and, consequently, quite hard to work. The resin can foul blades and saw teeth. Nails and screws are held securely. Paints and other finishes apply moderately well.	Best-quality pitch pine is used the world over for heavy building work—piles, spars, railway wagons, masts. (In the 19th century this was the wood for church pews and school desks.) Much of the world's rosin and turpentine comes from pitch pine's highly resinous timber.

Softwoods

The tree	Wood colour and quality	Technical profile	Applications
Radiata Pine *Pinus radiata* A native of California, also known as Monterey pine. It grows very fast in warm temperate regions: up to 200 ft/ 60 m in 40 years. As a result, it is the world's most commonly planted softwood.	Lack of contrast between the spring- and summer-wood gives a very even texture with indistinct growth rings. The heartwood is pinkish-brown, the 3–6-in/7–15-cm band of sapwood is creamy-yellow with fine brown lines.	Timber from young, fast-growing trees is mainly sapwood, which is not durable but absorbs preservative well. Immature trees also show spiral grain, which can cause warping. This wood works easily but tends to tear around knots.	As the large plantations of radiata pine in Australasia and South America reach maturity, this timber is replacing all other softwoods there, being used for building, crates, plywood, chipboard and pulp. The best is used in joinery.
Redwood *Sequoia sempervirens* (USA) This is the tallest living tree, growing up to 370 ft/112 m with a very straight trunk. The largest trees have a diameter of 28 ft/8.5 m at the base. Redwood is a native of California's coastal zone, which has a warm, foggy climate, but it grows well in other climates.	A narrow band of white sapwood surrounds the dark red-brown heartwood, which is straight grained with a fine, even texture and few knots. The timber resembles western red cedar, but lacks resin and has no smell. Timber grown outside America is lighter and coarser.	Lightness and durability are two important features of redwood. It also works easily and gives a good finish, but it tends to splinter and is susceptible to chip-bruising. Both nailing and gluing give good results, though alkaline glues stain the wood.	Because of its durability and lack of resin, redwood is used for vats and tanks. Resistance to fungal attack also makes it valuable for door and window frames, glasshouses, barns and garden benches. Some goes for plywood, and the fibrous bark is made into filters.
Scots Pine (European redwood) *Pinus sylvestris* Scots pine has a wide natural distribution from southern Spain to the Arctic Circle, and Siberia. It is recognized by the reddish bark on its upper trunk. The heartwood shares this colour, hence the names European redwood or red deal.	The great geographical range is reflected in the variable wood. Slow-growing trees from the cold forests of Russia have closely spaced growth rings, giving a fine texture. The warmer conditions of Europe give wider spaced rings and a larger area of pale sapwood around the red heart.	Scots pine finds a role in almost every timber-using industry. The best wood—slow-grown timber, or timber from mature trees—goes for furniture. The average grades are used for building, mine shaft supports and telephone poles. Pulp, boxes and plywood account for the rest.	Timber from fast-growing trees has broad bands of soft spring-wood, which tend to tear if the saw is at all blunt. Knots can be a problem—they may fall out. This wood takes nails well and can be glued unless very resinous. It is not durable, but absorbs preservative.
Spruce *Picea* spp. There are 50 species of spruce, some growing to 200 ft/ 60 m, though most are smaller. The European spruce, or whitewood, is well known as the Christmas tree. Of the six North American species grown commercially, Sitka spruce produces the best-quality timber.	Spruce is noted for its white, often lustrous colour; growth rings are faintly marked. It is light, and very strong for its weight. The heartwood is just like the sapwood in most species, but Sitka spruce has an ill-defined area of pinkish heartwood.	Spruce is non-durable and resists the application of preservative. It tends to tear unless cutting edges are sharp, and the knots may give trouble when sawing. It takes nails and glue well and contains little resin. Sitka spruce, grown in Britain, is of poor quality.	Quenching the world's thirst for news is spruce's main task: the whiteness of the wood makes it ideal for newsprint. Other uses include building, flooring, sheds, crates, violins, pianos and plywood. Sitka spruce, which is strong and lightweight, is used for boats and gliders.

The tree	Wood colour and quality	Technical profile	Applications
Western Red Cedar *Thuja plicata* This is not, in fact, a cedar, but a relative of the cypresses and junipers, whose leaves have a strong fruity smell. It grows from Alaska to California and east to Idaho, attaining heights of 150–250 ft/45–75 m.	A narrow band of white sapwood surrounds the heartwood, which varies from pink or red to dark brown. The wood is straight-grained, with marked, closely spaced growth rings. In fresh timber there may be bands of different colour.	This is the lightest softwood and, though lacking strength, it is durable. Sharp tools must be used to avoid compressing the soft springwood. Acidity in the wood will corrode iron nails and cause black stains; copper or galvanized nails should be used.	Durability and lightness make this wood ideal for glasshouses, sheds and finishing work, either external or internal. When used for cladding, weather-boarding or roof shingles, exposure changes the colour to silver-grey.
Western white pine *Pinus monticola* This tree is found in the upland forests of western North America, from British Columbia to California. It can grow up to 170 ft/50 m tall. Like yellow pine, it is attacked by the disease white pine blister rust, which limits planting.	White sapwood, only 1–3 in/2.5–7.5 cm wide, surrounds a straw-yellow or pale red-brown heartwood. Resin ducts are visible as fine brown lines, though the wood is not rich in resin. The grain is straight, and the growth rings indistinct, giving the wood an even texture.	Western white pine is very much like yellow pine but slightly more difficult to cut. It finishes well and takes nails, screws, paint, varnish and stain with ease. It also gives good results if glued. This is a slightly heavier and stronger wood than yellow pine.	Non-durable and fairly resistant to preservative, this wood is confined to interior uses such as joinery and panelling. It is used for engineering patterns but is not quite as useful as yellow pine, being more difficult to work. Some is made into plywood.
Yellow pine *Pinus strobus* Also called eastern white pine, since it is native to the eastern regions of North America, this tree produces one of the most valuable softwoods. It grows up to 150 ft/45 m tall; in pre-colonial times, trees 260 ft/80 m were known.	Varying from straw-yellow to pale pinkish-brown, the heartwood is barely distinguishable from the sapwood. Straight grain and faint growth rings combine to give a fine, regular texture. The wood is light, soft and only slightly resinous.	Provided sharp cutting-edges are used, this wood gives a superb finish. It takes nails, paint and stain well. But being weak and soft, it must not be used for structural purposes. Non-durable and fairly resistant to preservative, it is unsuitable for use outdoors.	The most important commercial use is in making patterns for engineering work, where a soft, even-textured and very stable wood is needed. Panelling and joinery account for the rest of the quality timber, while inferior grades are used for crates and boxes.
Yew *Taxus baccata* This small bush or tree can live to be a thousand years old. It may grow to 80 ft/25 m but is usually 35 ft/10 m or less. The fluted trunk is formed by the fusion of several shoots. Yew is found on dry soils in Europe, Western Asia, North Africa, and east to the Himalayas.	One of the heaviest softwoods, yew weighs about as much as pitch pine, and for strength and resilience it compares well with oak. The narrow white sapwood surrounds a reddish- or purple-brown heartwood, which has irregular growth rings but a dense, even texture.	The wood cuts quite easily, and straight-grained yew works well; planing, however, should be done with care if the wood has irregular grain. Yew is suitable for turning and steam-bending and polishes beautifully.	The main use for yew today is in decorative inlays and veneers, although some is employed for gate and fence posts, where durability is valued. In general, availability limits its use, especially since few trees produce long, clear planks.

Hardwoods

The tree	Wood colour and quality	Technical profile	Applications
Abura *Mitragyna ciliata* A tall, straight-trunked tree from the tropical swamp-forests of the West African coast. It grows to 100 ft/30 m or more, with an unbranched trunk up to 60 ft/18 m long and 3–5 ft/1–1.5 m in diameter.	Lack of seasonal variation in the tropics results in timber with no growth rings. Abura is a typical example of this phenomenon. A bland, yellow-brown or pinkish-beige wood, it is usually straight-grained and completely plain.	The wood works well but sometimes contains minute grains of silica, which can damage saws. Abura's main virtues are great stability when dry and uniformity. It can be glued and takes stain and polish well. Only thin nails should be used.	Abura is much used for the sides of drawers, furniture legs, and in other situations where a stable wood is essential. Its uniformity and fine, even texture also make it useful indoors for lipping and mouldings.
Afara (or Limba) *Terminalia superba* One of the most abundant trees of the West African and Congo basin rain forests. Several other closely related timber trees are found in the same region, for example idigbo. Afara grows to 150 ft/45 m, with an unbranched trunk up to 90 ft/27 m.	A variable wood, generally yellowish, rather like light oak (light afara), but occasionally having a dark heartwood with irregular grey or black figuring (dark afara). Dark afara sometimes resembles walnut. The texture is regular but fairly coarse.	Straight-grained wood works easily, but irregular grain may present problems. Afara can be nailed and glued, and it takes stain well, though the coarse grain needs to be filled. A strong wood, unless brittleheart (detected by the wood's light weight) is present.	Lack of durability confines this wood to internal use. Veneer and plywood are major applications, and the best samples of dark afara make excellent decorative veneers. Other uses include joinery, furniture production and coffins.
Afrormosia *Pericopsis elata* A West African forest tree, growing to heights of 149 ft/45 m, with a long, irregular, unbranched trunk, 3 ft/1 m in diameter. Tall forest trees often have buttress roots to give them extra stability; those of afrormosia stand 3–8 ft/1–2.5 m high.	A rich, yellow-brown when fresh, the heartwood turns dark brown with age. The thin band of sapwood is much lighter in colour. This wood has a fine texture with straight or interlocked grain, the latter sometimes giving a stripy appearance.	Wood with interlocked grain may tear unless carefully worked. The wood glues well but cannot be nailed without pre-boring. Iron nails cause black stains. A fairly strong, extremely durable and stable wood, it takes stain and polish reasonably well.	Afrormosia resembles teak (though lacking its oiliness and strong smell) and is put to the same uses: boat-building, joinery, furniture and flooring. Once used only for structuring teak furniture, it is now regarded as a useful substitute for teak throughout.
Agba *Gosswelerodendron balsamiferum* A tree of the African tropical forests, most exports coming from Nigeria, Angola and Cabinda. It grows to a height of 200 ft/60 m, with an unbranched trunk up to 100 ft/30 m long and 6½ ft/2 m across. The timber is also known as tola.	Pale yellowish- or pinkish-brown, with a heartwood generally a little darker than the sapwood, agba has a fine texture, and the grain is either straight or slightly interlocked. Wood with interlocked grain exhibits a banded pattern on quarter-sawn surfaces.	A fairly strong timber unless brittleheart is present (usually in large logs). Nailing should be done with care, as should sawing and planing on wood with interlocked grain. Though often extremely resinous, agba glues well. Only the heartwood is durable.	Lightness and strength recommend this timber to a variety of uses: joinery, flooring, planking for trucks, boat frames and robust furniture, especially school desks. It is often made into plywood. The resinous smell prevents its use in areas near food.

The tree	Wood colour and quality	Technical profile	Applications
Alder *Alnus* spp. These common trees of stream-banks and other damp places are found widely in the Americas and Eurasia. There are 30 species, all fairly small and slender, up to 80 ft/ 25 m tall. *A. incana*, grows well on dry soil.	The pale colour of freshly cut alder changes to reddish-brown with exposure to light. The red alder of America, *A. rubra*, has a rich colour, rather like mahogany. European alders (*A. glutinosa* and *A. incana*) have duller wood.	European alders give light, soft wood with straight grain and fine texture, easily worked with sharp cutting-edges. It has no natural durability but takes preservative well. The American red alder produces a more robust timber, which polishes well.	Red alder is the most widely planted hardwood on the west coast of North America, where it is used in furniture as a substitute for mahogany, and in paper-making. European alder is mostly made into plywood.
Apple *Malus sylvestris* The familiar fruit-bearing apple comes from Old World stock, but other species of *Malus* are found throughout the temperate northern hemisphere. All are small trees, up to 35 or 50 ft/10 or 15 m tall, often with a short trunk less than 1 ft/ 30 cm in diameter.	The fine, even texture and delicate, pinkish tinge make apple a particularly attractive wood. A subtle distinction of colour between the growth rings gives it a pleasing figure. However, trees with sinuous trunks may show highly irregular, spiralled grain.	Apple is one of the heavier hardwoods, comparable with European beech. It tends to distort in drying and soon blunts a saw. Where the grain is irregular, care must be taken in planing. The wood stains and polishes well but has no natural durability.	The fine texture of apple wood allows precise and delicate carving. Today, this quality is mainly put to decorative use, but in the past the cogs of small wooden clocks and other fine machine parts were often made of apple. The wood is also used for inlay work.
American Ash *Fraxinus* spp. Three different species supply this timber: white ash, green ash and black ash. All are native to the eastern states, but are planted elsewhere; green ash is grown for timber in southern Europe. The tallest of these trees is white ash at 120 ft/35 m.	The heartwood of white and green ash is grey-brown, often with a red tint; the sapwood is very pale. Black ash is darker in colour and has lower weight and strength. Both have a rough texture and, in general, straight grain.	White ash is of two types: 'tough' and 'soft'. The former resembles European ash in its toughness; it blunts tools and needs pre-boring for nails. Soft white ash, green and black ash are easier to work. Ash can be bent and glued.	Furniture and joinery are the main outlets for soft ash. Tough ash is sometimes used for these purposes, but its major use is in heavy-duty tool handles, spades, sports equipment and in other roles where outstanding toughness is required.
European Ash *Fraxinus excelsior* This is a common tree of Europe and western Asia, favouring damp soil but flourishing in almost any situation. It grows to 115 ft/ 35 m or more, and, if conditions are favourable, a long unbranched trunk is produced, 2–5 ft/0.6– 1.5 m in diameter.	A pale but attractive wood, lustrous grey-brown in colour, it may look slightly pink when newly cut. The summer-wood is darker and denser, producing a decorative figure, especially on flat-sawn timber and rotary-cut veneer. Some logs contain an irregular black heart.	Ash, especially timber with wide growth rings, has a great reputation for toughness. It can be worked fairly easily but should be pre-bored for nailing. Ash can be glued, gives a good finish and takes stain and polish well but is not durable and resists preservative treatment.	The best ash is used for hockey sticks, tennis racquets and handles for tools, especially picks, axes and hammers, which must withstand great stress. The bending properties of ash are useful in making boat and canoe frames, umbrella handles and bentwood furniture.

Hardwoods

The tree	Wood colour and quality	Technical profile	Applications
European Beech *Fagus sylvatica* Found throughout Europe, beech is easily recognized by its silver-grey bark and glossy, oval leaves. It is a tall, majestic tree, sometimes reaching 132 ft/40 m with a very straight trunk.	Beechwood varies from off-white to light brown, darkening in time and acquiring a reddish tinge. In southeast Europe, the wood is often steamed, which turns it pink or red. Flat-sawn surfaces show an attractive growth-ring figure.	A strong, heavy hardwood, usually with straight grain and a fine, even texture. It tends to burn during sawing and drilling and must be pre-bored for nailing. Beech is non-durable but takes up preservative well.	The furniture industry takes most of the available beech, which is valued for its turning and bending qualities. Use is also made of its strength in classroom furniture, sports equipment, tool handles and plywood. The timber also makes fair-quality flooring.
European Birch *Betula* spp. Silver birch, with its distinctive white trunk, and the greyish-barked downy birch, are found widely in Europe and Scandinavia. Both tend to be small, graceful trees though they can grow to 80 ft/25 m, with a trunk 3 ft/1 m across.	Birch is a pale brown or whitish timber, with a fine, even texture. The grain is usually straight and knots are commonplace, but there is little figure to the wood. The sapwood and heartwood are indistinguishable. The American paper birch produces similar timber.	The wood rivals ash for strength and toughness but is often flawed by knots. It usually works well, though knotted and cross-grained wood is prone to tearing, and should be pre-bored for nailing. Birch can be glued and takes stain and polish reasonably well.	The bulk of birchwood is produced in Russia and Finland, where it goes into ply. Some is used to make armchair frames, broom handles and pulp for high-quality paper. It is unsuitable for outdoor use unless pressure-treated with preservative.
Yellow Birch *Betula alleghansiensis* Like other birches, this is a delicate, slender tree, though it can reach 100 ft/30 m. More often it grows to less than 22 ft/7.5 m, with a trunk 2 ft/60 cm across. Native to eastern North America, it can be recognized by its yellow-grey bark.	The heartwood ranges from light brown to a deep russet colour, while the sapwood, which is often sold with it, is paler. The growth rings show as darker lines. Its grain is usually straight, but some wood has curly grain, (this may be sold as 'silky wood').	Wood with curly or irregular grain should be handled with care, for it may tear during planing and split around nails unless pre-bored. Gluing is possible and stain and polish give good results. This is a first-class wood for turning and bending.	Plywood is the main use, but whole timber is used for furniture and tool handles. Yellow birch is hard-wearing and makes suitable flooring for sports halls and schools. It is not durable and resists preservative, so must not be used outside.
African Blackwood *Dalbergia melanoxylon* An East African tree, related to the acacias and with a gnarled and stunted growth form, blackwood generally achieves a height of only 15–20 ft/4.5–6 m. The fluted trunk is cut into short lengths, averaging 4 ft/1.3 m.	The useful part of this tree is the heartwood, a dark-brown or purplish wood with dark streaks, which makes it look almost black overall. It has an extremely fine, regular texture and feels smooth and a little oily to the touch.	Blackwood is one of the hardest and heaviest woods; it rapidly blunts an ordinary saw: one with tungsten carbide or stellite teeth should be used. The wood can be turned, takes small screws without splitting and gives a fine finish.	The unique density of blackwood makes it impermeable to air. Since it is extremely hard, it can be cut to a sharp, precise edge. These qualities, together with its stability, are exploited in the making of oboes and clarinets. Some is also used for ball bearings and chessmen.

The tree	Wood colour and quality	Technical profile	Applications
Box *Buxus sempervirens* An evergreen species, box occurs in Europe, North Africa and the Middle East. It is often found as a bush or hedge, but also as a tree, up to 30 ft/9 m tall. Its trunk achieves a diameter of 4–12 in/ 10–30 cm.	A regular, matt wood, pale yellow in colour, with an exceptionally fine, even texture. The grain may be straight, but more often it is irregular, especially in wood from small trees growing in the colder northern climates.	A fairly difficult wood to work, especially if the grain is irregular. Sharp cutting-edges must be used to prevent burning, and nailing necessitates pre-boring. Box can be steam-bent and glued. It takes stain and polish well and is naturally durable.	Available only in limited quantities, box is used for various ornamental purposes and for small, specialized machine parts, skittles, chessmen and tool handles. Being cut on the end grain it is also the best wood for engraving.
Cherry *Prunus* spp. Cherrywood comes from the wild cherry of Europe (the parent of the cultivated fruiting cherries) and the American black cherry. The latter has glossy leaves, white flowers in a spike, and tiny black fruit. It grows to 100 ft/30 m, taller than European cherry trees.	This delicate pink-tinged wood matures to a deep reddish-brown. The heartwood is darker than the sapwood, and has a well-defined edge. Cherry trees produce a copious flow of gum in response to injury, and streaks of gum may be present in the timber.	Straight-grained wood works easily but other material requires care. Cherry is reasonably strong but has a tendency to warp and is not particularly durable. Gluing is possible, and the fine, even texture gives an excellent result with stain and polish.	Black cherry is widely used for furniture and panelling in America. European cherry is less readily available and only a small amount is employed in making high-quality furniture. The rest goes into parts for musical instruments and decorative inlays.
Dogwood *Cornus florida* A small, rather shrubby tree found in the eastern part of north America, dogwood bears large white flowers, followed by clusters of red berries. The trunk yields only about 3–8 ft/1–2.5 m of useful timber, 6 in/15 cm in diameter.	Only the sapwood is used, and this is an insipid pinkish colour. It has straight grain and surpasses most other woods in its fine, regular texture. The dark heartwood occupies only a very small area and is usually excised from commercial timber before it is sold.	Dogwood is not one of the easiest woods to work, but if sharp tools are used and care is taken, it gives a really superb finish. It is suitable for turning. Strength and toughness are the major qualities; it has little natural durability.	This robust wood gives an extremely smooth surface that will not wear, splinter or fray, despite continual abrasion. This unique quality has made dogwood useful in the textile industry for making shuttles and spindles. Dogwood has few other commercial applications.
Ebony *Diospyros* spp. A group of small rainforest trees found in South and Central America, Africa, India, Southeast Asia and Australia. Most, but not all, trees in this genus have black heartwood, and many produce edible fruit, too, the best known being the persimmon, or kaki.	The best ebony is pure, jet black, but often there are streaks of lighter wood. Some species are valued for their stripey patterns—for example zebra wood, with its whitish streaks. The black heartwood is of limited size in most species, and usually the pale sapwood predominates.	A hard, strong, but brittle, wood which is exceptionally difficult to work and rapidly blunts any cutting-edge. Pre-boring is required for nails. Ebony can be steam-bent if enough pressure is applied, and it gives a fine polish. The sapwood works most easily.	Ebony is most familiar as the black keys of pianos, although many instruments now have keys of stained hornbeam or plastic. Limited availability confines ebony to inlay work, the handles of knives, the fingerboards of violins and other parts of musical instruments.

Hardwoods

The tree	Wood colour and quality	Technical profile	Applications
Elm *Ulmus* spp. Large trees with distinctive oval leaves, there are 18 species of elm, all found in the temperate northern hemisphere, east of the Rocky Mountains. At least six are used for their timber. Elms grow up to 100 or 130 ft/30 or 40 m tall.	English elm and the Dutch elm hybrids are noted for their distinctive figure, which owes its character to irregular growth and large pores in the spring-wood. Other elms have a similar figure, but the American rock elm is much plainer.	Elm is fairly easy to work, except for rock elm, which is denser and stronger than the others. All elms nail and glue well and give good results with stain and polish. They are fairly strong and light. Elm bends well, but wych elm should not be steamed.	Light weight, strength and ease of bending make this wood useful for keels, rudders and other parts of boats. English and Dutch elms are also used for furniture. Rock elm and white elm—US species—are used for ice-hockey sticks, wheel hubs and tools.
Gaboon *Aucoumea klaineana* The timber of this tree is exported from the rain forests of central Africa in greater quantity than any other. Gaboon grows to heights of 130 ft/40 m, two-thirds being branchless trunk, often slightly curved.	Freshly exposed wood is light pink, becoming browner in time. The sapwood is greyer and merges with the heartwood without a distinct boundary. Gaboon is usually rather featureless and has straight grain, though occasionally it may be slightly wavy.	Gaboon is rarely used as a solid timber but is made into a plywood which is light, takes nails well and can be glued. Non-durability and resistance to preservatives largely restrict it to indoor use. The high silica content of the wood quickly blunts saw blades.	Gaboon is widely used in Europe for plywood covering material where weather resistance is not important. It is ideal for interior panels, doors, partitions and crates. Solid gaboon is also used as a constituent of blockboard.
Greenheart *Ocotea rodiaei* This tree is restricted to Guyana and parts of Surinam and is the source of one of the most commercially valuable timbers to be produced in South America. It grows to a height of 130 ft/40 m, much of this being a long, straight trunk.	Usually a shade of olive-green, but this is variable and the wood may have dark streaks. The grain is fine and usually straight, although sometimes it shows interlocking. The wood is so heavy that even after drying it will not float.	Greenheart timber presents problems in all stages of preparation. It has to be dried very slowly to prevent splitting, is difficult to saw and is unsuitable for nailing. However, it is exceptionally strong, and highly resistant to decay, even in sea water.	The strength, hardness and durability of greenheart are frequently made use of in marine piling, harbour timbers and sea defences. When sawn to smaller sizes, it is used in ship's decks, flooring, engine mountings and fishing rods.
Guarea *Guarea* spp. Black guarea and white, or scented, guarea both grow in tropical West Africa and produce timber which is usually treated as a single type. Both species grow to a height of 160 ft/50 m and have long, straight trunks, supported by buttresses.	Guarea wood resembles mahogany, although its figure is less marked. Scented guarea produces the best figure. Both guareas are resinous (scented guarea more so), and exuded resin may mark the timber after seasoning. The grain is often interlocked and the texture is fine.	Silica and resin in scented guarea may hamper sawing, and both woods produce an irritant dust. Scented guarea can be nailed without preparation, but black guarea requires pre-boring. Both woods can be glued and take polish fairly well once the coarse grain is filled.	Guarea wood is stable and highly durable and so is used for chairs, drawer sides and other joinery. In cars and trucks, guarea is used as a board timber, and it provides the frames and planking of caravans. It is sometimes made into rifle butts and stocks.

The tree	Wood colour and quality	Technical profile	Applications
Hickory *Carya* spp. Four commercially useful species of hickory grow from southeastern Canada to the southern USA; the differences in their timber are slight. Hickories reach a height of 60–120 ft/18–36 m, depending on species.	The heartwood, known as red hickory, is deep red or brown, while the sapwood, or white hickory, is pale. Sapwood makes up a large part of the timber. The grain is usually straight, but can be irregular. The texture tends to be somewhat coarse.	All hickory wood is renowned for its toughness, but, during steaming, it becomes pliable. It rapidly blunts saws, and for nailing, pre-boring is necessary. Hickory cannot be glued, has no durability and will not absorb preservative.	Hickory is found in wooden implements that have to withstand violent shock without splintering: hammers, axes, tennis racquets and baseball bats are typical examples. Drumsticks, heavy sea-fishing rods and parts of cars are also made of hickory.
Hornbeam *Carpinus betulus* Found in temperate Europe, hornbeam can reach 100 ft/30 m but is often smaller. The trunk may be fluted, bent or twisted, and, in poor conditions, the tree is low and spreading, with branches coming out close to the ground.	Both sapwood and heartwood are pale and dull, often with greyish streaks. Hornbeam has a fine, regular texture and is usually cross grained. Trees having crooked or sinuous trunks produce wood with acentric, wavy growth rings and irregular grain.	Hornbeam is prized for its hardness and smooth finish, but it tends to blunt tools. It glues well and is suitable for turning and steam-bending, even if slightly knotty. Although highly perishable, it can easily be treated with preservative.	A traditional material where toughness is required, hornbeam was once used for the huge cogs of windmills or, indeed, for smaller cogs and pulleys. Although hard to obtain, it is still used today for the moving parts of pianos, skittles, drumsticks, mallets and factory flooring.
Idigbo *Terminalia ivorensis* A tree of the West African rainforests, idigbo grows to a height of 150 ft/45 m, and usually has a straight trunk supported by buttress roots. The best wood comes from trees of medium size, which lack the brittleheart developed later.	This wood shows growth rings, unusual for a tropical tree; when flat-sawn, the figure is similar to oak. Idigbo is yellow to yellowish-brown, and the agent producing this colour is a strong stain. In older logs, brittleheart reduces the weight and strength of the wood.	A fairly strong, durable timber of medium weight, it can be sawn and nailed easily. When moist, the acid nature of the wood corrodes iron nails, causing black stains. Idigbo can be stained and polished once the coarse grain has been filled.	Idigbo is used for its attractive appearance and ease of working rather than for strength. It is suitable for joinery and domestic flooring and can be used for exterior work. Unfortunately it tends to corrode metals and stain fabrics when damp.
Iroko *Chlorophora* spp. This useful wood comes from two related tree species of tropical Africa. The larger of the two grows to a height of 160 ft/50 m, and produces a trunk that may lack branches for 70 ft/21 m and reach 8 ft/2.5 m in diameter.	The heartwood varies from yellowish-brown to dark brown, while the sapwood forms a narrow band that is noticeably paler. The grain is often interlocked and has a coarse texture. In appearance and weight, the wood is similar to teak but lacks teak's greasiness and odour.	Hard deposits of calcium carbonate hidden in the wood may cause sudden blunting of saws, otherwise iroko can be sawn and nailed quite easily. The heartwood is highly durable. During sawing and planing, the wood may produce an irritant dust.	Iroko is widely used as a substitute for teak. A combination of strength and durability makes it suitable for interior and exterior work, outdoor furniture, bench tops, boat building and marine pilings. It can also be used for domestic flooring.

Hardwoods

The tree	Wood colour and quality	Technical profile	Applications
Jelutong *Dyera* spp. Reaching a height of 200 ft/60 m, this tree grows in the forests of Indonesia and Malaysia and is valued both for its timber and its edible latex. The trunk is usually cylindrical and straight and branch-free for 90 ft/27 m.	Jelutong wood is pale with a yellowish tinge, fairly light (two-thirds as dense as oak) and quite soft. The fine, straight grain may be punctuated by rows of latex canals, each about 1 in/25 mm across. Sapwood and heartwood are usually indistinguishable.	Being soft, jelutong is easy to work, but it is quite a stable wood. Latex canals are usually avoided by using the timber in small sizes. This is not a durable wood, and, because of latex-tapping, it may become infected by fungi before felling.	Jelutong's fine texture and lightness enable it to be used for industrial patterns in place of yellow pine. It is also used for modelling and making drawing boards, but is ill suited for outdoor use. Its latex is a constituent of chewing gum.
Kapur *Dryobalanops* spp. Kapur, or Borneo camphorwood as it is known in the U.K., includes a number of similar species from Malaysia and Indonesia. The trees reach heights of 200 ft/60 m, and may have clear trunks 100 ft/30 m long, supported by buttress roots.	A coarse, strong wood, kapur is usually slightly heavier than oak. The heartwood is brown with a reddish tinge, while the sapwood is yellower or sometimes pinkish. It has straight or slightly interlocked grain. The camphor-like odour diminishes after cutting.	Kapur causes moderate blunting of saws, and the fibrous nature of the wood may make finishing difficult. The timber takes nails well, but, when damp, acids in the wood attack some metals, causing staining or corrosion. The sapwood can contain a yellow stain.	Despite being difficult to saw and finish, kapur is a useful wood where strength, durability and uniformity are important. It is used for outdoor furniture, door frames, window sills, and load-bearing exterior work such as stairways and harbour decking.
Keruing *Dipterocarpus* spp. Also called gurjun, yang, eng and other names: these cover several very valuable species found from Burma to the Philippines. The largest grows to 200 ft/60 m, and all have straight trunks, crowned with open, spreading branches.	The wood is usually brown, sometimes tinged pink or purple, with little figure. The heartwood is strong and heavy, with a coarse, regular grain, straight or slightly interlocked. The sapwood is grey. Some species are highly resinous, especially when young.	Some samples contain silica, which causes blunting; otherwise sawing is fairly easy. Resin exudation during steaming makes bending impracticable. Resin may also seep out in high temperatures, spoiling varnish or paints. Can be nailed, but gluing may be problematic.	Timbers of the keruing group are used as a substitute for oak, being slightly heavier and stronger. The wood is found in construction work, flooring and trucks. It is also used in boat-building, being fairly durable, though less so than oak.
Lignum vitae *Guaiacum* spp. This small tree, usually no more than 30 ft/9 m in height and 1 ft/3 m in diameter, grows in Caribbean countries and in northern South America. It was once exported for its supposed medicinal properties, hence the name, 'wood of life'.	Lignum vitae is twice as heavy as oak and a third as heavy as water. The heartwood is greenish-black in colour and has a very fine grain. It has an exceptionally high oil content, and is extremely hard, strong and durable. Its only weakness is a tendency to split tangentially.	Lignum vitae presents difficulties in sawing, since it quickly blunts blades, and it is unsuitable for nailing. However, the high density does make it ideal for turning, provided that greater than usual pressure is applied. Gluing is not usually successful.	The oil in lignum vitae acts as a lubricant, so the wood used for bearings, particularly propeller shaft bushes, and for machinery rollers. It is also useful where resistance to impact is required, as in mallet heads and 'woods' (balls) for the game of bowls.

The tree	Wood colour and quality	Technical profile	Applications
European Lime *Tilia vulgaris* A large, vigorous hybrid lime, often seen in city gardens and streets, it is recognized by its heart-shaped leaves. One of the tallest deciduous trees in Europe, it may reach 130 ft/40 m.	Both sapwood and heartwood are pale, sometimes yellowish, when freshly cut, darkening to a light brown. There is little figure, and the straight, fine grain gives it a uniform texture. Lime wood is light, soft, and correspondingly weak.	The timber presents few problems in sawing but may be torn by blunt blades. It shows reasonable strength in relation to its weight and can be steam-bent or turned. Gluing and nailing are both possible, and stain and polish give fairly good results.	Lime has long been favoured for carving and for many turned objects such as cotton reels and bobbins. It is used for handles, where strength is not required, eg, brushes. Although perishable, it can easily be treated with preservative for outdoor use.
Luaun *Shorea* **spp.** This is the name used in the Philippines for timber from a group of trees mostly belonging to the genus *Shorea*. They are tall forest species, some growing to 230 ft/70 m. Other names for the wood are red meranti (Malaya and Indonesia) and red seraya (Sabah).	Red luaun (dark-red meranti) is a red-brown wood with white resin streaks. White luaun (light-red meranti) is pinkish. Both have a narrow band of paler sapwood. Interlocked grain gives a stripy figure on quartered sections. The texture is coarse but regular.	Red luaun is a fairly heavy, strong wood, easy to saw, nail and glue. White luaun also works well but is lighter, not especially strong and much less durable. Both are rather stringy, but they can be stained and polished with reasonable success.	Plywood manufacture accounts for much of this timber. White luaun is also used for joinery and furniture but non-durability and resistance to preservative precludes outdoor use. Red luaun is used for building (both indoors and out), panelling, flooring and boats.
African Mahogany *Khaya ivorensis* A West African forest tree, reaching heights of up to 200 ft/60 m. It has short buttresses and produces a branchless trunk, up to 6 ft/2 m in diameter and 80–90 ft/25–27 m long. Other species of *Khaya* are sometimes shipped as mahogany.	A warm orange-brown wood with interlocked grain, which gives a pleasing stripy figure on quarter-cut surfaces. The colour is never as yellow as in the light forms of American mahogany. Whitish sapwood often merges with the heartwood. The texture is coarse.	This wood's main qualities are its stable nature and attractive appearance. The interlocked grain makes it a little difficult to saw and plane, and the dust may cause a skin rash. Mahogany nails and glues fairly well and is reasonably durable.	Although primarily a furniture and panelling wood, mahogany also finds a use in boat-building, especially in speed-boats where a lightweight timber is needed. Some is used for the interior fittings of cars and the rest goes to plywood manufacture.
American Mahogany *Swietenia* **spp.** The original mahogany, is a sturdy tree of the South and Central American forests, growing to 100 ft/30 m with a straight trunk up to 6 ft/2 m across and free of branches for 50 ft/15 m or more. It is related to the African mahoganies.	Mahogany is justly famed for its rich, lustrous colour, ranging from red or red-brown to brownish-yellow. Some has straight grain and is fairly plain, but wood with interlocked grain has a decorative figure. Unlike African mahogany this wood has growth rings visible on end grain.	Sawing and planing are relatively easy, although some wood gives a woolly finish unless sharp cutting edges are used. Mahogany can be glued and nailed, is durable, light, reasonably strong and extremely stable. It can be steam-bent, unlike *Khaya*.	Superior to other mahoganies in its colour and finish, but now in very short supply, this wood is used mainly for high-class furniture, panelling, and quality car and yacht fittings. Some is used for model- and pattern-making, where stability is valued.

Hardwoods

The tree	Wood colour and quality	Technical profile	Applications
Makoré *Tieghemella heckelii* A tall, slender, straight-trunked tree up to 150 ft/45 m high, the uniformly cylindrical trunk achieves a diameter of 4–9 ft/1.3–2.7 m. It is not spoiled by buttress roots.	This lustrous, tawny wood varies from pink to dark purplish-red. Straight-grained samples are rather featureless, but others show a subtle rippled figure, which looks attractive. Some wood has fine blackish veins. The texture is smooth and even.	The main drawback to makoré is its silica content, which defeats all but the toughest saws. It must be bored before nailing, and this, too, is difficult, often causing charring. The sawdust is an irritant. Steam-bending is possible with the heartwood.	Strong and highly durable, makoré is extensively used in boat-building, as solid timber or as plywood. Its stability and attractive figure are employed in making furniture and veneers. Some is used for doors, flooring and panelling.
American Maple *Acer* **spp.** The main timber maples of North America are the sugar maple and black maple (which yield a robust wood called rock- or hard-maple) and the silver maple and red maple (which yield a lighter, softer and weaker wood, known as soft-maple).	All the maples have a finely textured, creamy wood, with the heartwood and sapwood not distinct. Rock maple often has a reddish tinge and its grain may be curly. The fine growth rings form an attractive pattern. Soft maple is plainer and less lustrous.	Rock maple is strong, heavy and fairly difficult to work. It does not take nails well but can be glued. Steam-bending is possible. Soft maple is much easier to work and can be nailed, but this should be done carefully to avoid splitting. Gluing is not always a success.	Both types of maple are non-durable and resist treatment with preservative, so must only be used internally. Furniture and panelling are major uses. Rock maple's hardness and even grain makes a tough, smooth floor, useful for dance halls and squash courts.
Meranti *Shorea* **spp.** Also known as yellow seraya, these timbers come from a group of 12 closely related Malayan forest trees. They reach 200 ft/60 m, with trunks up to 5 ft/1.6 m in diameter, and belong to the same genus as the trees that produce luaun (red meranti).	This is a rather drab wood, yellowish in colour, turning darker with age. Its interlocked grain gives it a stripy figure on quarter-cut faces. The sapwood is greyish-yellow and 2–3 ins/5–7.5 cm wide. Although fairly coarse, the texture of the wood is superior to that of luaun.	Intermediate between red luaun and white luaun for strength and weight, this wood is fairly easily worked. It can be glued and nailed but tends to darken around iron nails. Once filled, it can be stained and polished, but this does not give very attractive effects.	Yellow meranti is a fairly durable wood which, however, cannot be treated with preservative. It can be used both internally and externally, although its preferred use is for interior joinery, construction work and flooring. It cannot carry heavy loads.
European Oak *Quercus* **spp.** The sessile oak and the pedunculate oak are both common throughout Europe; growing to 115 ft/35 m with a trunk 3–6 ft/1–2 m across, or up to 10 ft/3 m in some cases. They are similar and sometimes produce hybrids; their timbers are indistinguishable.	Oak is a mellow, golden-brown in colour, the heartwood having paler rays which give a pleasant, distinctive pattern when it is quartered. The grain is usually straight. Growth rings are less pronounced in slow-grown timber from central Europe than in north European wood.	The working properties depend on growing conditions: slow-grown timber is softer, lighter and weaker. Generally oak can easily be sawn, planed, steam-bent or glued, but it needs pre-boring for nails. Corrosion and staining will occur if oak is in contact with iron or lead.	An almost legendary wood that has become a by-word for strength and durability. Oak is used for fencing, boat-building and flooring and in construction work, particularly for doors and sills. The best decorative oak is made into furniture, panelling and veneers.

The tree	Wood colour and quality	Technical profile	Applications
American White Oak *Quercus* spp. Many different oaks contribute to timber of this name, but the main one is the true white oak, a tree up to 100 ft/30 m tall, with a spreading crown and grey, shaggy bark. It is native to North America.	The wood varies from light- to medium-brown, generally with a yellowish tinge. It has straight grain and pale golden rays, forming a decorative figure on quarter-cut faces. Fast-grown wood from the southern USA has wider growth rings.	A hard, strong wood, heavier than European oak but not as tough to work; the fast-grown timber presents most problems. Nailing is much easier if the wood is pre-bored. Acid in oakwood will corrode iron, lead and other reactive metals.	Like European oak, this wood is not only easily bent but durable, making it valuable for the staves of barrels (casks). Good-quality timber is used for furniture and panelling, and the rest in building work, flooring, fencing and vehicle construction.
Obeche *Triplochiton scleroxylon* A valuable West African tree which grows as tall as 180 ft/55 m, often with a branchless trunk for 80 ft/24 m of its height. However, the first 20 ft/6 m of this is likely to be marred by buttress roots. Timber from Ghana is called wawa.	Although very pale, varying from a light coffee-colour to almost white, obeche has a bright lustre, which gives it a pleasing appearance. The texture is coarse. Interlocked grain produces a broad stripe when quarter-cut. Heartwood and sapwood are identical.	Obeche is a light and easily managed wood, presenting few problems. When working on the end grain there is some tendency for it to chip or disintegrate. It can be stained and polished after filling. The unpleasant smell of the fresh wood soon disappears.	A stable wood that is useful for drawer sides, the frames of furniture, and other joinery work where strength is not essential. Some is used in organs and for model-making. Lack of durability and resistance to fungicide confine it to use indoors.
Padauk *Pterocarpus* spp. A widespread group of tropical trees, with representatives in Africa and Asia. One of the most valuable species comes from the Andaman Islands in the Indian Ocean. These trees grow to 120 ft/35 m, with a trunk up to 3 ft/1 m across, often with large buttresses.	An alternative name is vermilion wood, since most material is bright red when fresh, turning red- or purple-brown later, often with blackish streaks. Some timber is paler and yellowish. There is a broad band of grey sapwood. The texture is fairly coarse.	African padauk is often straight grained and thus much easier to work than the Asian types with interlocked grain. Nailing is problematic unless the wood is pre-bored, but gluing is possible. These are strong, hard, heavy and durable timbers, which finish well and can be turned.	The wood is widely used as flooring in public buildings, where resistance to wear is needed. African padauk is especially useful with underfloor heating, for it is unusually stable. Other uses include boat-building, construction, joinery, carving and veneers.
Pear *Pyrus communis* Well known as an orchard and garden tree, the pear originated in southern Europe and western Asia and has been cultivated from the earliest times. It rarely grows to more than 50 ft/15 m and is often lop-sided.	Pear is a pretty wood with rosy-pink colouring and a delicate, regular texture. The growth rings are faintly visible. Irregular grain is usually seen only in trees with mis-shapen trunks. *Sorbus* species (rowan, whitebeam and service trees) produce similar wood.	Pearwood is difficult to saw, especially if the grain is irregular, and it has a tendency to blunt tools. However, it turns well and gives an excellent finish. Stain and polish produce highly satisfactory results. Pear has no natural durability.	As their fruit yield declines, orchard pears are felled for timber. This is the main source of the wood and rarity restricts its uses. Most is made into turned pieces, bowls, brush handles, rulers, veneers and parts of musical instruments, notably recorders.

Hardwoods

The tree	Wood colour and quality	Technical profile	Applications
Plane _Platanus hispanica_ (USA: Sycamore) A vigorous hybrid tree, it is often known as the London plane. Rarely grown for timber, its immunity to pollution has led to widespread urban planting, providing a small supply of wood.	This warm, light-brown wood has numerous, broad red-brown rays that show up as a unique and highly attractive figure (lacewood) on quarter-sawn stock. The heartwood and sapwood look alike, but there is sometimes a darker core.	Plane wood is not too difficult to work, but sharp blades are needed for planing or the broad rays may flake, producing an irregular surface. It nails and glues easily, can be steam-bent and takes stain and polish, though care is needed for good results.	Plane is not particularly strong and has no durability, so it is used only for indoor work and then mainly as decoration. It is an interesting wood for inlays and veneer panelling. If regular supplies were available, it might be used more widely.
Purpleheart _Peltogyne_ spp. These giant trees of the Central and South American rainforests can grow to 150 ft/ 45 m tall. The trunk is relatively slender, up to 4 ft/1.2 m across, often with buttress roots. About 20 different species are felled for this timber.	An eye-catching wood, vivid purple in colour at first, but mellowing to brick-red or brownish-purple in time. The colour shows much variation. White sapwood 2–4 in/5–10 cm wide surrounds the heartwood. The texture of the wood is fairly smooth, the grain usually straight.	This is a heavy, strong wood, intermediate between beech and greenheart. Problems in working it may be aggravated by grain that is wavy or interlocked and deposits of resin on saw blades. Nailing requires care and gluing is not recommended.	Excellent strength and durability make purpleheart a prime timber for wharves, bridges and other heavy-duty construction work. As a flooring material, it can survive a great deal of hard wear. The wood is also used for carving, turnery and ornamental inlays.
Ramin _Gonystylus_ spp. A group of forest trees from the islands of southeastern Asia supply this timber. The trees grow fairly tall, over 100 ft/30 m, and generally have a long, branchless trunk, up to 60 ft/18 m long and 2–3 ft/60–92 cm across. Ramin is an important export for Sarawak.	This pale, rather featureless wood has a regular texture and straight or slightly interlocked grain. When freshly cut, ramin may discolour and often smells unpleasant. The staining can be prevented by dipping in a suitable solution; the odour wears off with drying.	Roughly equivalent in strength to beech, but with a greater tendency to split or splinter under stress. If the grain is interlocked, it may prove difficult to work. Nailing is not recommended, but gluing is possible. Ramin cannot be bent.	Ramin finds a use in furniture and joinery but should not be used where stability or durability is required. Some is made into moulding, handles, toys and other small items. Since water brings out its unpleasant smell, the timber is not suitable for articles likely to get wet.
Robinia _Robinia pseudacacia_ Also known as the black locust or false acacia, this tree is one of the pea family and bears showy white flowers. It grows to 90 ft/27 m, with a fluted trunk and heavily fissured bark. The trunk and branches are often sinuous and crooked, like an acacia's.	Greenish-yellow when newly sawn, the heartwood matures to a warm, attractive golden-brown. The summerwood is much denser than the springwood, giving bold growth rings and a coarse texture. It is straight grained, except where the trunk is bent or twisted.	Hard, heavy, and as tough as ash, robinia is no more difficult to work than would be expected. Nailing is problematic, however, and pre-boring is advisable. The wood can be glued, and gives fair results with stain and polish. It is excellent for steam-bending.	Robinia was much used by early settlers in New England for furniture, tools and carts. Some is still made into furniture, but most now goes for fences and posts, where its durability is valued. Robinia is grown for timber in Europe but only as an ornamental in Britain.

The tree	Wood colour and quality	Technical profile	Applications
Rosewood *Dalbergia* **spp.** These are Indian and South American trees, some reaching 125 ft/ 38 m. Their trunks are often forked or mis-shapen. Only old trees yield the richly coloured heartwood. Blackwood is a closely related African tree.	Rosewood is a dark timber with a muted purplish tinge and fine black streaks. Honduras rosewood has a smooth texture, but others are rather coarse. Indian rosewood has slightly interlocked grain. In others it is straight or a little irregular.	Strong, hard, heavy timbers, especially Honduras rosewood. All are fairly easy to work, but Brazilian rosewood may yield an irritant dust and is often oily, which precludes a high polish. Bending and turning are possible. Glue can be used.	The decorative aspect of rosewood is utilized in furniture, pianos and veneers, fancy turned goods and handles for knives and cutlery. Some is also made into parts for musical instruments; Honduras rosewood is the best wood for xylophone keys.
Sapele *Entandrophragma cylindricum* As its scientific name suggests, this West African tree has a long, straight cylindrical trunk extending to 100 ft/ 30 m without branches. The tree itself is generally about 150 ft/45 m tall, but some specimens top 200 ft/60 m.	A useful substitute for mahogany, sapele is rich golden- or reddish-brown in colour with a smooth texture. Interlocked grain shows up as a banded figure on quartered timber. Wavy grain, though rarer, produces an attractive fiddle-back pattern.	The main problem with sapele is its tendency to warp when drying. If seasoned carefully, it makes a sound timber that works fairly well and can be nailed and glued, but is unsuitable for steam-bending. Stain must be applied with great care, but polish gives superb results.	Rivalling beech in strength, but somewhat lighter, sapele makes excellent furniture, panelling, flooring and veneers wherever a mahogany-like appearance is required. Being fairly durable, it is also used for doors, window frames and boats, especially as plywood.
White Seraya *Parashorea* **spp.** One of the luaun-meranti-seraya group from southeastern Asia, but less variable than the others, since it comes from just two species. White seraya may be classed as white luaun in the Philippines—(white meranti is a different timber).	Like others in the group, this is a coarse, stringy wood, with slightly interlocked grain giving broad stripes on quarter-sawn planks. Shades of creamy-white, yellow or pinkish-brown are characteristic. The sapwood is much paler and duller.	A fairly light wood, not particularly strong, but slightly better than white luaun. It is stable and easy to work as long as blades are kept sharp. Surfaces tend to be fibrous but can be stained and polished after filling. Nailing and gluing are possible.	The bulk of the white seraya imported from southeast Asia is turned into plywood. This product has adequate working properties but is not recommended for outdoor use—it is usually not durable. Some white seraya is used for joinery and flooring.
Sweet Chestnut *Castanea sativa* This tree of the Mediterranean region was spread throughout Europe by the Romans. It has glossy, brown, edible nuts in prickly green cases. Heights of 100 ft/30 m are possible for mature specimens, and these trees often have spiralled bark.	Sweet chestnut is a relative of the oaks, and the wood has the same warm, golden-brown colour. However, chestnut lacks the rays that give oak its typical figure, and the texture is rougher. The grain is usually straight, but may become spiralled in old age.	Not as heavy or strong as oak, chestnut is easier to work and can be nailed or glued. Acidity in the wood corrodes iron, so galvanized nails should be used. If straight grained and knot-free, it can be bent reasonably well. Stain and polish give fair results.	Chestnut is put to many of the same uses as oak, including furniture and barrel staves. Some is used for fruit bowls, handles and cooking spoons. This durable wood throws up long, straight poles when coppiced, and these are valuable for split-chestnut fencing.

Hardwoods

The tree	Wood colour and quality	Technical profile	Applications
Sycamore *Acer pseudoplatanus* This vigorous maple is now naturalized in both Europe and in North America, where it is known as sycamore maple, the name sycamore denoting a species of plane tree. In Scotland, sycamore is known as plane.	When dried rapidly, sycamore is a lustrous white or straw colour. Slower drying causes staining, which is generally undesirable, but 'weathered sycamore'—a pale brown, slow-dried timber—is sometimes available.	Straight-grained wood works easily, but wavy grain requires care in planing. Sycamore is fairly strong, but light, can be nailed or glued and gives first-rate results with stain and polish. Knot-free wood bends well. Non-durable, it absorbs preservative.	Sycamore with wavy grain is highly decorative and is the best wood for violin backs. Some is also peeled for veneer. The plainer forms of sycamore are used as flooring, and for rollers in the textile industry, brush handles and spoons.
Teak *Tectona grandis* This mighty forest tree belongs to the verbena family and is found growing wild in southeast Asia and India. Its value as a timber tree has led to commercial planting in other parts of the world, notably Africa. Teak trees grow to 150 ft/45 m.	Golden-brown at first, teak becomes darker and more reddish in time. The finest natural teak from Burma is plain, but most teak has dark striations. Growth rings are present. The wood feels rough and greasy and has a pungent smell, reminiscent of leather.	An abrasive wood that calls for a saw with tungsten-carbide teeth, teak must be bored for nails and sanded before gluing. The sawdust may cause a skin rash. Teak's main virtues are its strength, stability, waterproof nature and outstanding resistance to decay.	Teak finds its major role in boat-building, where it can be used for almost all parts, except those that need to be bent. Its durable nature is particularly valued in the tropics. Other applications include flooring and furniture, especially garden seats.
Tupelo *Nyssa* spp. Two trees supply this timber, the tupelo gum and the black gum (also known as the pepperidge or sow gum); the latter grows wild in swamp forests but is also planted ornamentally. Both species reach about 100 ft/30 m. They have glossy leaves and blue-black berries.	Greyish sapwood merges with the creamy-yellow or pale brown heartwood. There is little growth-ring pattern and the overall appearance is rather dull. The grain is interlocked and irregular, although the wood has a fine, even texture.	Planing must be done carefully to avoid tearing the interlocked grain. Nailing is feasible, but tupelo does not always glue well. A fair result is obtained with stain and polish. If the timber is to be used outdoors, preservative must be applied.	These are weak and fairly light woods, though black gum is harder, stronger and heavier than tupelo gum and shows an unusual resistance to splitting. This makes it useful for railway sleepers and flooring. Some tupelo is used for furniture, plywood and crates.
Utile *Entandrophragma utile* A west African member of the mahogany family, utile is closely related to sapele, another commercially important timber tree. Utile grows as tall as 200 ft/60 m and may yield a branchless trunk 80 ft/25 m long.	Like sapele, this wood is a rich tawny colour and can be used as a mahogany-substitute. Its figure is not as appealing as sapele, the striations on quarter-sawn wood being broader and fainter. The grain is irregular and interlocked, the texture slightly rough.	This strong and fairly heavy wood is reasonably easy to work although care must be taken when planing to avoid tearing the grain. Utile can be nailed and glued. Once filled, it gives an acceptable effect with stain and polish.	Although less pleasing in appearance than sapele, utile is much easier to season and does not show the same tendency to warp. Thus it finds a use in furniture-making and panelling. Strong and durable, it is also employed for construction work.

The tree	Wood colour and quality	Technical profile	Applications
African Walnut *Lovoa trichilioides* Not a true walnut, this member of the mahogany family is found in tropical west Africa. It can achieve heights of 150 ft/45 m, but the trunk is rarely more than 4 ft/1.2 m across. Also called alona and Congo wood.	The only resemblance to walnut lies in the dark, narrow veins that decorate some samples. Most timber is plain, tawny in colour, and with a stripy figure on quarter-sawn faces typical of mahogany-type woods. The texture is fine.	Sharp tools and considerable care are needed or the interlocked grain will tear during planing. Otherwise this wood works well and can be nailed or glued. It gives satisfactory results with stain and polish, is very stable and fairly durable.	African walnut is a little lighter than beech, but much weaker and should not be expected to bear loads. It is used for furniture, doors, panelling and shop fittings. Some is peeled for decorative veneers and used for car fittings.
European Walnut *Juglans regia* Originating in Asia Minor, the walnut was widely dispersed by the Romans. Often a short-trunked, spreading tree, walnut can exceed 100 ft/30 m in a warm climate. It is grown for timber in Italy, France, Turkey and Yugoslavia.	When crushed, the leaves of walnut exude a brown juice, which also pervades the heartwood, creating the dark streaks that characterize this wood. American (or black) walnut is similar but has a slightly darker, more uniform colour.	A strong and relatively lightweight wood that presents no special problems for the woodworker. It is particularly easy to bend and takes a high polish. Walnut can be glued, or nailed with care, but should not come into contact with iron, which makes it stain.	The best walnut, with its intricate dark figuring and wavy grain, is a rare and valuable commodity obtainable only from burrs or stumps of old trees. This wood is used for panelling and furniture veneers. Other uses include turned goods and rifle butts.
American Whitewood *Liriodendron tulipifera* Well known as the tulip tree, this is widely planted in North America and in European gardens. The saddle-shaped leaves and greenish flowers are unique. A native of the eastern states, this tree grows up to 150 ft/45 m.	The heartwood is an unusual greenish-yellow or yellow-brown colour, hence the names 'canary wood' and 'yellow poplar'. The sapwood is paler: a broad white band in young, fast-growing trees, narrower and darker in older ones. The grain is straight and the texture fine.	One of the easiest hardwoods to work, American whitewood can be sawed, planed and nailed and gives an excellent finish. This lightweight timber has little inherent strength and no durability. It takes stain and polish with fair results.	Plywood manufacture accounts for most of this timber. Other uses include indoor joinery and furniture, sometimes as the main component, but more often as a secondary wood for interior sections. Stability and ease of working also makes it useful for machine patterns.
Willow *Salix* **spp.** These familiar waterside trees, with their slender twigs and small, narrow leaves, are found throughout the world; over 300 species are known. The only important timber species is the cricket-bat willow, a variety of white willow which shows very rapid growth.	A band of white, slightly lustrous sapwood surrounds the pale, pinkish heartwood. The width of the sapwood varies, being widest in the best cricket-bat willows. Fast growth produces straight grain, valuable for bats. The texture is smooth and even.	Willow is very easy to work, but blades must be kept sharp. Gluing is possible; nailing is not recommended. The wood can be stained or polished if required, but it is not especially attractive. It cannot be steam-bent, shows no durability and resists preservative.	Although light and weak, willow shows unusual resilience and will not splinter under the impact of a hard, fast-moving ball. It is this quality which makes it valued for cricket bats. Other uses include toys, crates for fruit, and artificial limbs.

Glossary

Abrade To rub down or smooth with abrasive paper when preparing a surface prior to finishing.

Across the grain At right angles to, or roughly at right angles to, the direction of the grain in the work surface.

Annual ring See **growth rings**.

Banding Decorative strips of veneer arranged around central panels of veneer, typically making a border.

Bare-faced With only one shoulder.

Beading Moulding with a generally convex profile, usually semicircular.

Bearer Any piece of timber or other material that supports or spreads a load.

Bench plane A plane with a flat bottom or sole (as opposed to an irregularly shaped sole seen, for example, in moulding planes) typically used on the bench for squaring up timber.

Bevel An edge which is formed at an angle other than 90° to the face side.

Burnisher Cylindrical steel rod used to 'turn over' the sharpened edge of a scraper into a hook profile for scraping. The rod is fitted with a wooden handle.

Burr or **burr edge** A 'wire' or rough edge left on a cutting edge after sharpening (honing) or grinding. The burr is always removed as the final stage in creating an incisive cutting edge.

Butt joint A plain side-to-side or edge-to-edge joint.

Carcase (alternative spelling carcass) Term used to describe the box-like assembly of a piece of furniture, such as a sideboard or chest, as opposed to the framework in tables, chairs and the like.

Chamfer (noun) Part of an edge which has been angled; (verb) to make a chamfer.

Cheeks (of a carcase) The vertical outer sides.

Cheeks (of a saw) The upright pieces of the frame of some bow saws.

Chuck Adjustable device for grasping a drill bit or auger, or for holding wood when turning on a lathe.

Countersink To bore out extra material in the surface around a screw hole to permit a screw head to sit flush with the wood surface.

Cross member A component which crosses others.

Dado A groove sunk across the grain of a piece of timber to carry a second piece of timber. If the whole end of the second piece fits into the dado, a housed joint is formed.

End grain Grain exposed at the end of a piece of cross-cut timber.

Face side The best surface of a timber component—that which has been chosen to be 'on view'—in the finished piece. It should be planed perfectly true.

Fence A stop, fixed or adjustable, against which work can be held steady or guided.

Figure The grain pattern on a wood surface.

Gauge To mark a line on timber by scoring it with the spur of a gauge.

Gauged line Line gauged parallel with the edge of a piece of timber.

Glue block A block of wood glued to the inside of a joint to give it extra strength.

Grain The arrangement and direction of the fibres which constitute wood. They can be visualized as fine tubes, like drinking straws, which is how they appear when magnified. See also **End grain**.

Groove To sink a channel along the grain.

Ground The base on which a veneer is laid.

Growth rings The concentric rings exposed when a tree trunk is cut through horizontally. They mark the successive formation of a new layer of timber each year on trees in temperate climates where the graining seasons are clearly defined.

Hardwood Timber from a broad leaved tree; the wood is not necessarily hard. See **Softwood**

Hone To put an incisive edge on the already ground bevel of a cutting tool.

Jig A pattern or device enabling tools, such as drill bits, to be repeatedly and accurately positioned in relation to work on which they must operate.

Key To roughen a surface, either with abrasive paper, saw teeth or a rasp, so that adhesive bonds better with that surface.

Kerf Cut in wood made by a saw blade.

Keying Reinforcing a mitred joint with a strip of timber, usually hardwood, for added strength.

Kicker Device, usually a timber strip, fitted to a carcase rail above a drawer to prevent a drawer tipping when pulled out.

Mitre Joint where the two pieces are bevelled, usually at 45°, at their junction.

Mortise A recess or hole, rectangular in shape; the recess that receives a tenon.

Oversailing Fitting a top to carcase cheeks so that it projects on one or more sides, front and/or back.

Pitch The angle of a sloping surface.

Rabbet Alternative form of rebate, used generally in the USA. See **Rebate**.

Rail Horizontal piece of timber joining vertical pieces in a carcase or frame.

Rays Tissues radiating in bands from the pith toward the bark of a tree.

Rebate A step-shaped reduction cut along the edge of, or in the face of, a piece of timber, usually to receive the edge of another piece. See also **Rabbet**.

Scribe Mark out with a sharp point.

Shoulder After cutting a tenon, the end grain surface perpendicular to the tenon surface.

Size To seal a porous surface with diluted glue or adhesive.

Softwood Timber from coniferous trees; the wood need not be soft. See also **Hardwood**.

Spindle (in machine tool) A vertical rotating shaft.

Stile The vertical sides in a frame.

Stopped Not cut right through.

Credits

1/6   Clive Corless

12   Forestry Commission

19/21   Crown copyright; reproduced by
           permission of the BRE Princes
           Risborough Laboratory

26/27   Crown copyright; reproduced by
           permission of the BRE Princes
           Risborough Laboratory

33   Fidor

170   Tom Leighton/The World of Interiors

172/192   Clive Corless

Acknowledgements
Thanks to Caroline Weeks, Patricia Sunley,
Ann Snow, David and Maya Seligman, Edith
Paul, Ken Mellor and David Giles, Catharina
Mannerfelt
Flowers from Hillier and Hilton, 61 Church
Road, Barnes, London SW 13
Antiques from Portmeirion Antiques, White Hart
Lane, London SW 13, Guinevere, 578 King's
Road, London SW 6, M & D Seligmann, 37
Kensington Church Street, London W8